WISCONSIN THROUGH 5 BILLION YEARS OF CHANGE

Byron Crowns

Photos by Ralph V. Boyer

Published by
Wisconsin Earth Science Center
430 E. Grand Avenue
Wisconsin Rapids, Wisconsin

Cover: Devils Lake nestled among the hills of the Baraboo Range, in Sauk County.

WISCONSIN THROUGH 5 BILLION YEARS OF CHANGE

Library of Congress Catalog Card Number: 76-46151

Consulting editor — John Rupnow; Book design — Thomas W. Jewell

I dedicate this book to Elizabeth, my mother, who struck the spark to the tinder, and to Gail, my wife, who kept the flame from flickering out.

FOREWORD

"God called the dry land Earth" — 1 Genesis 10

When God created rock, He held it in such esteem that He made the Earth of it. Although changeable in form, rock is the wonderful, indestructible substance that dates back to the dawn of time. Nothing endures like "the rock of ages" . . . the girders and building blocks of the mountains, the primordial slabs forming the continents, the solid basins beneath the oceans. The Creator prized rock so highly that He fashioned it in every color of the rainbow, produced it in an almost endless variety of crystalline forms, invested it with sublime order and endowed it with beauty — both delicate and bold. No one can study rock without eventually pondering its role in the great mysteries of the universe.

Table of Contents

As the years go by, Wisconsin's landscapes are continually changing . . . Oldest known engraving of the mouth of the Wisconsin River.

I
Wisconsin's Changing Countenance

The rocks of Wisconsin are products of interacting geologic processes that have operated since the solid earth formed. The processes generally are cyclical, progress slowly, extend over millions of years and change the state's appearance continually.

A Story Of Change

Can you visualize a Wisconsin (quite unlike the one we know today) with majestic mountains towering toward the sky? Or a Wisconsin with volcanoes pushing up, erupting and covering the countryside under a blanket of fiery hot lava? Or a Wisconsin buried below a solid sheet of ice — up to two miles thick? Or a Wisconsin submerged beneath the waters of a warm sea, teeming with weird creatures, alien to our present-day world? Sounds fantastic? Yes, but surprisingly, it's true! There have been such richly varied occurrences in the state.

The Wisconsin we see today has not always been the same. Over the ages gone by, it has worn many faces, because time is an efficient face-lifter — a plastic surgeon without peer. The beautiful landscapes unfolding as we travel around the state — with a diversity of hills, valleys, prairies, rivers, lakes, marshes and glacial sculptures — are made up of surface features of comparatively recent origin. Similarly, the rocks that crop out in some places, and everywhere underlie the surface, reach only part way back into geologic time. Both today's surface features and rocks represent merely the latest phase in a development begun long ago. All are the temporary details in a long sequence of change. A succession of great recurring events, marked with high drama, leads to the things of the present.

Wisconsin's land mass, as a part of the earth's crust, has been, sporadically, uplifted by mysterious, powerful forces operating from within the earth and then worn down on the outside by weathering and erosion. In the course of diminishing the rocks exposed at the surface, water, air and ice have carved away at the land, reduced it in size, transported it long distances in the form of tiny sediments and flushed it, eventually, into the sea. All this has been followed, in turn, by a new uplift, in a perpetual cycle of

change. Thus, for eons, Wisconsin's countenance has been continually changing.

Wisconsin's climate has not always been the same. It, too, has experienced many changes. During some periods, there has been arctic cold; during others, very mild, almost tropical conditions; and during others, moderate extremes as we witness today.

Ages ago when warmer climate prevailed, almost certainly, palm trees thrived in the state. These climatic changes, as with most earth processes, have developed slowly.

The story of Wisconsin's changing countenance is the story of a relentless rhythm of change occurring on and within the earth. Essentially, as we shall see, it is the story of Wisconsin's rocks and their role in the natural order.

It begins in a distant misty yesteryear when the earth formed as a solid planet.

The Earth — A Ball Of Rock

The earth is a big ball of rock, 7,927 miles in diameter, weighing about 6.6 sextillion tons (66 followed by 20 zeros). Slightly flattened at the poles, the earth technically is an oblate spheroid. It has a volume of about 260 billion cubic miles and an average density of 5½ times that of water. The earth is estimated to be growing in size at the rate of a few thousand to a few million tons each year because of the accumulation of meteoritic dust continually falling from the heavens.

On the outside, the earth has many outcroppings of rock but most of its surface is covered with water and soil. These external features are rather shallow. Not far below the bottom of the seas and the soils supporting vegetative growth on the lands, the earth is girdled with solid rock. It is wrapped in great concentric layers of rock called strata. (The word strata comes from Latin meaning that which is spread out.)

Inside, the earth is composed of a very heavy core and several massive rock layers, denser near the core and lighter toward the surface. The outer layers press down upon the inner layers, exerting awesome pressure that results in extreme heat, sufficient to melt solid rock to a plastic or liquid substance. Rock temperature rises at a fairly regular rate: one degree Fahrenheit for every 60 feet of depth. At about three miles down it becomes hot enough to boil water. This is shown at some locations by geysers spouting scalding hot water.

The crust of the earth, rarely over 40 miles thick, rests upon a mantle of hot jelly-like rock that reaches downward for 1,800 miles. Below this is an outer core of molten nickel-iron about 1,300 miles thick. The inner core, forming the most compact mass of the earth's interior, has a radius of about 860 miles. This very dense core is composed of nickel-iron compressed probably into a solid, almost four times as dense as granite.

In comparison to the total mass of the earth's globe, the crust is quite thin. It is thickest beneath continents (up to 35 to 40 miles or so) and thinnest beneath oceans (as little as three to four miles). However, all efforts by geologists so far to drill through

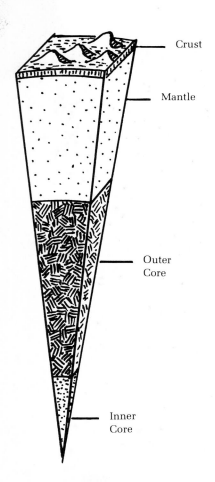

A core section of the earth showing the massive layers forming the interior.

8

the crust to reach the mantle have failed.

The earth's structure may be compared to that of a peach. The skin of a peach is thin and outermost, resembling the earth's crust. The fleshy part of a peach, bulkiest of all, is comparable to the earth's plastic mantle and molten outer core. Finally, the peach pit, densest and innermost, is equivalent to the earth's solid inner core.

Nearly three-fourths of the earth's surface is drowned in oceans. The remainder (not taking into account islands) is comprised of continents that rise as great plateaus of rock with an average elevation of about one-half mile above sea level.

The earth's highest mountain is Mt. Everest (in Nepal), towering majestically to an elevation of 29,028 feet above sea level, and its deepest basin is the 35,800-foot-deep Marianas Trench in the western Pacific.

The outside of the earth is very smooth in relation to its total size. Traveling around upon the surface, we are not aware of this because we judge the earth's exterior features in relation to our own diminutive size. A billiard ball, which to us appears highly polished, may be used to illustrate how smooth the outside of the earth really is. If we were to magnify the billiard ball to the size of the earth, the imperfections in its surface would appear as ridges higher than the earth's highest mountains and as valleys deeper than its deepest ocean basins.

We have only scratched the surface of the earth. The deepest mine in the world goes down into the outer shell a mere two miles, penetrating only a small fraction of the average thickness of the crust.

Wisconsin, as we all know, is part of continental North America. Continents are large blocks or "islands" of granitic rock floating upon denser and darker basaltic rocks which girdle the earth and underlie the ocean basins. These rocks together comprise the crust of the earth. A continent floats on basaltic rocks much as an iceberg rides in the water of an ocean. With immense weight, the continental blocks press down deep enough to dimple the underlying mantle.

The Oceans

The Pacific, Atlantic, Indian, Arctic and Antarctic Oceans all comprise one vast connected body of salt water, which surrounds the continents. The statistics of this extensive body of

A seascape.

9

A continent, shown at the top in this profile, floats on basaltic rock, shown in black, which completely wraps the earth. With great weight, the massive continent presses down on the basaltic rock and the mantle below.

water are impressive. It has a total surface area of 140 million square miles, an average depth of 2 1/3 miles and a volume of 330 million cubic miles (representing 0.15% of the total volume of our planet). In addition, it contains 98% of all water on earth while serving, also, as the principle source of our fresh water supply, because 80,000 cubic miles of water evaporate each year from the oceans and fall again as rain and snow.

The oceans, like all geographic features of the earth's surface, are continually changing. Wisconsin illustrates the far-reaching sweep of these changes. Although now situated high above sea level, Wisconsin lay below the waters of shallow seas for long periods in the distant past. It was then that the oceans spread out and advanced inland, flooding large tracts. Many of the rocks exposed at the surface in the state today formed then from sediments accumulating on ocean floors.

Sea floors are not level, featureless basins as generally depicted; rather, they have a rich variety of topographical features, including undersea trenches, in some instances, deep enough to swallow Mt. Everest. The underwater world is one of our last frontiers on earth and we are only now making headway in the exploration of the ocean depths. Fantastic new experiments suggest the possibility of man's eventually adapting to an undersea environment.

The oceans are of peculiar importance to life. Almost certainly, somewhere in their vastness, eons ago, the first forms of life on earth originated. We shall discuss later the significance of this great event.

The Atmosphere

The earth is enveloped by an atmosphere consisting of an invisible mixture of air, water vapor, smoke and dust. The atmosphere surrounds the earth like a protective shell, screening out the lethal rays of the sun and most cosmic rays from outer space. It insulates the earth from the cold beyond and holds in the warmth received from the sun.

Extending skyward, perhaps, as much as 40,000 miles, the atmosphere is the theater of operation for the interacting forces that produce weather. The phenomena of weather — wind, rain, snow and ice — are agents of erosion on the earth's exterior. Without an atmosphere to return water through precipitation to rivers for stream-flow, the earth's surface would remain largely ungroomed throughout eternity. Unless periodically being worn down into tiny fragments, the rocks exposed at the surface would not convert into soil necessary to support life. Without the atmosphere's renewable supply of oxygen and carbon dioxide, all living things would eventually perish.

The atmosphere plays an important part in the story of the rocks of Wisconsin. As our story unfolds, we shall look into its role in more detail.

The atmosphere, too, is subject to change. Earth scientists believe that the atmosphere was devoid of oxygen for a long time after the solid earth formed. An oxygen-free atmosphere was not

10

conducive to the emergence of life on earth in the form we know today because oxygen is essential to all present-day forms of life. Only after oxygen was introduced by natural occurrence did life forms finally appear in great abundance. This was a significant natural change that took place long ago. But one of the latest changes is of our own doing. During the last 35 years we added radioactive fallout particles to the atmosphere through our nuclear explosions. We haven't yet fully assessed the long-term effects of this change.

The Theory Of Plate Tectonics

The earth's crust is made up of a patchwork of seven giant plates and at least 20 smaller ones — all differing in size and shape. The largest of the plates extends beneath most of the Pacific Ocean. The smallest forms the floor for Greece and part of the Aegean Sea. Wisconsin occupies part of an immense plate underlying most of North America.

The plates are rigid and rather thin, enclosing the earth somewhat like the shell on a walnut. Comprised mostly of basalt, granite and other relatively light materials forming the earth's crust, they ride upon the denser hot plastic rocks confined below. The main ingredient of the inner rocks is olivine, a compound of iron, magnesium, silicon, oxygen and other elements.

Sliding about slowly, the plates are driven by heat locked deeply within the earth. The fiery underworld thrusts up molten material, under great pressure, in the form of giant pipelike plumes. The gargantuan plumes are each about 100 miles in diameter. They generate fierce currents in the hot jellylike rock beneath them, thus becoming the driving force that produces earthquakes and volcanoes and moves the continents. They may be thought of as heat engines that furnish the power for major changes in the dynamic earth.

The plumes were first discovered in 1970 by a University of Princeton geophysicist as a result of his studying the fact that satellites circling the earth experience a dip in orbital pattern whenever passing over an area of increased gravity. He reasoned that a gravity high is caused by something extra heavy in the earth's makeup. The concentration of a huge mass of heavy dense plastic rock in the form of a subsurface plume fit the description and provided an answer to the puzzle.

Most earthquakes occur near the edges of the massive plates (indicated with dashed lines) that patch together the earth's crust.

With fault lines marking their edges, the plates are driven laterally to one another, at the rate of a few inches a year, producing continental drift. As the continents drift apart, the seafloors lying between them become spread. Where the plates butt, earthquake activity is frequent.

Scientists refer to earth movements related to the plates as plate tectonics.

The Rock Of Ages

We tend to think of rock as a permanent and indestructible substance. Similarly, we regard landforms, such as mountains and hills, as timeless and immovable surface features. But, in

Ancient Badwater Greenstone, showing pillow structure, cropping out in Florence County.

Jumble of fragmented basalt at Dresser, in Polk County.

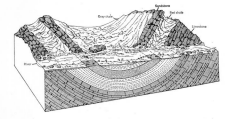

Earth science detectives study and compare rock formations around the world to reconstruct the events of the past. This cross section shows the same rock layers surfacing at two separate places. Thus, geologists would conclude that such layers have become folded since deposition, suggesting a period of crustal deformation.

reality, rock is not permanent and the earth's outer crust is neither stationary nor static. Ever since forming, the earth's exterior has experienced continuous changes. It is always in some stage of being raised, lowered, spread, compressed, twisted, incised or otherwise altered while rock, at the same time, is in the process of being formed or decomposed. Vigorous tectonic forces act on the earth from within, while weather and erosion are busy on the outside manicuring the earth's surface. From day to day, we are seldom aware of these activities but they take place in a subtle manner, much like the aging of living things. We cannot see a person growing older nor a plant developing from a sprout, but we know, by comparing past observations to present ones, that aging and growth occur. Sometimes we see small differences on the earth's exterior, such as a river changing course, a lake drying up or a gully cutting into a hillside. We may have the rare experience in our travels of observing an eruption of an active volcano. But perceptible or not, changes occur continually in the structure and features of the earth's outer crust. Geology deals with the story of the changing earth.

The Greatest Detective Case

By studying rocks exposed at the surface, geologists try to decipher the events of the geologic past. At best, Mother Nature has left a cold and spotty trail. The reconstruction of what took place during the long period of the earth's history, covering the mind-boggling span of about five billion years, is the most challenging of all detective cases. The task requires super sleuthing. Every lead must be pursued. Every scrap of evidence must be gathered and weighed. Every available scientific tool must be pressed into service in order to set straight the disarrayed facts. No stone can be left unturned. The forces that alter, destroy or replace rocks have been busy for eons scrambling clues of the earth's past.

A succession of great changes, continually modifying the composition and structure of the earth's outer crust, clouds and often obscures any backward look into time. Throughout the ages, forces operating both inside and outside the globe, have combined to despoil much of the evidence of earlier events. Thus, it is small wonder that geologists regard many of their conclusions about the occurences of the past as tentative and subject to revision as further research brings to light new information.

Obscure Beginnings

Wisconsin's geologic history spans the long period of the earth's existence from the onset of the first major division of geologic time, called the Precambrian Era, to the present. It includes the shadowy beginning, the undeciphered events of the early years, the periods of great deposition and great erosion, the building and destruction of mountains, the flooding of the land, the subsidence of the oceans, the emergence and evolution of life, the invasion by the glaciers and, most recently, the occu-

12

pancy by man — all advancing the story over an incredible length of time.

Radiometric dating of Precambrian rocks from different parts of North America shows a variance in age from 925 million to 3.5 billion years. The oldest known rocks on earth crop up in Soviet Antarctica and have been dated at 4 billion years. Greenland has rocks dating back to 3.9 billion years. Certain meteorites fallen from outer space have yielded dates in a range of 4.5 to 4.8 billion years, while rock samples brought back from the moon by the astronauts show an age of 4.7 billion years. These data suggest a maximum age of the earth and other planets of about 4.7 to 5 billion years.

Cycles Of Change

By studying rock formations around the world, geologists have learned that, ever since forming, the earth has experienced slow, recurrent cycles of great change. Forces operating within the mantle are largely responsible for these changes. Earth materials lying below the crust exert a variable amount of pressure on the solid crust, especially below continental blocks. These fluctuations in pressure usually develop at an unhurried pace over millions of years. Exactly what causes the pressure changes is not yet fully understood, but they are believed to result from activities associated with plate tectonics. Just as an automobile tire becomes pumped up by introducing more air pressure or deflated by releasing air pressure, the earth's subcrustal pressure has a dynamic influence upon the rocks of the crust.

Continents, in relationship to sea level, are uplifted when subcrustal pressure pushing upward exceeds the crustal pressure pushing downward upon the mantle. With the upward movement of the continents, the rocks of the crust undergo great stress, eventually becoming deformed and displaced. It is then that long periods of mountain building ensue, with volcanoes pushing up and the outer shell wrinkling, buckling and breaking. In time, upland plateaus dominate much of the land and mountain ranges reach toward the skies. As the cycle continues, the internal pressure of the earth is temporarily relieved and long periods follow of only slight crustal disturbance. The upland plateaus and mountains are then slowly eroded and carried away by rivers and streams, accumulating as sediments in the oceans. In time, much of the surface of the continents becomes nearly flat and featureless, while oceans rise and spread gradually over the land. The continents, in the process of becoming denuded, lose a great amount of bulk but the ocean basins, in contrast, take on great weight from a buildup of deposited sediments. Sooner or later, a new uplift of the crust takes place; the continents rise; mountains build; and the cycle, once again, begins.

The same processes responsible for shaping the crust in the past are shaping it now. In the earth's long history so far, there have been, perhaps, ten fully or partly completed cycles. At the present, we appear to be near the beginning or, possibly, middle of a period of new uplift.

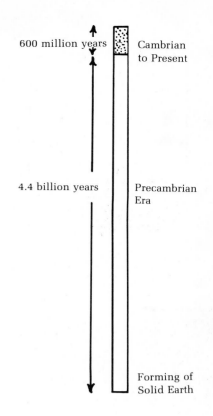

Cycle of change

13

The folds in this very old rock in the Quinnesec Formation in Florence County, illustrate severe crustal deformation.

Folding of crustal strata.

These very old rocks in Portage County are remnants of an episode of mountain building in the distant past.

In Wisconsin, geologists continue to study the rock record, in the long perspective of the earth's history, to determine how many episodes of mountain building may have occurred within the state. Unfortunately, the clues to these events generally are disarrayed and frequently missing. Some conclusions are drawn from rocks still existing that served as building blocks for the most recent of Wisconsin's ancient mountains; but not enough information can be gleaned from the rocks found in the state to reconstruct a full account of the past. Additional information is sought from rocks in other areas, especially those in neighboring states and Canada, indicating what may have happened in Wisconsin. Based on the best evidence so far uncovered, current estimates are that Wisconsin may have experienced, at least, five periods of major mountain building.

The internal and external forces causing these great changes in the earth's outer crust are grouped into three major processes: volcanism, diastrophism and degradation. Because of the importance of these processes to an understanding of how the rocks of Wisconsin formed, we shall take the time to describe each in some detail. Volcanism and diastrophism work from within the earth; but, degradation, in contrast, works on the outside of the earth and concerns the weathering and erosion of surface materials. Mother Nature's orchestration of change through these geologic processes is the greatest symphony of all.

Volcanism

The Romans called their god of fire Vulcan, and volcanism has come to mean the melting, movement and eruption of fluid rock

14

materials because of intense heat locked within the earth's interior. Some writers have described the conditions in the hot underworld as "the fires within the globe". Temperatures there are believed to be in the range of 4000 to 8000°F. Protected on the surface by the insulation of the mantle and crust, we are seldom reminded of the earth's searing interior. But hot springs and geysers suggest locally that great heat prevails below. And volcanoes, in a spectacular way, offer even greater proof of the nature of the fiery underworld. With outpourings of white-hot lava and gas fed from subsurface sources, volcanoes are fired by the same forces that maintain the earth's locked-in heat.

In pushing to the surface, lava usually follows extensive fractures in the crust (fissures) associated with earthquakes. Frequently, it thrusts up through weak spots in the crust where earthquake activity is prevalent and crustal plates butt together. Earth scientists have not yet learned exactly what triggers an eruption.

Two views of the lava flow at Little Bull Falls, north of Pittsville, Wood County.

Volcanoes

Few things in nature are as dramatic as a volcano in action. When we view today's relatively placid setting, a feature in Wisconsin's landscape as spectacular as a volcano seems incredible. But evidence of past volcanic activity is found in numerous exposures of Precambrian rock around the state.

Wisconsin, from time to time, had great volcanoes among its prehistoric mountains. In some parts of the state, the outpourings of bygone volcanoes can still be traced in the bedrock.

An ancient volcanic belt is believed to have extended through central Wisconsin, west and south of Wausau.

Widespread volcanic activity occurred in the area now forming the Upper Fox River Valley in south-central Wisconsin. Extensive deposits of rhyolite and other rocks developing from molten materials are found in scattered outcrops, including those at Berlin, Utley, Montello, Marquette, Alboa, Marcellon, Observatory Hill, Endeavor and Baraboo. Some of the bedrock there shows flow structure suggesting that great eruptions took place at the time of deposit. However, no remains of any volcanic vent nor pipe have been found.

Rib Mountain, towering near Wausau, is part of a complex of rocks representing the roots of an ancient volcano whose underground chamber collapsed long ago.

In addition, you can see hardened sheets of volcanic rock at Saint Croix Falls, in northwestern Wisconsin, which originally flowed great distances overland as lava.

When active, a volcano is an impressive sight — a mountain of fire, spewing gas and lava. But volcanoes differ greatly in appearance. Some develop into stately cones while others erupt with only little relief showing above the surface.

Usually, during the initial stage of an eruption, immense clouds of smoke and ash, belched from the volcano, darken the skies. Fires from the volcano's vent reach through the darkness in eerie fingers of light. Sulphur fumes permeate the air of the lower

A forcible explosion in a volcano results from an accumulation of gas beneath a hardened plug of lava. As stresses build, eventually the volcano blows its top.

15

Magma pushing up (shown in black) sometimes domes upper strata.

"Rotten granite" (syenite), formed from magma long ago, is quarried near Mosinee in Marathon County.

Red granite, another rock originating from magma, outcrops north of Wausau in Marathon County.

atmosphere. Earthquakes shake the land. Thunder rumbles ominously underground. Showers of ash and pumice rain down, burying the countryside under a suffocating blanket of debris. Through these stirrings, the volcano is clearing its massive throat for an impending outburst. Then a sudden, terrifying blast signals the release of molten materials that burst to the surface and gush forth until the eruption subsides. The eruption is both violent and beautiful. Lava ejected from the volcano moves as an all-consuming force, overcoming almost all obstacles in its path. An incandescent mixture of molten rock, gas and steam, the lava, with fires flaring up from escaping gas, flows in streams down the volcano's flanks, spreads out, starts cooling, slows down, stops flowing and eventually hardens into solid rock.

Flows vary greatly in behavior depending upon the volume, composition and temperature of the lava. Some flows travel slowly, but others race overland at speeds up to 35 miles per hour. Flows differ, too, in the rate of cooling — ranging from those composed of lava that cools rapidly and hardens almost immediately upon reaching the surface to those that retain white hot heat for a long time, travel long distances and cool very slowly. The texture of rocks forming when lava solidifies, as we shall discuss later, is influenced significantly by the rate of cooling. Crystalline textures in such rocks are characteristic of slow cooling, while glassy textures, such as in obsidian (volcanic glass), are characteristic of rapid cooling.

Magma

Not all volcanism manifests itself in the form of erupting volcanoes. The process involves all movement of molten materials including that taking place below the surface. Most volcanism, in fact, occurs underground when hot magma (a mass of molten material) squeezes upward and forces itself among older rocks.

Contrasted with lava which pours out on the surface, magma cools and hardens underground, not emerging to the surface while in molten form. Rocks developing from magma come to light later, only after erosion wears away their cover of upper strata and exposes them at the surface. A formation developed from magma solidifying below the surface is called an intrusion.

Sometimes when magma, gradually pushing upward, approaches the surface, it lifts the strata beneath the surface instead of breaking through. This action produces a dome-shaped blister at the surface under which the molten material spreads out. The older rocks forming the blister are left conspicuously arched.

Wisconsin has numerous outcrops of ancient magmatic rocks that originated underground. An example is rotten granite (syenite) exposed in Marathon County; another is Wisconsin's official state rock, red granite, cropping up near Wausau.

Geologists believe that the molten rock feeding a volcano or intrusion has no connection with the superheated, very dense liquid rock comprising the earth's outer core. The two forms of melted rock differ greatly in mineral content. In other words,

16

there are no pipelines reaching outward, as once thought, through which magma moves from the outer core to the crust and surface. Rather, the sources of molten materials associated with volcanism are thought to be located in the upper mantle and crust. But geologists are uncertain as to what brings about the melting of rock at such relatively shallow depths. Incredibly high temperatures, of course, are required to convert solid rock under pressure to a liquid state. The most popular theory is that radioactivity from materials entombed in the crust and mantle generates sufficient heat to produce pockets of magma, which generally have a temperature range of 900 to 2500 degrees F. Probably a reduction in subcrustal pressure brought about by the fracturing or warping of deep layers of crustal rock actually triggers the formation of magma. Such a release of pressure would counteract the constant downward pressure exerted by upper strata which normally keeps subsurface rock compressed in a solid state. This condition would allow the subsurface rock to expand and melt.

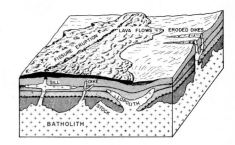

Diagram showing the structural relations of igneous rock masses.

As a melt of rock, magma is mainly silicate in composition, typically containing up to 11% steam and other gases dissolved under pressure. A magma of more than 50% silica is called acid and that with less than 50% silica is called basic.

Subsurface reservoirs of magma thus formed are known as magma chambers. Corrosive gases released from magma eat away subsurface strata as the magma gradually squeezes upward, commonly taking into solution many of the rocks with which it has contact. Magma is lighter and more mobile than solid rock. Hence, it tends to rise toward the surface, forced up by the great pressure upon it of surrounding rock. Sometimes, magma engulfs huge masses of subsurface rock which may become wholly or only partially absorbed into it.

Magma welling up, but not reaching the surface, collects in large subsurface masses called plutons.

Earth activities associated with volcanism occurring underground are described as being plutonic (from the Greek and Roman god, Pluto, the master of the underworld) whereas those pertaining to materials erupted upon the surface are described as being volcanic. Both, generically, are referred to as thermal activities (from the Greek *thermos*, meaning hot).

Diastrophism

Volcanism is usually associated with the second great geological process, diastrophism (from the Greek word for thorough turning over). Working from within the earth, diastrophism is responsible for the periodic disturbance and dislocation of the crust. The process is active when the crust is uplifted, tilted, fractured, folded and then dragged down from below. It generally operates on a large scale producing widespread changes in crustal rocks.

When the continents are raised or lowered, the rocks of the crust are exposed to great stresses, commonly wrinkling in folds and fracturing along faults and joints. A fault is a fracture in the crust along which a section of the crust slips up or down. This vertical movement of the crust is known as displacement. Parallel fractures along which no displacement takes place are called joints. Folding is another common characteristic of crustal deformation, resulting from the warping or bending of rock layers. Folding and faulting, when sufficiently intense to dislocate the surface, lead to mountain building.

Volcanism is always active during a long period of diastrophic change. At the same time as folding and faulting occur, volcanism, as already discussed, is usually responsible for further mountain building.

Earthquakes

Traveling in shock waves, earthquakes are convulsions of the crust and mantle generated commonly by faulting. Some geologists believe that earthquakes are produced primarily by the collision of crustal plates. Earthquakes reflect the restless nature and great power of forces lurking in the underworld. Sometimes earthquakes of great intensity, wracking through rigid crustal rocks, severely fracture the earth's outer shell. Thus, they weaken the structure of crustal rocks and leave them more susceptible to other forces associated with diastrophism and volcanism.

The Defense Civil Preparedness Agency reports on earthquakes: "An earthquake is the oscillatory, and sometimes violent, movement of the earth's surface that follows a release of energy in its crust generated by a sudden dislocation of segments of the crust or by volcanic eruption. When subjected to deep-seated forces, the crust bends. As flexible strength of the rock is exceeded, the crust breaks and assumes a new position. In the breaking process, seismic waves are generated. They travel outward from the break, in all directions. They move along the surface of the earth and through it at varying speeds, depending on the medium through which they move. This causes the entire planet to quiver or ring like a bell."

Ever-Changing Crustal Rocks

As the crust is deformed, crustal rocks undergo great changes in structure. Most become severely tipped, bent or otherwise distorted. At the same time, new rocks develop on or below the surface from molten materials pushing up from subsurface sources. These hot fluid materials come in contact underground with older rocks, sometimes causing them to melt and become absorbed into magma. Frequently, they produce recrystallization in the older rocks, short of melting, as the older rocks become soft from the heat of the magma, somewhat like butter becomes soft on toast and then hardens again when the toast cools. But some of the older rocks experience recrystallization not from direct contact with the magma but from heat and pressure generated by the weight of great quantities of new materials deposited in upper strata or upon the surface. Thus, through volcanism, younger rocks replenish, replace and reinforce older ones.

The rocks of Wisconsin, as elsewhere, enjoy an amazing state of equilibrium. While some are being destroyed, others are being

Extreme folding of the crust produces mountains.

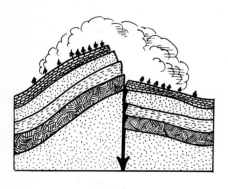

Mountains sometimes develop from severe faulting.

18

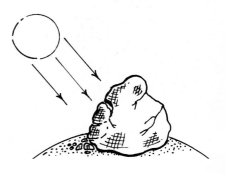

This wall of severely fractured basalt along the St. Croix River near St. Croix Falls, once part of a massive lava flow, shows the effects of sustained weathering and erosion.

Weathering decomposes rock.

formed. The distribution of rocks is kept constant by a natural balancing between the forces that ravage rocks and the events that lead to the formation of new ones.

Degradation

Unlike volcanism and diastrophism, the third great geological process, degradation, operates externally upon the earth's surface. Degradation is responsible for lowering the elevation of land areas by wearing down and carrying away rocks exposed at the surface. Degradation includes all processes that cause weathering, erosion and transportation of surface materials. For our purpose, we shall refer to degradation simply as "weathering and erosion".

Weathering

Weathering is the process by which rocks are broken down and decomposed through the action of external agents, such as wind, rain, temperature change, plants and bacteria. It is the first step in the long series of activities that lead to the stripping off of the surface (denudation). Weathering always attacks rocks where they are (in situs) and no movement nor transportation of sediments to a different place is involved; this factor distinguishes the concept of weathering from that of erosion.

The two types of weathering, relentlessly at work, are mechanical weathering and chemical weathering. Although it is helpful for the purpose of discussion to distinguish between these two types of weathering, they are almost impossible to separate in the field because they work closely together in the breakdown of rocks.

Mechanical weathering is produced chiefly by temperature changes causing rock expansion and contraction, frost wedging and exfoliation. Exfoliation, an onion-skin-like peeling of the surface of a rock, results from the unequal expansion of different mineral components in a rock when strongly heated by the sun. Mechanical weathering also includes plant growth pressure.

Chemical weathering is brought about mainly by the action of chemical substances dissolved in rainwater. The solutions attacking rock are usually acidic in character and wash out or leach rock rather vigorously. Chemical weathering results from several processes which we shall mention but not describe in detail. These are oxidation (chemical alteration by the addition of oxygen), carbonation (attack by carbonic acid), hydrolysis (decomposition by taking up the elements in water), hydration (another type of alteration by the addition of water) and chelation (change in metallic ions). All cause rock to decompose.

Erosion And Transportation

Erosion is the wearing and moving away of the land surface by several natural agencies, the most important of which is water in various forms — rain, runoff, streams, rivers and the sea. Wind, frost, melting snow and ice (especially glacial ice) also contribute to the process of erosion.

Plants also act as an erosive force. Their roots frequently pry rocks apart, helping to reduce into smaller and smaller fragments the primordial slabs of which mountains are made. Brightly colored lichens, seeming to require almost no soil in order to thrive, are found encrusted on rocks in brilliant shades of red, yellow and orange. They are usually the first plants to appear on barren ground as rock decomposes. In the process of growing, they produce an acid that further breaks down rock into soil.

The movement of dislodged earth materials from one place to another is called transportation. Some of the same forces that erode the surface carry away the products of their efforts. Water, wind and ice are Mother Nature's common carriers, variously transporting rock fragments toward their final destination in the oceans. Winds and glaciers normally provide shorter hauls, but rivers operate in branching networks from coast to coast.

Rivers are busiest in the springtime in Wisconsin.

Flowing water carries mud and sand in suspension but stones

Flowing water transports rock particles.

Stream erosion is evident along the Yellow River in Wood County where it has carved a valley through solid granite.

20

are rolled and bounced along river and stream bottoms. At the same time, water transports other mineral materials in solution.

The mass movement downslope of unconsolidated earth materials after weathering includes landslides, earthflow, slumping and soil creep.

As a stream slows down, it drops its load of suspended rock particles — first the largest and then, progressively, the smaller ones. Thus, the deposited materials become uniformly sorted in size.

Sorting Of Sediments

A major service performed by flowing water is the sorting of its load of suspended materials. A stream's capacity to carry sediments in suspension and to push larger particles along the bottom is in direct ratio to the speed of its flow. The faster a stream flows, the greater its potential load. When the current slows, a stream's carrying capacity is correspondingly reduced and some transported materials are automatically dropped. The largest particles are unloaded first and the smallest last. Through this process, a stream sorts deposited materials as though they were passed through a series of screens and graded in particle sizes. The sorting of sediments is important in the distribution of most stream-deposited soils and sedimentary rocks. Similarly, the sorting of materials accounts for most gravel deposits.

This evenly sorted gravel was deposited by glacial meltwater in the South Kettle Moraine Area, in Waukesha County.

Materials Carried In Solution

Water carries minerals in solution after leaching them from rocks with which it has contact. This is another means of transportation of weathered substances incidental to stream flow. Some of the dissolved minerals eventually accumulate in oceans and cause seawater to be salty. The salts of seawater account for about 3.5% of its weight.

Water, The Master Sculptor Of Landforms

The primary agents of transportation — rivers, glaciers and winds — by themselves are capable only of minute abrasive action on rocks over which they pass but, when they gird themselves with hard particles weathered from other rocks, they become powerful agents of erosion. Like sandpaper, they become equipped to be efficient forces of abrasion. By scraping against one another, rock particles become reduced in size, with the softer substances wearing down more rapidly than the harder ones. The property of rocks permitting them to withstand abrasion is called resistance, i.e. a harder substance like granite is more resistant than a softer substance like shale.

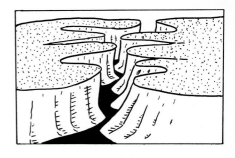

Water is the master sculptor of landforms.

Valleys are good examples of the power of flowing water to erode the land. A valley is carved by a river or stream as it seeks the level of its ultimate drainage basin.

Valleys are classified according to their stage of development as being in *youth, maturity* or *old age*; and the terms are just as descriptive of the characteristics of valleys as when applied to human beings. Excavated and occupied by a swift-flowing river that cuts rapidly down toward base level, a young valley is V-shaped and steep sided. In comparison, a mature valley is deep with flaring sides and gently rounded slopes. A valley in old age, the victim of a long period of erosion, has gentle slopes and a

Sandstone sculptures along the Wisconsin River at Wisconsin Dells.

broad undulating plain where the river flows sluggishly in a meandering course. When all the valleys in a region advance to old age and the divides between them are leveled almost to base level, the land stretches out in a nearly featureless expanse known as a peneplain.

Water, in one form or another, is the hardest working and most versatile of all the agents of weathering and erosion. Three examples of this are raindrops, ice wedging and waves.

Drops of falling rain pound the soil with a force of 2.3 pounds per square inch. In an average downpour, some five million raindrops fall every second on one acre of land. The total impact of raindrops on a field is more than that of a pile driver.

Similarly, ice wedging in the pores or fractures of a rock is a persistent force that, in time, can level mountains. A single crystal of ice expands with a pressure of 400 pounds per square inch. Multiplied by a great number of crystals, the resulting force eventually becomes too much for a rock to bear. The rock cleaves

View of Wisconsin Precambrian peneplain in Portage County.

22

the same as a log split by a wedge.

Driven by strong winds, waves, too, can be a devastating force. Recent tests show that waves breaking against the coast of Scotland have a force up to 6,000 pounds per square foot.

Deltas

As a river empties into an ocean, it comes to a virtual halt, dropping much of its load of suspended materials at the mouth. The loss in velocity of sediment-laden freshwater, lighter than saltwater, results from its tendency to float and spread over the saltwater. As the fresh and saltwaters come in contact and mix at the river's mouth, a large proportion of the sediments "rain" onto the bottom. The deposit that builds up is called a delta. A river builds a delta from borrowed materials — sediments carried from the lands over which it flows. Most of the sediments are particles eroded from rocks cropping up somewhere within the watershed of the river. But some, if the river flows through glaciated areas, come from rocks and soil that were transported into the river's watershed by glaciers during the Ice Age. Some are dust particles from distant places, blown into the river's watershed by winds. And a few are stardust fallen from the heavens.

Oceans As Repositories

In the erosion cycle, ocean basins serve as repositories or dumping grounds for all the wastes of the land. We could think of them as graves where all the pulverized continents would be laid to final rest if nothing ever counteracted erosion. Ocean waters are salty from a residuum of mineral materials dissolved out of rocks, while ocean floors are covered with sediments of the land. Currents and undertows distribute this accumulation to every part of the oceans, but the greatest buildup of bottom deposits is concentrated near river deltas and along continental shelves extending under the waters of the oceans. Shallow water is characteristic where sedimentary materials have been deposited extensively on continental shelves. Such areas are usually very fertile and teem with plant and animal life, setting the stage for the formation of marine fossils for the future rock record.

Water Occurrence And Movement

The Wisconsin Geological and Natural History Survey explains the occurrence and movement of water in Wisconsin as follows:

"All water comes to us in the form of precipitation, either as rain or as snow. Some of this water immediately runs off in rivers and streams to the ocean. Some of it soaks into the ground to replenish groundwater supplies and to form the base flow of many streams. A larger amount is evaporated from water surfaces or transpired by plants back into the air. From here the water comes to us again in the form of precipitation. This continuous circulation of water is known as the hydrologic cycle.

"Once it reaches the earth, water continues to move in a hydrologic system. Part of this system is on the land surface and we

The Wisconsin River at Wisconsin Rapids, in Wood County, is typical of the many rivers and streams that carry the state's surface waters.

recognize it as the streams and rivers in which the water moves. Another part not so easily visualized is underground where the water moves through the small openings and cracks in soil and rock formations.

"Although Wisconsin receives a lot of water in the form of precipitation, only about one-third of that amount is available for use by its people. This is because much water is lost through plants, which is known as transpiration, and from water surfaces and moist soil, known as evaporation. The combination of these two losses is known as evapotranspiration and averages more than 20 inches annually in Wisconsin.

"Water in lakes, ponds, rivers, and streams and flowing over the surface of the ground is called surface water. Wisconsin has a plentiful supply of such water although it varies considerably from place to place and from year to year.

"Runoff is that part of the precipitation that finally appears in surface streams. Compared to the annual average of 28 to 32 inches of precipitation that falls on Wisconsin, the average annual runoff in rivers and streams ranges from 6 to 20 inches, generally increasing from south to north. There are, of course, wide deviations from these averages, and during some of the drier years of record, runoff has totaled less than two inches for some smaller drainage basins in central and southern Wisconsin."

Groundwater

Wisconsin has large reserves of groundwater in its soils and underlying rocks. Groundwater, according to a report of the Ground Water Council, comprises 97% of the total water associated with land areas in the world. Less than 3% of such total supply is surface water — collected in lakes, rivers, streams and wetlands. (These figures, of course, do not include the enormous

Groundwater provinces.

24

amounts of water collected in the oceans.) For example, there is considerably more water under Wisconsin than in all the Great Lakes and the state's thousands of inland lakes combined. Groundwater moves through beds of subterranean rocks. A rock unit that transmits groundwater is called an aquifer (from the Latin words for water bearer). Rocks that serve as aquifers are said to be permeable. Permeability may be defined as the ease with which water moves through a material and depends upon the amount, size and interconnection of pore spaces in such material. Groundwater also moves through fractures in substrata. Rocks, of course, vary considerably in degree of permeability. Sandstone is one of the most permeable of all rocks.

The principal aquifers in the state are shown in the drawing at the bottom of the preceding page.

Geologic Time

Two principal kinds of dates are referred to in geology: relative dates and absolute dates. Relative dates concern qualitative age relationships. In other words, one geologic feature is either older or younger than another. Absolute dates, on the other hand, concern the actual ages of geologic features in thousands, millions or billions of years. It is somewhat easier to comprehend the geologic history of Wisconsin if we consider relative dates in comparing the sequence of events that leads to the present.

Principles Pertaining To The Relative Ages Of Rocks

Relative ages of geologic events and features may be established by comparing one rock formation with another and applying several principles relating to the sequence of rock formations which are universal in application but nevertheless remarkably simple.

- *The Law of Superposition.* In a sequence of stratified rocks that formed one layer at a time, the oldest layer occupies the bottom level, the higher layers are successively younger, and the youngest layer lies on the top. This arrangement

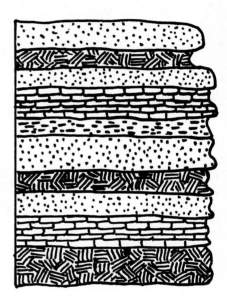

This sequence of strata illustrates the law of superposition.

These rocks at Copper Falls State Park, near Mellen in Ashland County, are set on edge (tilted vertically) illustrating abrupt folding of the crust.

25

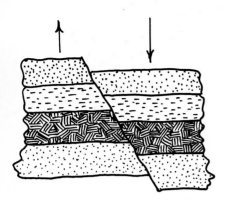

The position of opposing strata along a fault shows the cross-cutting relationship.

The pebbles found in this quartzitic conglomerate in Florence County are older than their host rock.

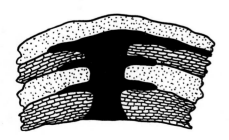

The igneous rock (shown in black) is younger than the strata it intrudes.

assumes that the layers were deposited originally on a horizontal floor and that they have not been folded nor faulted since deposition to such a degree that older layers now rest above younger ones.

- *The Law of Initial Horizontality.* Sedimentary and volcanic rocks are deposited horizontally in a sequence of layers. Evidence of folding after deposition exists where such rocks are found tilted. A disruption in the continuity of a layer along a plane shows faulting after deposition.

- *Faunal and Floral Succession.* There is a regular progressive change in fossil organisms within a sequence of rock layers. The order and direction of this change are usually rather easy to determine because higher layers are successively younger. The more primitive the fossils, the older the rock stratum in which they are formed. Life forms evolve progressively from simple origins to increasingly more complex forms and diversity in numbers. Faunal and floral (animal and plant) succession provides a useful tool in establishing the comparative age and sequence of sedimentary beds deposited since life first appeared on earth.

- *Cross-cutting Relationships.* A fault is a fracture in a bed of rock along which there has been some displacement and through which units of rock are cross-cut. For example, a block of rock on one side of a fault line is always found slipped downward in comparison to the block of rock on the other side. Layers of rock of a corresponding age rest at a lower level in the downthrown block and at a higher level in the upthrown block. Thus, the cross-cutting relationship is such that, in every case, the feature that is cut is older than the feature that cuts across it. Cross-cutting relationships also occur with unconformities and igneous intrusives, both of which are discussed later.

- *Inclusions.* A material is called an inclusion when it becomes enclosed in another material. Inclusions are always older than the rocks in which they are enclosed. As an example, a rock called breccia is composed of an assortment of rock fragments cemented together by another material. The fragments obviously represent older rocks that existed before the cementing material bound them together.

- *Intrusions.* An intrusion occurs in a body of rock when it is invaded underground by fresh molten material (magma) that forces itself into the older rock. A rock that is intruded is older than the rock that intrudes it. As an example, the subsurface layers in a very old unit of rock may be spread and filled with granite injected as a fluid from a deep well of magma. Later the granite cools and hardens, resembling a sandwich filler in the older rock. One may readily deduct that the granite is younger than the host rock.

- *Unconformities.* An unconformity is a break in a depositional sequence of rock beds. Traces of erosion on the top of a layer before the next layer above was laid down is an example of an unconformity. Where an unconformity separates

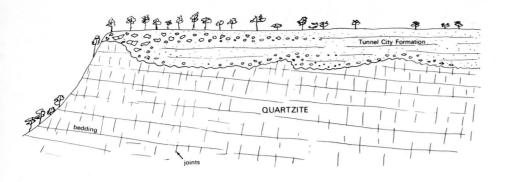

These sketches of the La Rue Quarry near North Freedom, Sauk County, show an unconformity (note deep fracture in bottom sketch filled with quartzite blocks at right) between the quartzite and sandstone strata.

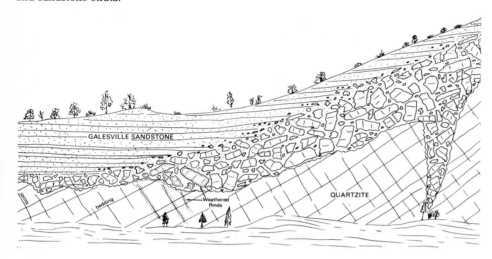

two layers of rock, it represents a gap in geologic time between the period of deposition of each layer.

Radiometric Dating Of Rocks

The dating of igneous and metamorphic rocks (in order to obtain absolute ages in millions and billions of years) has become possible in recent years through a scientific technique devised by geologists known as radiometric or radioactive dating. The method is based upon the fact that rocks containing radioactive elements are subject to radioactive decay. Starting at the time of

This cross section of the Upper Narrows of the Baraboo River shows how a comparison of geologic features helps earth science detectives reconstruct the events of the past.

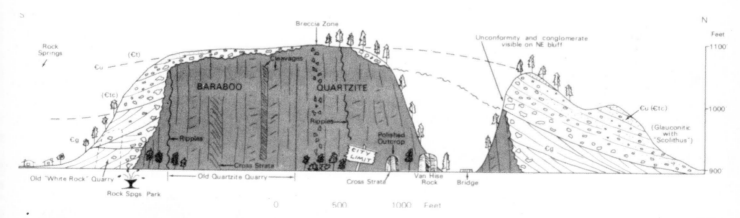

27

the crystallization or recrystallization of the rocks, decay causes daughter products to form as radioactive elements break down through a spontaneous emission of energy. This process occurs at a constant rate and permits a calculation of the age of the rocks through a determination of the amount of the daughter product present and the rate at which it formed.

Geologists study several radioactive elements to date rocks. Uranium, thorium, rubidium and potassium are elements with radioactive isotopes. Radioactive potassium, as an example, de-

No.	Location		Geologic data	Age in million years		
	Town or other location	Sec. T.–R.		Biotite		Other
				Rb–Sr	K–Ar	
1	Mellen	24–45N–3W	Granite porphyry	. . . .	990	. . . .
2	Aurora	38N–19E	Granite	. . . .	1160	. . . .
3	Hogarty.	4–29N–10E	Pegmatite in granite.	1200	. . .	. . . .
4	Wausau.	10–29N–6E	Pegmatite in syenite	1230	. . .	. . . .
5	Mountain . . .	31N–16E	Rhyolite porphyry.	. . . .	. . .	1300^1
6	Stevens Point .	31–24N–8E	Gneiss and schist.	1320	. . .	. . . .
7	Aurora	11–38N–18E	Quinnesec Formation.	1350	1340	. . . .
8	Prairie R. Dells	14–32N–7E	Gray granite.	1370	. . .	. . . .
9	Marion	18N–11E	Coarse schist in granite. . . .	1390	. . .	. . . .
10	Rib River. . . .	31–30N–5E	"Hamburg slate"	1390	. . .	. . . .
11	Waterloo. . . .	9N–13E	Muscovite in granite	. . . .	. . .	1410^2
12	Big Falls	26–25N–12E	Granite	1420	. . .	. . . .
13	Lohrville	18–18N–12E	Granite	1420	. . .	. . . .
14	Praire R. Dells	14–32N–7E	Mafic dike in granite	1420	. . .	. . . .
15	Stevens Point .	18–24N–8E	Granite	. . . .	. . .	1430^3
16	Waterloo. . . .	9N–13E	Pegmatite in quartzite			1440^4
17	Waupaca	29–22N–12E	Rapikivi granite	1440	1430	. . . .
18	Marion	18N–11E	Granite	1440	. . .	. . . .
19	Mosinee Hills .	22–28N–7E	Microgranite	. . . .	. . .	1450 ± 10^3
20	Plover River. .	9–23N–8E	Granite	1460	. . .	. . . .
21	Utley	36–15N–13E	Rhyolite porphyry	. . . .	. . .	1490^3
22	Marion	18N–11E	Inclusion in granite from locality no. 18	1520	. . .	. . . .
23	Wausau.	23–29N–6E	Moonstone pegmatite.	1530	. . .	. . . .
24	Wausau.	22–29N–6E	Biotite-rich gneiss	1530	. . .	. . . .
25	Plover.	8–23N–8E	Gneiss and schist.	1540	. . .	. . . .
26	Neillsville . . .	14–24N–2W	Gneiss and schist.	1570	. . .	. . . .
27	Athens	5–29N–4E	"Hamburg slate"	1250	. . .	1600^4
28	Wausau.	34–30N–8E	Red granite	. . . .	. . .	1600^3
29	Baraboo	21 and 22 12N–7E	Rhyolite under quartzite. . .	. . . .	. . .	1600^3
30	Black River Falls	15–21N–4W	Gneiss and schist.	1610	. . .	. . . .
31	Port Edwards .	36–22N–5E	Gneiss and schist.	1620	. . .	. . . .
32	Nekoosa	3–21N–5E	Gneiss and schist.	1640	. . .	. . . .
33	Monico.	21–36N–11E	Rhyolite	. . . .	. . .	1640^3
34	Wausau.	19–29N–8E	Rhyolite	. . . .	. . .	1640^3
35	Mosinee	4–26N–7E	Rhyolite	. . . .	. . .	1640^3
36	Butternut. . . .	29–41N–1W	Granite cuts iron-formation	. . . .	. . .	1660
37	Niagara.	18–38N–20E	Hoskin Lake Granite	1360 ± 10	1230	1350^2 1500^4 1520 ± 300^1 1720^5
38	Powell.	25–42N–3E	Kyanite-mica schist	. . . .	1720	. . . .
39	Trapp River . .	18–30N–8E	Highly altered slate	1720	. . .	. . . .
40	Merrill	18–31N–7E	"Hamburg slate"	1510	. . .	1800^4
41	Amberg.	5–36N–20E	Newingham granodiorite and Amberg Granite . . . . 30–33N–20E.	. . . .	. . .	1860 ± 15^6
42	Aurora	19–38N–20E	Marinette Quartz Diorite . .	1350	1370	1870^5
43	Dunbar	13–37N–18E	Dunbar Gneiss	. . . .	. . .	1880 ± 15^6
44	Fisher Lake . .	34–38N–19E	Hoskin Lake Granite	. . . .	. . .	1890 ± 15^6
45	Conant Rapids	8–23N–8E	Gneiss and schist	1900	. . .	. . . .
46	Mill Creek . . .	15–23N–7E	Gneiss and schist	1940	. . .	. . . .

Geochronologic data of Precambrian rocks, Wisconsin

28

cays to form argon as a daughter product. The ratio of potassium 40 to argon 40 is used commonly to determine the age of rocks, especially those containing mica.

Radiometric dating reveals rocks on the earth as old as 4 billion years.

Another method of dating, using the radioactive isotope of carbon (carbon 14), is useful in measuring the age of carbonaceous materials, such as wood, bone or coal. This method is based upon the fact that all living matter contains a fixed ratio of carbon 12 and radioactive carbon 14. As soon as a living thing dies, the carbon 14 begins to decay back to nitrogen. This technique can be used to calculate the length of time since an organism ceased to have life. Recent experiments show that this method tends to produce age measurements that are somewhat too young because of exposure of the object tested to varying amounts of carbon 14 derived from the atmosphere. However, a formula for making the necessary correction has been devised.

Radiocarbon dating is used extensively in archeology and glacial geology. But the method is ineffective for substances more than about 40,000 years old, the period of time required for carbon 14 to become so depleted as to prevent accurate measurement.

Radiometric dating of rocks and other objects is a useful tool in deciphering the complex geologic history of Wisconsin. It permits the dating of the geologic time scale in years. However, because of inherent inaccuracies in the measurement of the amount of the daughter product produced by radioactive decay, it is not yet possible, in many cases, to date rocks with any degree of pinpoint accuracy. Error may arise in the determination of the age of a rock if the decay of the parent element to the daughter product is influenced by the introduction of additional quantities of either (or the partial removal of either) through natural causes. It should be noted that the absolute dates obtained by studying different radioactive elements in the same sample of rock commonly show some discrepancies. Moreover, rocks without radioactive elements present at the time of crystallization cannot be dated in this manner. This is the case with sedimentary rocks whose age is determined through a comparison of fossils. Hopefully, improved techniques in the future will make radiometric dating more accurate. The committee on the Measurement of Geological Time observed more than 20 years ago, "These figures (radiometric dates for rocks) are as railway time-tables say, subject to change without notice."

Geologic Time Chart

The recognition of the immensity of geologic time and the development of methods for subdividing geologic time into comprehensive units are among the most significant achievements of geologists. Geologic time deals with the interrelationship between rocks and time. The sequence of events in the earth's long history resulting in the deposition of rocks of different ages is portrayed graphically in what is known as the

GEOLOGIC TIME CHART

ERAS	PERIODS	EPOCHS	DURATION IN MILLIONS OF YRS.	BEGAN MILLIONS OF YEARS AGO
CENOZOIC	Quaternary	Recent * Pleistocene	(Late archeo-logic and his-toric time) 1	 1
	Tertiary	Pliocene Miocene Oligocene Eocene Paleocene	12 12 11 22 5	13 25 36 58 63
MESOZOIC	Cretaceous Jurassic Triassic	(Early, middle or late)	72 46 49	135 181 230
*PALEOZOIC	Permian Pennsylvanian Mississippian * Devonian * Silurian * Ordovician * Cambrian	(Early, middle or late)	50 30 35 60 20 75 100	280 310 345 405 425 500 600
*PROTEROZOIC	* Keweenawan * Huronian		900	1,500
*ARCHEOZOIC	Timiskaming Keewatin		3,500	5,000

PRECAMBRIAN

*(*Most significant in Wisconsin's geologic history)*

geologic time chart. This calendar of the past serves as a frame of reference for bygone geologic events. It is fundamental to any study of historical geology. The product of the combined efforts of many geologists, the time chart represents a condensation of a great deal of information about the ages of rocks. It should be scrutinized carefully. Memorizing it is recommended because it is just as indispensable to the story of the rocks of Wisconsin as the alphabet is to reading.

The oldest time interval is shown at the bottom of the time chart and later ones progressively toward the top. It is designed to be read from the bottom upward, the order in which geologic events develop and successive rock strata usually form.

The largest segments of geologic time shown on the chart are called eras. Historically, eras are separated from one another by major mountain-building episodes, which were substantially worldwide in scope and had a profound effect upon life on earth. Each era is named after a characteristic type of life flourishing during the interval of time represented. All the era names end in the suffix zoic (which comes from the Greek word for life). Thus, the eras are called: *Archeozoic* (era of ancient life), *Proterozoic* (era of former life), *Paleozoic* (era of old life), *Mesozoic* (era of middle life), and *Cenozoic* (era of recent life). The rock units formed during an era are referred to as groups.

Eras are subdivided into periods, which are separated from one another by less extensive episodes of mountain building, more local in scope than those separating eras. Many of the names assigned to periods relate to places where rocks of the age covered by the period were first discovered. For example, the Cambrian Period is defined as the period of time in which certain sedimentary rocks cropping up in Wales were deposited. Cambria is the Latin word for Wales. These rocks furnish the prototype for all Cambrian rocks with which rocks everywhere are correlated and compared. The rocks of Wisconsin which we call Cambrian are of the same sequence as those found in Wales and are presumed, therefore, to have formed during the same geologic time interval. This same principle is followed for the names applied to other geologic periods.

The Ordovician rocks of Wisconsin are of the same system as those found immediately above the Cambrian in Wales. The name is derived from an early Celtic tribe, the Ordovices, who inhabited Wales.

Wisconsin's Silurian rocks correspond to those found in Wales next to and above the Ordovician sequence. The name is taken from the Silures, another early borderland tribe of the region.

Devonian rocks, stratigraphically, follow the Silurian in Wisconsin and elsewhere. They belong to the same horizon of rocks as the sedimentary strata found immediately above the Silurian near Devonshire, England, from which the name is derived.

The further subdivisions of the time chart are self explanatory.

The vast span of time covering all that transpired before the beginning of the Cambrian Period (600 million years ago) is commonly referred to as the Precambrian Era. As we shall learn later, this is a significant division of time in Wisconsin's geologic history.

In recent years, geologists have adopted a system of subdividing the Precambian Era into three major geologic time intervals — Late, Middle and Early — replacing the older terms — Archeozoic and Proterozoic Eras — to describe the same span of time.

Mind-boggling Span Of Geologic Time

If we assume that our story spans a period of 5 billion years and compare the events that took palce in the geologic history of Wisconsin to a period of one year in our life, then one minute to us would be equivalent to 9,511 years of geologic time. The ticking away of one second on a watch would mark the passage of 158 years of the earth's history. The Precambrian Era would take 321 days of the year to unfold. It encompasses about 88% of the earth's history. The Cambrian Period would last slightly more than one week. Everything that has happened since would occur in 36½ days. The Ordovician Period would come and go within 5½ days, the Silurian in less than 1½ days and the Devonian in less than 4½ days. The Ice Age would begin and end during the last 3 hours. Christ would be born with 12 seconds of the year remaining. The Declaration of Independence would be signed during the last 2 seconds. Our own lifespan would cover about ½ of the last second! Our longest sustained efforts (like reading every word in this book) would involve less than a fleeting moment!

II Wisconsin's Building Blocks

The rocks of Wisconsin differ not only in origin but also in mineral content. All serve as structural components for the earth.

Physical Properties Of Rocks

What are rocks? If we conducted a poll at random to find an answer to this question, the chances are that most persons would describe rocks simply as stones (unconsolidated fragments of mineral matter) — the kind typically that make up gravel, rock gardens or stone fireplaces. Certainly, this definition would cross the mind of a farmer, with an aching back, who has just finished clearing his fields of glacial cobbles and boulders. Probably, others would refer to rocks as the materials of which mountains are made. A skier who has raced the wind down rocky slopes, likely, would think in this vein. Less likely, some would describe rocks, on a grander scale, as the mineral matter forming the entire earth. In fact, rocks *are* the earth's structural components or "building blocks" as we shall call them. They form Wisconsin (and the earth everywhere) from the solid crust to the massive layers and super-heated core below.

Rocks have some amazing physical properties which we seldom consider. Even a cursory study of these properties would show that they are ideally suited to serve as the earth's building blocks.

The earth, as a big ball of rock suspended in space, contains a force that keeps material things from spinning away into the void beyond. This remarkable force holding things where they are is called the power of attraction. The familiar name for attraction is gravity. Important to our story of the rocks of Wisconsin, gravity pulls fragments of rocks from hillsides and water from high to low elevations, thus contributing to the movement of materials fundamental to the processes of erosion. Similarly, it forces dust particles to alight from the atmosphere and sand and mud grains to settle on ocean bottoms.

Rocks have the property, too, of being rigid. Without rigidity, the earth would not maintain its shape nor would there be any

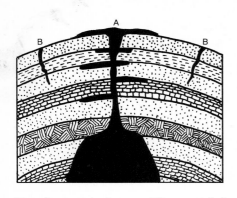

Deep fractures in the crust (A) are mended with molten materials pushing up from below, while shallow fractures (B) are mended with mineral matter precipitating out of ground water.

high nor low places. It is this quality of rocks that gives structure to the continents, islands and ocean basins. Moreover, rigidity allows fragments splintered from bedrock to assume and keep their shapes. If rocks broke down and disintegrated solely into forms of gas and liquid, no soils would develop and terrestrial plant life, as we know it, could not exist.

Another characteristic of rocks, counterbalancing their rigidity, is that of their being somewhat elastic. If the earth's crust could neither be squeezed nor bent, it would break and shatter whenever stress became intense. Earthquakes would soon bring an end to life on our planet. Fortunately, Mother Nature has tempered the rigidity of rocks with a certain degree of elasticity.

The property of rocks to melt fulfills the continuing need to replenish and reinforce the crust as a result of the unending destruction wrought by erosion upon rocks at the surface. Hot fluid materials, periodically welling upward from subsurface sources, replace the bulk of the continents as they become worn down and carried away to the oceans in the form of sediments.

A corollary to the melting of rocks is their ability to solidify when a molten mass cools. This quality, too, is important for keeping crustal rocks in a state of equilibrium.

When the crust becomes deeply fractured, Mother Nature welds it back together with magma and lava. The broken units of rock are bonded together like steel. In addition, when superficial fractures occur, the outer shell is "glued" together by mineral matter precipitating out of underground water. Fractures are mended according to a variable schedule; some, for good reason, are allowed to go unchecked for extended periods. Faults and joints that persist for a long time are usually necessary if units of crustal rock are to have freedom to expand or contract and to lift up or drop down in the face of changing geologic environments. After Humpty Dumpty's fall, all the king's horses and all the king's men couldn't put him back together again; but the earth is kept in a 100% state of repair, where duly required, through natural processes inherent in rocks.

The physical properties of rocks variously contribute to the operation of the counterbalancing forces of diastrophism and volcanism, on the one hand, and weathering and erosion, on the other. If rocks didn't contain a gravitational pull and didn't stretch, bend, break, expand, contract, lift up, drop down, mend, melt and harden, the great cycle of change that keeps our planet stable would go out of kilter.

All Rocks Are Not The Same

Even without looking closely at the rocks exposed at the surface, we are aware that different kinds of rocks exist because we see a variety of them used as building materials in our everyday world. We observe granite, sandstone, limestone, slate and fieldstones in walls, walkways, steps, fireplaces, planters and many other forms of construction.

It is obvious to us that all rocks are not the same. We know from our previous discussion that rocks have different origins. In

34

addition to differences in origin, each kind has its own individuating qualities and these provide a basis for identifying, classifying and assigning a name.

However, before we discuss the classification of rocks, let's consider the distinction between rocks and minerals.

Distinction Between Rocks And Minerals

Rocks, as we have already mentioned, are the building blocks of the earth. Minerals, in contrast, are the natural chemical substances making up rocks. But these generalizations leave some questions unanswered.

How do minerals compose rocks? And what, in turn, are minerals composed of? We can't develop a meaningful appreciation for rocks and minerals unless we first learn the clear-cut distinction between the two. To do this, we must look from something as large as a mass of rock to something as small as an atom.

An atom is the smallest part of an element. All matter on earth is made up of one or more of some 100 known elements. This includes all solids, liquids and gases. Meteorites fallen from space and lunar samples brought back by the astronauts contain identical elements to some of those found on earth. The same basic materials probably comprise the whole universe. An element is a pure substance. There is no chemical means of breaking it down any smaller.

An essential property of atoms, the minute components of elements, is that they are gregarious. Seldom do atoms exist in a solitary state. Almost universally, they join up with other atoms, sometimes with their own kind, sometimes with other kinds. They band together through electrical force and form molecules.

As an example, if an atom of oxygen combines with another atom of oxygen, a molecule of oxygen is formed. But if two atoms of hydrogen join together with one atom of oxygen, a molecule of water is created. This combination of atoms produces a new substance called a compound. The symbol for hydrogen is H and for oxygen O. Thus the formula for water is H_2O.

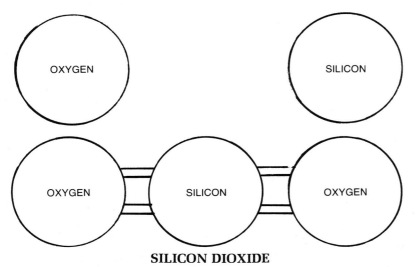

SILICON DIOXIDE
The simple elements oxygen (O) and silicon (Si) band together to form the compound silicon dioxide (SiO_2), which, as a mineral, is called quartz.

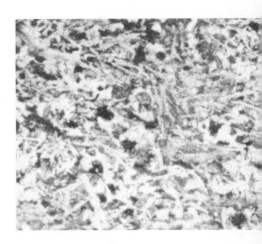

This photo, with a magnification of approximately 100X, shows the mineral distribution in a specimen of Precambrian greenstone from the Central Wisconsin Volcanic Belt near Wausau.

35

Like an element, a compound is a pure substance. No matter how divided, it has exactly the same composition. Homogeneous is the term for describing this uniform nature of a compound. (Homogeneous is derived from the Greek words meaning of the same kind.)

Compounds all have properties not shared by the elements of which they are composed and there are millions of compounds making up most things on earth. But we should distinguish between compounds and mixtures. A mixture, too, is a combination of two or more elements.

But in a mixture, the different kinds of atoms are not banded together by electrical force and each retains its own identity and characteristics. Each can be separated from the other by physical processes. The components in a mixture are not joined together to form a new substance as in a compound. Air is an example of a mixture. It is made up principally of nitrogen and oxygen, with each gas keeping its own identity. Each can be isolated physically. All substances are either elements, compounds or mixtures.

There are two distinct families of molecules. The small or lighter ones comprise all inanimate things — such as stone, metal, air and water. The large or heavier ones, on the other hand, are the stuff making up life. All life forms — animal and vegetable — are comprised of the heavier molecules, which are called polymers. Thus, all things of organic origin contain polymers but other substances not of organic origin do not contain polymers. So for our purposes, let's make a distinction between substances of organic origin and those of inorganic origin.

Now to the definition of a mineral. A mineral is a structurally homogeneous solid of definite chemical composition, formed by the inorganic processes of nature. Simply stated, a mineral is a natural inorganic solid substance formed as a single element or a compound. But it is never a mixture. It doesn't contain any polymers, with only a few exceptions.

This definition even includes ice as a mineral. But coal is excluded because of its organic origin. We do, however, regard some substances to be minerals that began as the shells of marine animals, frequently the main constituents of limestone. The only exception to our definition that a mineral must be a solid is native mercury (quicksilver), which is a liquid.

In our definition the terms "of definite chemical composition" are not synonymous with being "of fixed or constant composition" because a given mineral may include a range of slightly different compounds. Its composition may be variable between certain limits, which are defined in terms of what the chemists call end members. An example of this is the olivine group of minerals. The formula for the olivines is expressed in terms of two compounds Mg_2SiO_4 (forsterite) and Fe_2SiO_4 (fayolite). Mg is the symbol for magnesium, Si for silicon and Fe for iron. The variation in the composition of the olivines pertains to differences in their iron and magnesium content. The general rule is that minor variations in composition which do not markedly

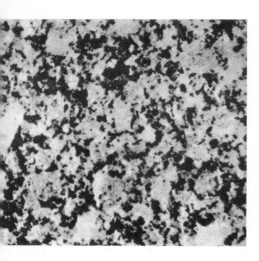

Granite. An aggregate of light and dark mineral grains.

36

alter the fundamental properties of a mineral are discounted. Slight variations in the chemical content of two compounds can be found among the members of a given mineral group. But we don't mean to suggest that a mineral within the end limits of its group is not homogeneous. On the contrary, it does, without exception, have a uniform, orderly internal structure.

Minerals, as we have explained them, are the building blocks of *almost all* rocks. Some rocks, however, aren't formed of minerals. Coal is such a rock. So are natural deposits of paraffin and asphalt. This is also the case with volcanic glass, which is called obsidian. It cools so fast when solidifying from lava that it doesn't develop an orderly internal structure qualifying it as a mineral.

Quartz crystals

All minerals, in addition to all other characteristics, are crystalline. By that, we mean they always have orderly internal structures, capable of being stated in chemical formulas.

All minerals are composed of either one or more elements. Examples of minerals formed from only one element are copper and sulfur, both of which are metals. In the nonmetals, graphite and diamond are formed solely of carbon. Most minerals, however, are a compound of two or more elements. An example of this is quartz whose chemical name is silicon dioxide (SiO_2).

Minerals are classified as metals or nonmetals. The most common minerals are the so-called rock-forming minerals, essential to the composition of all rock. In addition, many important minerals constitute ore bodies. These yield metals and are known as metallic minerals. They, of course, are of great economic importance. Some nonmetallic minerals are of little economic importance even though they are distributed throughout the earth. But some of the nonmetallics are used for their chemical properties, especially for medicines. The basic difference between the metallic and nonmetallic minerals pertains to the way their atoms bond together.

Twin crystals of staurolite

But where do crystals fit into the picture? Most minerals, as we know, do, on occasion, form crystals. A crystal is a three-dimensional solid body, with bounding surfaces arranged symmetrically. In a given mineral, a crystal has constant angular relationships, which arise from the regular atomic structure of the mineral. But to be a crystal, a specimen must be so formed as to present an outward manifestation of its orderly internal structure.

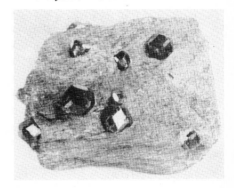
Garnet crystals in schist

On the other hand, all minerals are *crystalline*. All have an orderly internal structure despite the fact that many do not necessarily occur as geometric crystals that can be plainly seen. In other words, a mineral may not form as an obvious crystal even though it is always crystalline. This distinction between crystal and crystalline is important to remember for our further discussion of minerals.

In summary, we may consider that rocks, in general, are composed of minerals and that minerals, in turn, are either elements or compounds. In short, we may think of rocks as mineral aggregates.

Common Elements Composing Minerals

Although there are some 100 known elements, more than 98% of the earth's crust in Wisconsin and elsewhere is composed of only eight elements, which are shown in the following table.

Element	Symbol	Atom %	Weight %	Volume %
Oxygen	O	61.85	46.40	94.27
Silicon	Si	21.40	28.15	.88
Aluminum	Al	6.51	8.23	.47
Iron	Fe	2.15	5.63	.48
Magnesium	Mg	3.64	4.15	.58
Calcium	Ca	1.26	2.36	.68
Potassium	K	1.26	2.33	1.65
Sodium	Na	1.94	2.07	.99

Classification Of Rocks Based On Origin

All rocks are classified in three major groups based upon how they formed: igneous, metamorphic and sedimentary.

Wisconsin has numerous outcrops of rocks belonging to each of these groups offering clues to the events in its complex geologic history.

Igneous Rocks

Igneous rocks form from the cooling and solidification of molten materials. Lava and magma are the hot mother liquids of all igneous rocks. Igeneous comes from the Latin word meaning fire. The size of the mineral grains in igneous rocks depends upon the rate of cooling of the molten material.

The igneous rocks that develop from lava (which by definition is extruded upon the surface) are called extrusive igneous rocks. Because lava cools rapidly in most cases when spreading out on the surface with much of its heat escaping into the atmosphere, the grain size of most extrusive igneous rocks is fine or even indistinguishable. The other kind of igneous rocks (always forming from magma solidifying below the surface) are called intrusive igneous rocks. Because fiery hot magma cools slowly in most cases with much of its original heat trapped underground where it dissipates at a very slow rate, the grain size of most intrusive igneous rocks is large or coarse. But, apart from difference in grain size, the two kinds of igneous rocks have many common characteristics. The same subsurface masses of molten materials feed both volcanoes and subsurface intrusions. Consequently, for each variety of extrusive igneous rock, there is an intrusive igneous equivalent of substantially the same mineral composition.

In Wisconsin and elsewhere, principal intrusive igneous rocks are: granite, diorite and gabbro. Their extrusive igneous counterparts, in the same order, are: rhyolite, andesite and basalt. In addition, peridotite is a locally common intrusive igneous rock.

Ancient extrusive igneous rock from an outcrop west of Wausau

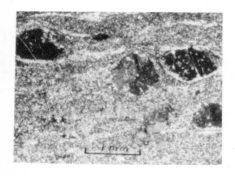

Precambrian intrusive igneous rock from the Eau Claire Dells east of Wausau

38

Granite

Granite is one of the most common intrusive igneous rocks. Essential minerals for classification as a true granite are quartz and potash feldspar, while optional (but commonly present): plagioclase feldspar, biotite mica or amphibole (hornblende). Some granites contain random grains of muscovite mica as well as minor accessory minerals such as apatite, magnetite and zircon.

Usually a handsome rock with a prominent crystalline texture, granite comes in a wide range of colors. Wisconsin's granites are mostly red, green, mottled black and white (salt and pepper) and pink. Wisconsin's official state rock is red granite, a beautiful ruby red rock quarried near Wausau. Other varieties of granite are found at many scattered places around the state, with concentrations between Wisconsin Rapids and Wausau, along the Wolf River in Menominee County, in northern Marinette County, along the Black River in Jackson and Clark Counties and in northern Waupaca County.

Syenite is another intrusive igneous rock similar to granite but containing little or no quartz. Extensive outcrops of syenite occur in Marathon County.

Rhyolite

Rhyolite is the extrusive counterpart of granite. In texture, its most prominent grains are quartz but potash feldspar and biotite mica are also common. Rhyolite is found as bedrock in many places, such as in the central part of the state, northwest of Wausau and around Mountain, in Oconto County.

Diorite

Another intrusive igneous rock, diorite is less common than granite and generally contains various dark minerals such as biotite mica, amphibole (hornblende) and pyroxene (augite). Plagioclase is the dominant feldspar but potash feldspar also is usually present. Diorite crops up in many places in northern Wisconsin, including a concentrated area between Wisconsin Rapids and Wausau and another southeast of Rhinelander.

Andesite

Andesite is the extrusive equivalent of diorite. Somewhat characterless, it shows mostly feldspar grains. Andesite crops up west of Rudolph, in Wood County, and extensive flows of andesite are found in company with basalt flows in northwestern Wisconsin.

Gabbro

Gabbro, an intrusive igneous rock, is a sinister-looking dark rock. Its principal minerals are pyroxene (augite) and plagioclase feldspar (usually labradorite). In addition, it frequently contains hornblende and olivine. A wide-bedded gabbro crops up around Mellen, in Ashland County.

Granite boulders scattered around by the glaciers (top: near Mosinee, Marathon County; bottom: near Amherst, Portage County)

39

Very old gabbro surfaces near Mellen in Ashland County

Basalt

Basalt, the most abundant of the lavas, is the extrusive counterpart of gabbro. It is a fine grained rock, popularily referred to as trap rock. Commonly, small spherical or ellipsoidal cavities are contained in basalt and result from bubbles of gas that became trapped when the rock solidified from lava. These cavities are called vesicles. In time they fill with materials precipitating out of solution from underground water or gas. Common vesicle-fillers are quartz, calcite, epidote and a number of other minerals. Lake Superior agates originate from the filling of vesicles in the basalt forming part of the bedrock around Lake Superior, which extends as far west as St. Croix Falls and beyond

Basalt bluffs border the St Croix River near St. Croix Falls in Polk County.

40

the boundary line of the state into Minnesota. A large scale quarry of basalt is in operation at Dresser, in Polk County.

Peridotite

Commonly dark green in color, peridotite is an intrusive igneous rock consisting chiefly of olivine and pyroxene. Extrusive equivalents of peridotite are rare. Outcrops of altered peridotite are found in the vicinity of Rudolph, in Wood County.

Metamorphic Rocks

Metamorphic rocks are formed by the alteration in texture or composition of rocks underlying the surface. This transformation is called metamorphism (from the Greek for change + form). Metamorphism results from rocks experiencing a changed geologic environment in which their stability can be maintained only by a corresponding change in physical and chemical makeup. Heat, pressure and fluids are the major agents bringing about the change, which is characterized by the development of new textures, new minerals or both in the altered rocks. The process operates without the rocks melting. Instead, new textures are produced by a recrystallization of the grains in the altered rocks. The mineral grains develop into larger crystals, with a different orientation than before. Typical structures in metamorphic rocks are described as wavy, banded or foliated (leaf-like), due to a parallel arrangement of platy or elongated mineral constituents. When cleaved, such rocks have a tendency to separate along lines of foliation.

New minerals are created through metamorphism when minerals form new partnerships. As the minerals recombine, minor impurities take on more significant roles, influencing the chemistry of the altered substances. Even though a number of minerals are distinctively of metamorphic origin, most metamorphic rocks are similar in overall chemical composition to the antecedent rocks from which they transformed.

Metamorphism usually takes place in rocks when they become

These ridges are composed of extremely old metamorphic rocks (left: Baraboo Range, Sauk County; bottom: Penokee Range, Iron County).

41

deeply buried, when the crust becomes severly folded, when hot gas solutions develop from a magma or when physical contact is made underground with a mass of magma. Most of these circumstances arise during periods of violent crustal deformation and mountain building. However, materials building up on the surface for other reasons may produce sufficient heat and pressure for metamorphism to occur in deeply entombed strata.

Metamorphic rocks may develop from any kind of rock — igneous, sedimentary or previously metamorphic.

Gneiss

Common metamorphic rocks are found in many places in Wisconsin. One of the most abundant is gneiss, a coarsely layered metamorphic rock, consisting of alternating layers or lens of unlike appearance. Felspar and quartz layers — the dominant constituents in most gneisses — are more granular and lighter in color than those rich in biotite mica, amphibole (hornblende) or garnet. Ancient gneiss crops up in the Black River Falls-Neillsville area, commonly pink to red or grey to green in color. Some geologists believe that most gneiss results from the metamorphism of granite.

Schist

Gneiss grades into schist, another abundant metamorphic rock, when platy or mica constituents dominate. In schist, visible minerals tend to be more uniform in appearance and composition, with little feldspar present and adjacent layers generally consisting of the same minerals. Schist is extremely foliated, causing it to split readily. Varieties of schist are referred to on the basis of the most prominent mineral present such as mica schist, talcose shist, garnet schist, hornblende schist or chlorite schist.

Greenstone schist is found abundantly in the Penokee Range, in Iron and Ashland Counties. Sericite schist, with or without garnet, is a common rock in the iron formations near Black River Falls.

Slate

Slate is metamorphosed shale, characterized by the way it splits easily into smooth, lustrous plates (slaty cleavage). The blackboards in old-time school rooms commonly were slabs of slate. Normally having a carbon content in the form of graphite along with some iron and manganese, slate varies in color with black or gray prevailing and red not uncommon. Outcrops of slate are found northwest of Wausau, in Marathon County, and near Florence in Forest County.

Phyllite

Phyllite is a metamorphic rock representing a transition in texture between schist and slate. It tends to break into slabs metallic in appearance, with surfaces showing minute crumpling. Some phyllite associated with schist is found in the Black River Falls area.

Closeup of a specimen of slate from Florence County. Piece of twig shown is one inch long.

42

Marble

Marble, a massive, nonfoliated crystalline rock, results from the metamorphism of either limestone or dolomite. Impurities present during the time of transformation produce striking patterns in marble making it much in demand as a construction stone. A green dolomite marble is quarried at Grand View, in Bayfield County.

Quartzite

Quartzite is a very common metamorphic rock in Wisconsin, composing many striking landforms, such as the hills of the Baraboo Range, in Sauk County. Quartzite results from sandstone that has been thoroughly altered by metamorphism. When fractured, it has a glassy surface because it breaks indiscriminately through the original sand grains and cement enclosing them rather than separating around the grains like the fracturing of unmetamorphosed sandstone. Quartzite is one of the most durable of all rocks with great resistance to weathering and erosion.

Among other prominent outcrops of quartzite in the state are the Blue Hills, in Barron County; Rib Mountain, near Wausau; the Flambeau Ridge, near Holcomb, in Chippewa County; McCaslin Mountain, in northeastern Wisconsin, and scattered mounds in central Wisconsin.

Quartzite crops up at many other places including areas west of Waterloo, in Jefferson and Dodge Counties, and north of Lake Mills, in Jefferson County.

Sedimentary Rocks

Sedimentary rocks are the most abundant of all exposed rocks, sheathing about 80% of the earth's surface. They form from the broken and dissolved remains of older igneous, sedimentary and metamorphic rocks which have become disintegrated through weathering and erosion. Sedimentary rocks develop either through an accumulation of sediments — usually deposited by

These topographic features formed from Paleozoic-age sedimentary rocks (top: limestone bluff on shore of Green Bay in Door County; left: sandstone sculpture along Wisconsin River at Wisconsin Dells).

rivers draining into ocean basins — or through precipitation from solutions. Those developing from solid sediments form clastic sedimentary rocks. Clastic is derived from the Greek word for broken piece. Those developing from the deposition of dissolved mineral matter are called precipitated or nonclastic sedimentary rocks. However, precipitated mineral matter also contributes to the cementing of clastic materials.

Unconsolidated fragments of older rocks accumulating on ocean floors or in other basins where sediments collect become buried beneath a gradual buildup of other sediments and in time develop into a mass of compact rock, through a process known as lithification. Lithification results from the close compaction of buried sediments due to the weight of other sediments accumulating above, the cementing together of the buried sediments by mineral matter precipitating out of underground water and the chemical alteration and recrystallization of such buried sediments, especially when the spaces between them become filled with other mineral matter. Thus, a compacted sedimentary rock is described as being lithified.

As younger deposits of sediments cover older ones, buried layers transform very slowly into solid rock. Sedimentary rock takes a long time to build up. To start with, sedimentation usually occurs at a snail's pace. For a layer one foot thick to develop, the average estimated time required for shale is 100 years, for sandstone 450 years and for limestone 6,000 years. Because it forms the fastest, shale is the most frequently occurring sedimentary rock. In contrast, limestone accumulates the slowest because it derives from the shells and skeletons of aquatic life, which are much less plentiful than sediments deposited by rivers draining into oceans. Calcite oozes developing from concentrations of microscopic marine remains turn into a very fine-grain compact form of limestone. A noticeably different variety of limestone, called coquina, is composed of coarse, loosely compacted organic fragments, principally of shells but sometimes of crinoid stems and plates, pieces of coral or algae.

As a result of Wisconsin's having been covered by oceans for long periods during the Paleozoic Era, all the common types of clastic and precipitated sedimentary rocks are now found abundantly at the surface — mostly in the southern portions of the state where they have more successfully resisted erosion.

Conglomerate

Conglomerate is naturally cemented gravel. Varying greatly in size, the fragments making up a conglomerate may come from any kind of rock. But quartz and chalcedony pebbles are most common. Usually the interstices between the fragments are filled with sand grains. When the fragments consist of relatively uncommon rubble with sharp edges and pointed corners, the conglomerate is called sedimentary breccia.

The Great Conglomerate beds in northern Wisconsin, extending down from Upper Michigan, are estimated to be as much as 2,200 feet thick. Outcrops of conglomerate are found along the shoreline of Lake Superior. An ancient variety occurs as bedrock near Powers Bluff, in Wood County.

Sandstone

Sandstone is made up of cemented grains of sand. Quartz is the principal mineral in most sandstones. But many other minerals are usually present, including the placer minerals, such as magnetite, rutile and zircon. Placer minerals are those that are heavy and very resistant to weathering and thus become concentrated as sediments by running water or along beaches. If deposited in sufficient quantity, the placer minerals act as coloring agents, producing black or yellow sands. But in most cases, the color of sandstone is determined by the nature of its cement. Red and brown sandstones are held together with a cementing material containing a great deal of iron. Arkhose is a variety of sandstone containing a large amount of feldspar in addition to quartz. Graywacke is a sandstone in which dark rock fragments predominate, such as particles of slate or fine-grained igneous rock.

An interesting green sandstone (glauconitic sandstone) is found in random places in western Wisconsin; its moss green

This sketch of the sedimentary rock outcropping at Irvin Park in Chippewa Falls, Chippewa County, illustrates the wide range of size in particles comprising various sandstones.

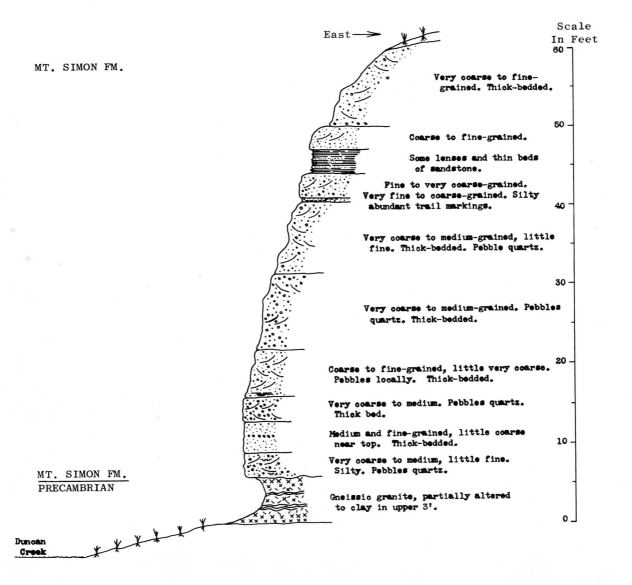

45

color results from the presence of a high percentage of the mineral glauconite.

Wisconsin's sandstones represent a broad range of geologic periods. The sandstones exposed along the shoreline of Lake Superior are of Precambrian age. A graywacke of even more ancient vintage crops up north of Wausau. The castellated formations around Camp Douglas, in Juneau County, and the Wisconsin River sculptures at Wisconsin Dells are formed of Cambrian-age sandstones. And the most plentiful of all, younger sandstones of the Paleozoic Era compose landforms in many places in eastern, western and southern Wisconsin.

Shale

Sediments smaller than sand grains form shale, the most abundant sedimentary rock on all the continents. Shale is composed of lithified mud (silt and clay) — the smallest rock particles of all. Hence, it has a fine texture, appearing homogeneous to the unaided eye. But usually some grains of mica and quartz are present. Sandy shales are called *arenaceous*. When organic matter is sufficiently present to color shale black, it is called *carbonaceous*.

The widespread shales of western, southern and eastern Wisconsin, represent the entire span when the state was submerged intermittently below Paleozoic seas — from the Cambrian Period into the Devonian Period. Most of these shales are fossil-bearing. A whimsically named shale of even more ancient origin, Nonesuch Shale, crops up south of Lake Superior. It has a measurable copper content and has been mined successfully in Upper Michigan. But all efforts to mine it in Wisconsin have been unsuccessful.

Limestone

Limestone is the most common of the nonclastic sedimentary rocks. Most limestones build up on ocean floors from an accumulation of shells and skeletons of marine organisms. A great variety of hard-shelled sea creatures grow resistant parts through the removal of calcium carbonate from seawater. When these creatures die, their shells remain as a rock-forming material. This material is the major ingredient of limestone. Spaces in a developing mass of limestone are filled with the same material, either in a powder form created by pounding waves or as a chemical precipitate from sea water.

Because it is composed of calcium carbonate, limestone is classified chemically as a carbonate. All minerals classed as carbonates are composed of carbon, oxygen and other elements. The chief mineral component of limestone is calcite, which is easily tested because it effervesces in cold acid.

Some of the state's carbonates of sedimentary origin are limestone but most are dolomite.

Dolomite

Resembling limestone in most ways, dolomite is formed when magnesium replaces part of the calcite in limestone. The process

46

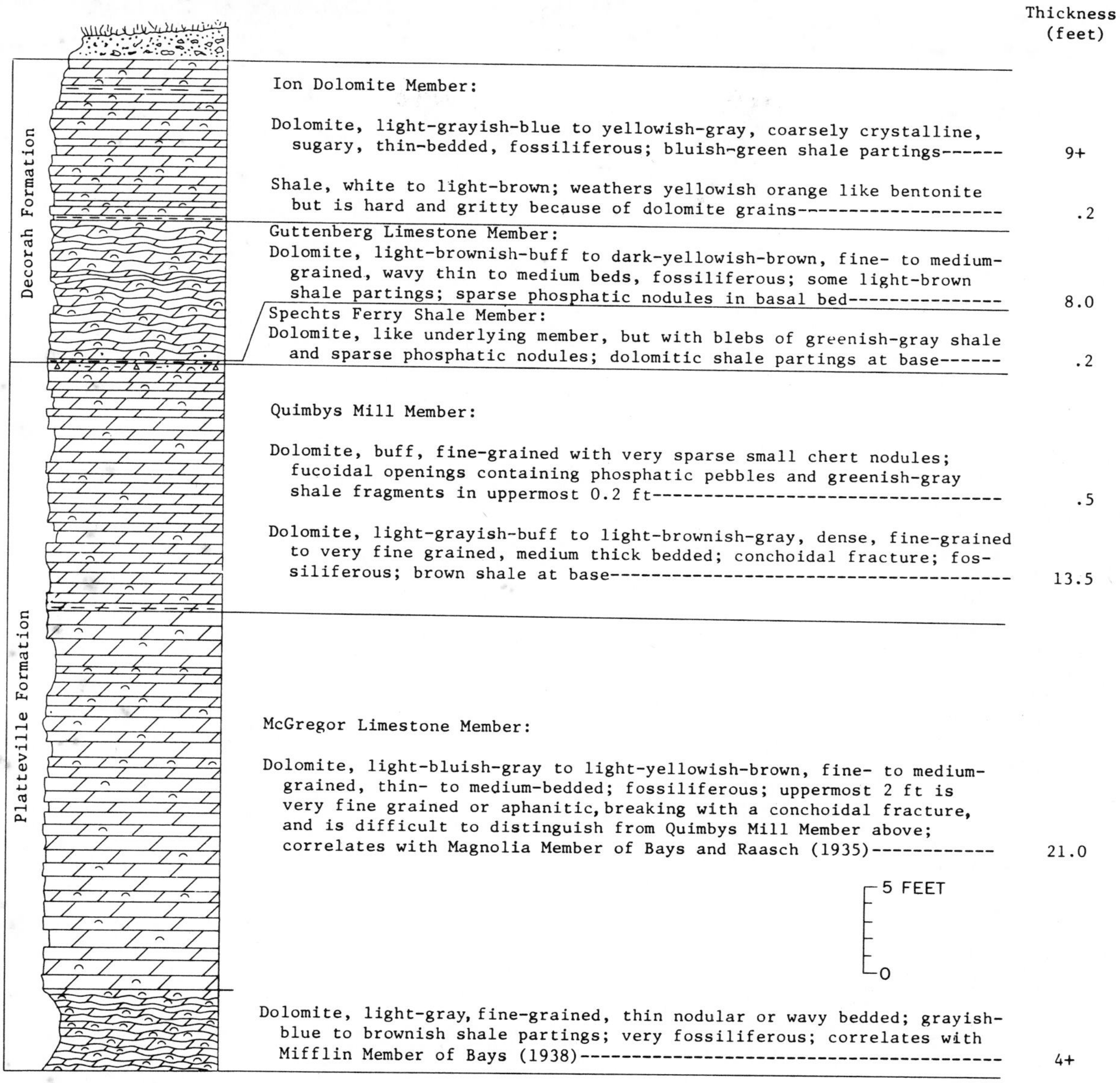
Thickness (feet)
Decorah Formation
Ion Dolomite Member:
Dolomite, light-grayish-blue to yellowish-gray, coarsely crystalline, sugary, thin-bedded, fossiliferous; bluish-green shale partings------ 9+
Shale, white to light-brown; weathers yellowish orange like bentonite but is hard and gritty because of dolomite grains------------------- .2
Guttenberg Limestone Member:
Dolomite, light-brownish-buff to dark-yellowish-brown, fine- to medium-grained, wavy thin to medium beds, fossiliferous; some light-brown shale partings; sparse phosphatic nodules in basal bed--------------- 8.0
Spechts Ferry Shale Member:
Dolomite, like underlying member, but with blebs of greenish-gray shale and sparse phosphatic nodules; dolomitic shale partings at base------ .2
Platteville Formation
Quimbys Mill Member:
Dolomite, buff, fine-grained with very sparse small chert nodules; fucoidal openings containing phosphatic pebbles and greenish-gray shale fragments in uppermost 0.2 ft---------------------------------- .5
Dolomite, light-grayish-buff to light-brownish-gray, dense, fine-grained to very fine grained, medium thick bedded; conchoidal fracture; fossiliferous; brown shale at base-------------------------------------- 13.5
McGregor Limestone Member:
Dolomite, light-bluish-gray to light-yellowish-brown, fine- to medium-grained, thin- to medium-bedded; fossiliferous; uppermost 2 ft is very fine grained or aphanitic, breaking with a conchoidal fracture, and is difficult to distinguish from Quimbys Mill Member above; correlates with Magnolia Member of Bays and Raasch (1935)------------ 21.0
5 FEET
0
Dolomite, light-gray, fine-grained, thin nodular or wavy bedded; grayish-blue to brownish shale partings; very fossiliferous; correlates with Mifflin Member of Bays (1938)-- 4+

This profile shows the dolomitized strata at a quarry one mile north of Darlington, in Lafayette County.

by which dolomite forms is called dolomitization. Limestone develops in deeper water but dolomitization usually occurs in warm shallow, more saline waters. Dolomite, as a mineral (calcium magnesium carbonate), is somewhat harder and heavier than calcite (calcium carbonate); it is less soluble in acid and effervesces in cold acid only after being freshly scratched or pulverized. Most of the so-called limestone formations throughout the southern, eastern and western portions of the state actually are composed of dolomite. Because they are more resistant to erosion than most other exposed sedimentary rocks, Ordovieian-age dolomites remain often as pronounced ridges throughout much of the landscape.

Chert

Underground water sometimes precipitates quartz (silica) from solution, slowly forming large masses of a rock called chert — a nonclastic sedimentary rock. Powers Bluff, near Arpin, in Wood County, is believed to be composed of chert that has been metamorphosed since its original deposition. Chert nodules frequently occur as cavity fillers in beds of limestone and dolomite. Agate is a form of chert.

Rock-Forming Minerals

Now that we have discussed briefly the classification of rocks into three major groups based upon their mode of origin, let's consider the most common minerals found in Wisconsin relating to each of these groups. Although these minerals, in each instance, can be described by chemical formula, our getting to know them may be easier if we pass over their chemical composition, and stress instead their physical characteristics. Many books are available on the subject of the chemical composition of minerals.

In the next chapter, we shall discuss in more detail the matter of mineral identification.

Minerals Of Igneous Origin

Feldspar

A scant number of minerals form most igneous rocks found in Wisconsin. The most abundant of these are the feldspars, a group of silicate minerals. All the feldspars are composed of aluminum, silicon and oxygen. Additional elements distinguish the members within the group. The potash-soda feldspars (mainly orthoclase and microline) contain potassium (potash) and sodium (soda). The soda-lime feldspars (plagioclase) contain sodium and calcium (lime). All tend to be tabular in shape and show good cleavage — the manner of breaking into fragments. Orthoclase is derived from the Greek words for right and to break. It describes the feldspars' two chief cleavages which are at right angles. Thus, fragments of feldspar typically are domino-shaped.

Quartz

One of the most important and, certainly, the most widespread of all minerals is quartz, with the word possibly derived from the old Greek word for ice. Commonly ice-like in appearance, quartz can be recognized in igneous rocks as a glassy, colorless or gray mineral, without noticeable crystal shape because it forms late as molten materials cool and fills the irregular spaces left between earlier-formed mineral grains. The handsome six-sided crystals of quartz, proudly displayed by mineral collectors, formed, most likely, in caves or cavities in preexisting beds of rock and not from a molten mass.

Mica

The mica group of minerals is remarkable because of its flaky texture and elastic properties. Mica in some instances peels in sheets like the pages of a book. It is so resilient that it will actually snap back after being bent abrupty. The thin, semitransparent sheets are sometimes too thin to handle. Mica is also incorrectly called isinglass, suggesting its widespread use in the

Feldspar (orthoclase)

Amphibole (hornblende)

Mica (muscovite) and quartz

48

past as a material for window panes. The old fashioned base burner stoves glowed through ports fitted with mica. The three main series of mica, present in a diversity of igneous rocks, are biotite (the most common and dark to black in color), muscovite (white mica known as muscovy glass because of its popularity in Muscovy, Russia, as window glass) and lepidolite (a lithium-bearing pink form).

Pyroxene

The pyroxene minerals follow right behind the feldspars as the most universal constituents in igneous rocks, especially those forming early as molten materials cool. Generally dark green or brown, the common members of the pyroxene group are diopside, enstatite and, most abundantly, augite. Pyroxene is a combination of words from the Greek for fire and for stranger. Actually, the name is inappropriate because pyroxene is a fairly common ingredient, far from a stranger in many igneous rocks.

Amphibole

The amphibole family is another major group of rock-forming minerals, composed of silicates of various metals. Crystallizing later than pyroxene from magma or lava, amphibole, none-the-less, bears a strong resemblance to pyroxene. Amphibole is distinguishable, however, because of its large-angled cleavage and greater tendency toward elongated crystals. Hornblende, an extremely complex mineral, is the most common species of amphibole.

Olivine

One of the first minerals to precipitate from molten materials while still very hot, olivine as its name suggests (think of olives) is green in color. Generally glassy looking but sometimes sugary in texture, it is easily recognized.

Zeolite

Zeolites commonly fill cavities left by gas escaping from lava and appear variously in igneous extrusive rocks as little pinwheels (thomsonite), sheafs of grain (stilbite) or clusters of delicate needles (natrolite). Zeolite is derived from the Greek word meaning to boil because it tends to bubble when heated with a blow pipe.

Minerals Of Metamorphic Origin

Minerals of igneous and sedimentary origin, of course, are essential components of most metamorphic rocks. In addition, other minerals are typically of metamorphic origin. Let's consider briefly some of the latter which we are likely to encounter in Wisconsin's very old metamorphic rocks.

Pistachio green in color, epidote forms in masses and, less commonly, as complex crystals in cavities in metamorphic rock.

Idocrase, with crystals of green and brown, closely resembles epidote. This mineral was formerly known as vesuvianite be-

Epidote

Kyanite

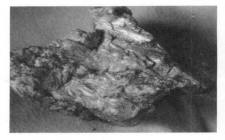

Actinolite

cause it was identified as one of the rocks altered in the eruption of Mount Vesuvius.

Ranking among the principal minerals developing in metamorphic rocks, the garnet group crystallizes in the isometric system. Red colored almandite garnets are the most common variety found in Wisconsin. They sometimes form crystals as large as dimes in host rocks, such as in the garnet schist cropping up east of Black River Falls.

A metamorphic member of the pyroxene group, diopside forms in crystals of transparent pale green or white, most commonly as an ingredient in marble.

Grading into actinolite, tremolite is a member of the amphibole group of minerals.

Other fairly common metamorphic minerals are andalusite, kyanite and sillimanite — all composed of aluminum silicate.

Minerals In Sedimentary Rocks

All the minerals associated with igneous and metamorphic rocks are represented in the many sedimentary rocks which are formed from the broken and dissolved remains of older rocks of diverse origins. Sediments compose all sandstones, shales, clay stones, siltstones and conglomerates. However, some sedimentary rocks such as limestone are formed of the mineral calcite. The word calcite, is derived from the Latin word for lime because it becomes lime when heated. Calcite is the most abundant of the carbonate minerals. It is also the most diversified of all known minerals, described in more than 300 different forms, including nail-head, dog-tooth and twinned crystal forms. Highly soluble, it is deposited from dripping water in caves as stalactites and stalagmites. Reacting as a carbonate, it fizzes in dilute acid.

The most common clay mineral is kaolinte. It is easy to identify as a specimen because of its earthy appearance and peculiar property of sticking when touched with the tongue.

Bowen's Reaction Theory

When magma, from the depths of the underworld, wells up as a hot melt near the earth's surface, it gradually cools and hardens into rock. Minerals precipitate from the cooling magma and form as crystals according to an orderly sequence. In a typical basaltic melt as the temperature falls, the minerals crystallize in the following sequence: first olivine, then pyroxene, amphibole and biotite, concurrently with calcic plagioclase turning to sodic plagioclase, followed by potassium feldspar and muscovite and, finally, by quartz. This crystallization sequence in igneous rock is called Bowen's Reaction Series because it was first described by the American geologist, N.L. Bowen. He also suggested that chemical reactions occur between the crystals forming early in a melt and the still liquid portion of the melt, influencing the mineral composition of the rocks finally formed.

Metallic minerals usually precipitate from a magma near the end of a melt and, generally, in association with quartz. Thus, exploration for metals like gold and silver is directed commonly

Stalactitic calcite

Quartz (chert)

Calcite (coquina)

50

toward formations containing large concentrations of magmatic quartz.

Classification Of Rocks Based On Age

All of the bedrock of Wisconsin is classified in two major groups based upon age as Precambrian or younger. The Precambrian rocks — all older than 600 million years — are mostly ancient crystalline rocks, extensively contorted as a result of folding and faulting after deposition. These old rocks are the gnarled survivors of distant geologic periods. The younger rocks, in contrast, are seemingly flat-lying sedimentary rocks, dating back to the Paleozoic Era, deposited during the Cambrian, Ordovician, Silurian and Devonian periods.

"Crystalline" Rocks

Many of the earth's crustal rocks, including those composing Precambrian outcroppings in Wisconsin, are referred to as crystalline rocks because they are made up of a mass of intergrown crystals. The individual crystals forming many of these rocks are large enough to be seen by the naked eye; but in some rocks they are indistinguishable because of their microscopic size, in which case, the rocks are referred to as being crytocrystalline. (The prefix, cryto, is derived from the Greek word cryptos meaning hidden.) The so-called family of crystalline rocks includes most igneous and metamorphic materials. Crystalline rocks are generally distinguished from typical sedimentary rocks which are composed of a mass of compacted sediments. The term crystalline is loosely used in this context because, technically, in atomic science, all solids by definition are crystalline. This is true because solids are composed of atoms which always form with an orderly arrangement. The term is misleading, too, because some precipitated sedimentary rocks like chert have a definite crystalline texture, although they are not of igneous nor metamorphic origin.

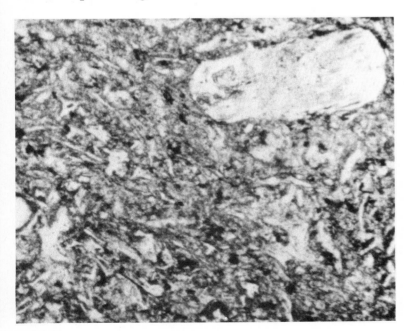

This closeup (magnification approximately 140X) shows feldspar phenocrysts in rhyolite cropping up at Wausau.

51

Porphyritic texture in syenite. Crystals of feldspar in a fine-grained matrix.

Phenocrysts

Sometimes, in a crystalline rock, the crystals of one mineral grow to a noticeably larger size than the crystals of other minerals. Standing out like dandelions in a lawn, these large conspicuous crystals are known as phenocrysts. The fine material in the rock is called groundmass. Common phenocrysts are formed of feldspar, hornblende or epidote. When phenocrysts are present, an igneous rock is referred to as being porphyritic. Such rocks are named after the ground mass rather than the dominant crystal. Typical are granite porphyry, syenite porphyry and andesite porphyry.

Glacial alluvium — unsorted deposits of gravel left by streams of glacial melt water — found in northern Wisconsin commonly contains pebble and cobble-size specimens of porphyritic rock, sometimes suitable for lapidary use.

The Rock Cycle

In the rock cycle, rocks through the operation of recurring geologic processes commonly change in time from one form to another. Sediments may lithify into sedimentary rock; sedimentary rock may transform through metamorphism into metamorphic rock; metamorphic rock may dissolve into an invading magma and, when the magma cools and solidifies, become igneous rock; and, finally, igneous rock when exposed at the surface may convert, through weathering and erosion, into sediments — and the rock cycle begins once again. The cycle, however, doesn't always go full circle; each stage is determined by geologic events occurring in the upper crust or upon the surface. Sometimes, stages take place out of order from those portrayed in the conventional cycle. Periods of sedimentation may be followed by periods of erosion without the intervention of any events associated with diastrophism or volcanism; in such a situation, thick layers of sedimentary rock build up, separated by uncomformities respresenting the periods of erosion. In some instances, igneous rock may be metamorphosed before being diminished by weathering and erosion and in other instances, metamorphic rock may be reduced to sediments by weathering and erosion without first being taken into solution by plutonic activity.

In each stage of the rock cycle, rocks experience chemical changes. At the same time, underground water and gas are busy leaching minerals from substrata, transporting them in solution and redepositing them in new host rock; by this means — called hydrothermal activity — new mineral partnerships also form.

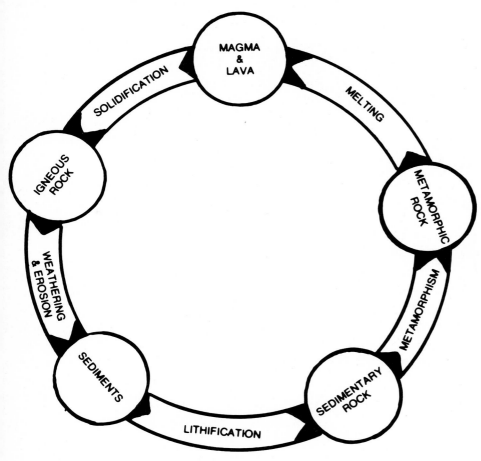

The rock cycle

III Identifying Wisconsin's Minerals

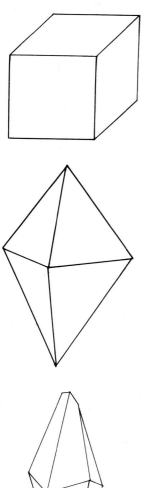

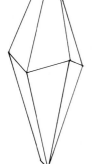

Minerals composing Wisconsin's rocks are classified on the basis of their physical and chemical characteristics. These properties help identify mineral specimens found in the field.

Getting To Know Minerals

Of the world's 2,500 mineral species, only about 150 are commonly found. A good museum collection consists of about 500 different mineral specimens.

Mineralogy is the science pertaining to minerals. In mineralogy, all minerals are compared and identified on the basis of their chemical and physical characteristics. Among physical properties compared are color, hardness, streak, specific gravity, luster, cleavage, fracture and crystal form. These properties and others may be tested in laboratories using sophisticated equipment. However, simple field testing, in most cases, will lead to an accurate identification of specimens.

A table for identifying some of the minerals found in Wisconsin is set forth on pages 78-83.

Color

A mineral's color offers the first clue pointing to its identity. In most metallic minerals, color provides a reliable bit of information. But, in individual specimens of some common minerals, such as quartz, calcite, agate, tourmaline and garnet, color varies greatly and should be used as an identification aid only with caution. Impurities present when a mineral forms often influence its color. Iron oxide is a common coloring agent. As an example, Lake Superior agates are found usually in shades of red because iron oxide was present along with the principle mineral quartz during the agate-forming process. But other specimens of these agates come in brown, green, grey, black or white; some even have amethyst centers.

Luster

A mineral's luster depends upon the absorption, reflection or refraction of light by its surface. Luster is a useful characteristic

Calcite cleavage
(right angle)

Galena cleavage
(cubic)

Quartz fracture
(uneven)

The Way Minerals Break

Siltstone fracture
(earthy)

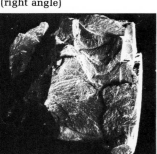
Slate cleavage
(slaty)

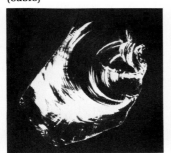
Obsidian fracture
(conchoidal)

Mica cleavage
(sheet-like)

Fluorite cleavage
(octahedral)

in identifying specimens. A given mineral may be vitreous (glassy) like quartz, earthy like kaolin, silky like asbestos, adamantine (brillant) like diamond, greasy like serpentine, resinous like sphalerite, pearly like mica or metallic like galena.

Cleavage And Fracture

The way minerals break into fragments differs among mineral families. Some minerals split along planes related to their molecular structure and the surfaces created by their breaking are referred to as their cleavage. However, if minerals break other than along planes, the surfaces created by their breaking are called their fracture. Cleavage and fracture provide useful information for mineral identification. As an illustration, galena cleaves in perfect cubes, mica in sheets and fluorite, sometimes, in octahedral fragments.

The Prehistoric Indians made projectile points from materials such as obsidian and flint that flake with a conchoidal (spoon-shaped) fracture. But the fracture of other minerals is described as earthy, fibrous, splintery, hackly, even or uneven.

Hardness

The hardness (H.) of minerals differs from that of the softest, talc, to that of the hardest, diamond. Hardness is a very useful tool for identifying minerals.

The degree of hardness of a mineral specimen may be readily ascertained because it will scratch only softer substances and, in turn, can be scratched only by harder substances. By using other mineral specimens of known degrees of hardness, a little scratching with or upon the specimen to be identified will lead quickly

Mohs' Scale of Hardness, although arbitrary, is useful in mineral identification. It is based upon ten well-known minerals, ranging from the softest (1) to the hardest (10):

1. Talc	6. Orthoclase
2. Gypsum	7. Quartz
3. Calcite	8. Topaz
4. Fluorite	9. Corundum
5. Apatite	10. Diamond

In field testing the following materials may be used to compare the hardness of a specimen:

2.5 fingernail
3.0 penny
5.5 window glass or knife blade
6.5 steel file or razor blade
7.0 agate

55

to its correct classification of hardness, through the process of elimination.

Mohs' Scale of Hardness is based upon the comparative degree of hardness of ten well-known minerals. It should be noted, however, that the numbers on this scale do not reflect equal divisions in the range of hardness. For instance, diamond (#10) compared to corundum (#9) is many times harder than corundum (#9) compared to topaz (#8) or gypsum (#2) compared to talc (#1).

Most books describing minerals list the hardness of most common minerals according to Mohs' Scale and provide an easy reference for confirming the identification of specimens.

Streak

Most metallic minerals produce a streak when rubbed across an unglazed porcelain surface called a streak plate. The back of a piece of ceramic tile makes an excellent streak plate. The streak results from the color of the powered mineral. The color differs depending upon the mineral species. As an example of how streak helps in identification, magnetite, hematite and limonite are all iron ores found in Wisconsin, sometimes with much the same general physical appearance. They may be easily distinguished, however, through a streak test. Magnetite streaks black, hematite dark cherry red and limonite yellow-brown.

Specific Gravity

The specific gravity (Sp. Gr.) of a mineral is the ratio of its weight to that of an equal volume of water. Because various rocks of the same size differ considerably in weight, specific gravity measurements are widely used in mineral identification. As an illustration, galena, a relatively heavy mineral, has a specific gravity of 7.5, whereas graphite, hardly a feather weight itself, has a specific gravity of 2.0. Both are dark colored minerals. Graphite is used as the "lead" in wooden pencils and galena is the common ore of the metal lead. With such a widespread in comparative weight, it is unlikely that these two minerals would be confused for each other.

Crystals

Crystals, so varied in form among mineral species, are the architectural masterpieces of Mother Nature. Sometimes they are so magnificent in their beauty and symmetry that it is difficult to believe that they are natural. They reveal amazing mathematical relationships. They were referred to by one pioneer French geologist as "the flowers of the minerals".

A crystal's shape (habit) is the external expression of its internal structure which is composed of molecules attaching to one another according to an orderly plan and forming a latticework. Somewhat as square tiles are laid — side by side — forming a square floor, a crystal is made up of microscopic-size parts, precisely arranged, with each having a habit identical to that of the crystal. Each integral part is a miniature reproduction of the

A typical streak test

Specific Gravities of some common and uncommon minerals found in Wisconsin are as follows:

2.0	Graphite
2.2- 2.7	Serpentine
2.6	Orthoclase (feldspar)
2.7	Quartz
2.72	Calcite
2.7- 2.8	Soapstone
2.85	Dolomite
2.0- 2.5	Muscovite (mica)
3.0	Tremolite
3.2	Apatite
3.6- 4.0	Limonite
3.5	Augite
3.9- 4.0	Malachite
4.0	Sphalerite
4.5	Barite
4.7	Zircon
4.89	Marcasite
5.02	Pyrite
5.2	Magnetite
5.3	Hematite
7.5	Galena
8.9	Copper
15.0-19.3	Gold

SYMMETRY CLUES

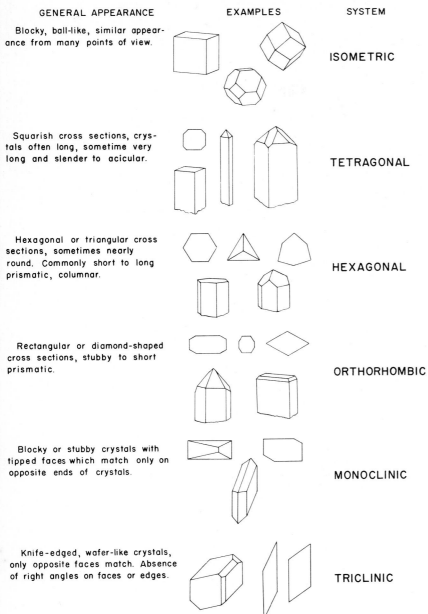

GENERAL APPEARANCE   EXAMPLES   SYSTEM

Blocky, ball-like, similar appearance from many points of view. — ISOMETRIC

Squarish cross sections, crystals often long, sometime very long and slender to acicular. — TETRAGONAL

Hexagonal or triangular cross sections, sometimes nearly round. Commonly short to long prismatic, columnar. — HEXAGONAL

Rectangular or diamond-shaped cross sections, stubby to short prismatic. — ORTHORHOMBIC

Blocky or stubby crystals with tipped faces which match only on opposite ends of crystals. — MONOCLINIC

Knife-edged, wafer-like crystals, only opposite faces match. Absence of right angles on faces or edges. — TRICLINIC

From *Mineralogy for Amateurs* by John Sinkankas © 1964 by Litton Educational Publishing, Inc. Reprinted by permission of Van Nostrand Reinhold Company.

external shape of the crystal itself. A crystal is described, therefore, as a mass of crystalline material bounded by natural growth surfaces.

Whether growing alone or as a member of a cluster, a crystal is a systematically proportioned mass, with obvious geometric relationships on its face. From the smallest to the largest, it represents an embodiment in stone of nature's supreme beauty and order.

The science dealing with crystals is called crystallography. The study of crystal forms is called morphology.

Crystals are classified, according to their shape, in six major systems: cubic (isometric), tetragonal, hexagonal, orthorhombic, monoclinic and triclinic.

Garnet

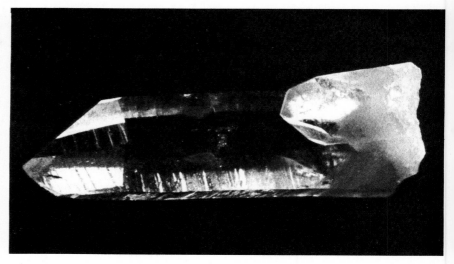

Quartz

Calcite

Calcite

If the crystal form of a mineral specimen is prominent enough to be visible to the unaided eye, it is referred to by rockhounds as a crystal, otherwise, it is called a mineral specimen. Although this distinction is somewhat unscientific, it is followed in this text.

Specimens of crystals are found in many places in Wisconsin. Clusters of exceptionally fine elongated quartz crystals occur as cavity-fillers in the quartzite at Rock Springs in Sauk County. Some of the best millerite cyrstals (nickel sulphite) found anywhere come from the sedimentary rocks at Estrabrook Park, in Milwaukee. Sphalerite, galena, calcite, pyrite and marcasite crystals are plentiful in the rocks of the lead and zinc region of southwestern Wisconsin. Pyrite, marcasite and calcite crystals occur abundantly in the dolomite of eastern Wisconsin.

A study of crystal forms is extremely helpful in mineral identification.

Unfortunately, any discussion other than this bare introduction into the fascinating world of crystals would go beyond the scope of this presentation. But many books and journals treat this subject in detail.

Rock Oddities

Adding a touch of the bizarre and mysterious, rock and mineral oddities are found occasionally throughout Wisconsin. These include such varied natural curios as geodes, concretions, ripple marks, fulgurites, meteorites and small specimens of rock spectacularly sculptured by weathering and erosion.

Geodes, only infrequently found in the state, are hollow balls of mineral matter lined with crystals. Highly prized by collectors, they are minature caverns, adorned with sparkling crystal terminations. Rarely, Lake Superior agates are formed as small but beautiful geodes, with cavities encrusted with crystals of amethyst.

A *concretion* occurs in sedimentary rock where a mass of cementing material concentrates during the process of lithification and later erodes out of neighboring softer rock in some

58

fantastic and complex shape. Concretions commonly are spherical but may be flat or elongated. They range in size from less than an inch to several feet. Common cementing materials forming concretions are quartz, calcite, iron oxide and dolomite. Sandstone concretions, in a seemingly endless assortment of little spherical sculptures, are found near Arcadia in Trempealeau County. Some of these resemble bunches of grapes. Shale concretions, in a myriad of bizarre shapes, are found at Waverly Beach in Ashland County, along the shoreline of Lake Superior. Some bear an amazing resemblance to shrunken human heads.

Fossil-like in appearance, *ripple marks* are formed in sedimentary rocks, at the time of deposition, by the action of waves in a shallow sea. These interesting impressions of prehistoric wave action arrested in stone are found in many places around the state, almost anywhere that clastic rocks of the Paleozoic crop up.

Fulgerites are sometimes called petrified lightning. A product of the intense heat contained in lightning, they are formed by the fusion of grains of sand, in narrow hollow tubes, marking the spot where lightning strikes the ground. Reaching downward several inches, they appear commonly as branches or forks, with glass threads hanging like whiskers from the inside of the tubes. Specimens of fulgerites are found in the sandy bed of old Glacial Lake Wisconsin — in Wood, Adams and Juneau Counties. They are found, also, in sandy areas around Portage, in Columbia County.

Meteorites, from time to time, fall on Wisconsin. These wonderous stones from outer space are the only objects available to us with an origin outside our own planet — except for the lunar samples brought back to earth by the astronauts. Meteorites are of two kinds: iron or stoney. Iron meteorites are called siderites and consist almost entirely of iron alloyed with nickel. Stoney meteorites are known as aerolites and are composed of silicate minerals with only small amounts of nickel and iron. The Mil-

Shale concretions from Waverly Beach

Sandstone concretions from Arcadia

Typical ripple marks preserved in sedimentary strata (above). At left, ripple marks, shown with arrow appear on a vertical face of the quarry wall at Rock Springs, in Sauk County. This is a good example of extensive tilting of strata that was originally deposited on a horizontal plain.

59

Representative iron meteorite.

An iron meteorite polished and acid-etched on the surface to reveal the Widman-Staettin pattern — showing the crystal pattern of the iron and/or nickel.

waukee Public Museum has specimens on display of both types of meteorites, representative of those that have fallen on Wisconsin. Included are a 21-pound stoney meteorite from near Colby, in Clark County, and a 27-pound five-ounce siderite meteorite from the town of Trenton, in Washington County.

Weather and erosion sculptures are rock oddities produced by the weathering and erosion of exposed rock. Water is a master artist, creating masterpieces in stone, ranging from those as grandiose as the Grand Canyon to those as small as pebble-size art forms that especially appeal to collectors. Sometimes water augers through extremely hard rock, leaving boulders or cobbles with holes resembling the finger-holes in bowling balls. Plated and pillared sculptures are produced by differential weathering which results from varying degrees of resistance in layered rock; small hand-size specimens are common in many gravel deposits. Sometimes, these sculptures resemble a stack of plates of different sizes.

Sandblasting, too, fashions some interestingly shaped pebbles known as *ventifacts*. Sand, hitting a pebble on the side facing the prevailing wind, produces a concave polished surface. Most ventifacts have several such wind pitted surfaces, three being common. Another word for ventifact is the German dreikanter, meaning three edges.

Gemstones

Gemstones are described as minerals with ornamental value. Cut and polished, they are used for personal adornment, generally as settings in jewelry. They represent the nobility of the mineral kingdom.

Gemstones are classified according to their degree of rarity. The most valuable of all, *precious stones* include only diamonds, rubies, sapphires, and emeralds. The next most valuable, *semiprecious stones* include a number of infrequently occurring transparent crystals such as beryl, spinel, tourmaline, topaz, zircon, spodumene, garnet, amethyst and citrine. In addition, jade and opal are considered semiprecious. The jewelry stones of lesser value not classified as precious nor semiprecious are called *gems* or *gemstones*. These, including the great family of quartz gemstones, make up the cutting materials most commonly worked upon by rockhounds. The quartz gemstones consist of numerous varieties of quartz, agate, jasper, flint, chert, amethyst, opal, true onyx, chalcedony and many petrified substances.

When set in a jewelry mounting, a transparent stone is referred to as a *jewel*.

Gemstones — precious, semiprecious and gem quality — are found in Wisconsin in varying degrees of abundance. These include diamond, corundum (both ruby and sapphire reported from near Seymour, in Outagamie County), zircon (from west of Wausau, in Marathon County), beryl (from the Embarrass River, near Tigerton, in Shawano County), fresh water pearls, garnet, jade, amethyst, rock crystal (clear transparent quartz), smoky, quartz, labradorite, peristerite, agate, jasper, chert, coquina, ser-

60

pentine, epidote, jaspilite, breccia, aventurine and other less well-known cutting materials.

The chief characteristics distinguishing gemstone materials are beauty, hardness, color, durability and rarity. Other traits are transparency, in the case of faceting grade gems, and pattern, fire, scenic quality or chatoyancy (shimmer), in the case of translucent or opaque cutting materials.

Gallery Of Wisconsin Specimens

Wisconsin offers a rich variety and abundance of rocks and minerals — from jade to junkite (the whimsical term used by rockhounds to describe a rock or mineral that is virtually worthless). Unfound rock and mineral treasures await discovery almost everywhere. Of course, there isn't a gem under every toadstool, but there's something of interest in just about every deposit of rock. The photos on the following pages portray some of the fascinating members of the mineral kingdom found in the state. These include rocks, crystals, minerals, gemstones, ores and stone oddities. The specimens shown are representative of those available in the field but, generally, are of better than average quality because they have been selected from several outstanding collections.

Smoky Quartz. This hexagonal crystal of smoky quartz is from western Marathon County, found in a vug in "rotten granite."

Quartz. Quartz is one of the most common minerals in the earth's crust. This elongated crystal is from McCaslin Mountain, near Townsend, in Oconto County.

Calcite. Appearing in more than 300 different forms, calcite is the most diversified of all minerals. Crystals are found almost everywhere dolomite or limestone outcrops, especially in southern and eastern Wisconsin.

Millerite. The hairlike, radiating crystals of this beautiful specimen of millerite, from Estabrook Park in Milwaukee, are typical of this nickel sulfide mineral.

Galena and Calcite. Galena is Wisconsin's official mineral. The cubic crystals in this specimen, occurring with calcite, are typical. Found abundantly in southwestern Wisconsin.

Pyrite. One of the most common metallic minerals, pyrite is also known as "fool's gold." From Lutz's Quarry, Oshkosh, in Winnebago County.

Smithsonite. Forming as zinc ores weather, smithsonite usually appears as a crystalline crust. The original source of zinc in southwestern Wisconsin, smithsonite was known as "dry bone."

Dolomite. Formed from the remains of Paleozoic-age marine organisms, dolomite is a very common rock and mineral. The crystals, uncommon in Wisconsin, are often saddle-shaped, pink and vitreous. From Linden, in Iowa County.

Actinolite. This fibrous crystalline variety of actinolite is from east of Rudolph, in Wood County.

Aragonite. Chemically the same as calcite, aragonite crystallizes in the orthorhombic system. This specimen is from Platteville, in Grant County.

Goethite. Formed from the weathering of iron-rich rocks, goethite frequently appears as a pseudomorph replacing pyrite. From Hurley, in Iron County.

Garnet in Matrix. An important rock-forming mineral, garnet is a constituent in some of Wisconsin's ancient metamorphic rocks. This specimen is from near Black River Falls, in Jackson County.

Sphalerite. A common mineral in southwestern Wisconsin, sphalerite, known as "black jack," is an abundant ore of zinc.

Petrified Wood. This gnarled specimen of petrified wood was found in glacial drift near St. Croix Falls, in Polk County.

Feldspar. These unusual twinned crystals of orthoclase developed in syenite. From west of Wausau, in Marathon County.

Marcasite and Calcite. Through successive stages of crystallization, two or more minerals often combine to produce masterpieces of design. Typical is this beautiful specimen of marcasite sprinkled with little darts of calcite. From Platteville, in Grant County.

Calcite and Marcasite. These beautifully formed citrine-colored calcite crystals have grown upon a mass of marcasite crystals in this specimen from Racine.

Garnet in Schist. Garnet is a common rock forming silicate minerals, as in these specimens of very old mica schist from the Jackson County Iron Mine near Black River Falls, in Jackson County.

Cockscomb Marcasite. One of the most striking crystal forms of marcasite, with a pale-brassy color. From Racine.

Andesite. This specimen of andesite has a fracture filled with diorite, showing faulting. From Little Bull Falls, in Wood County.

Dogtooth Calcite. This cluster of crystals formed in a limestone vug near Racine.

Quartz. This pincushion-like cluster of quartz crystals was formed in a vug in the quartzsite at Rock Springs, in Sauk County.

Iridescent Marcasite. Blazing in a rainbow of color like a peacock's plumage, this specimen is from Shullsburg, in Lafayette County.

Amethyst. A form of purple quartz believed by the early Greeks to prevent intoxication when worn. The word amethyst comes from the Greek meaning "not drunken." From south of Sparta, in Monroe County.

65

Pyrolusite. The pyrolusite dendrites (resembling tree branches) on the surface of this metasedimentary rock from western Marathon County were deposited by underground water.

Antigorite. A platy variety of serpentine, green antigorite from north of Milladore, in Wood County, has been marketed under the name of "jade-X."

Book Mica. A common ingredient in metamorphic rocks, muscovite (also known as book mica) is a potash mica of variable chemical composition. From a glacial boulder near Waupaca, in Waupaca County.

Massive fluorite. Attractive masses of purple fluorite are found in syenite at the site of an abandoned thorium mine, west of Wausau, in Marathon County.

Gabbro. Resembling a man-made artifact, this specimen of gabbro is a good example of differential weathering. From Ashland County.

Cave Onyx. This banded cave onyx (travertine) is a form of compact calcite deposited by underground water in subterranean caverns. From near Westby, in Vernon County.

Jaspilite. A form of crytocrystalline quartz, jaspilite combines red jasper and steel grey hematite. (Found in glacial alluvium in northern Wisconsin.)

Fluorite and chalcopyrite. This beautiful specimen contains crystals of multicolored chalcopyrite on white quartz and purple fluorite. From the Turner Quarry, west of Pittsville, in Wood County.

Graphite. A soft mineral occurring in metallic-gray sheetlike masses. From east of Black River Falls, in Jackson County.

Acmite. Moss green crystals of acmite, generally associated with massive fluorite, are found in syenite outcropping west of Wausau, in Marathon County.

Shale. As indicated by the trilobites in this specimen, shale is commonly fossil-bearing. From Milwaukee.

Labradorite. One of the most widely known cutting materials from Wisconsin, labradorite (also known as Wausau Moonstone) is a gem variety of plagioclase feldspar. When polished it shows an iridescent sheen in blue or green. From the Town of Weston, in Marathon County.

67

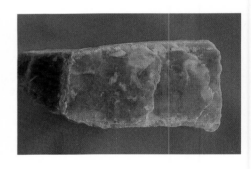

Drusy Quartz. Formed as a botryoidal crust in a dolomite cavity, this sparkling drusy quartz is from near Wilton, in Monroe County.

Float Copper. The Prehistoric Indians pounded implements from float copper deposited by the glaciers at many places in Wisconsin. This specimen is from a gravel pit near Plainfield, in Waushara County.

Copper in Epidote. Boulders containing inclusions of copper are found occasionally in glacial alluvium in northern and eastern Wisconsin.

Sulfur. A by-product of the smelting of zinc sulfide ores from southwestern Wisconsin, sulfur is not found in crystalline form in the state. From Mineral Point, in Iowa County.

Barite. A common mineral in Wisconsin's zinc/lead region, barite is easy to identify because of its high density. From Platteville, in Grant County.

Azurite. The soft blue color distinguishes the copper mineral, azurite, from malachite, its frequent companion. From Eberle Mine, near Highland, in Iowa County.

Wavellite. Encrusted on sandstone, this unusual form of wavellite, believed to have once been associated with radioactive materials, is from east of Black River Falls, in Jackson County.

Aventurine. A spangled variety of quartz, glistening with flecks of mica, aventurine outcrops in several places near Veedum, in Wood County. It is found in both a vivid green and plum color.

Jade. Nephrite, one of the two forms of true jade, ranging in color from green to black, is found in western Marathon County.

Augite. Usually serving as an important dark mineral in igneous rocks, augite, associated with feldspar and epidote, outcrops west of Rudolph, in Wood County.

Malachite. With a rich green velvety luster, malachite is a copper mineral and gem, frequently associated with azurite. From Esofea, in Vernon County.

Iceland Spar. Large clear crystals of calcite cleave into rhombohedral fragments. A variety, first observed in Iceland, has the property of producing a double image when used as an eyeglass. Hence, the name "Iceland Spar." From Platteville, in Grant County.

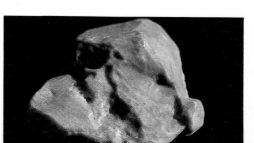

Calcite The calcite crystals in this beautiful specimen developed on marcasite crystals that lined a cavity in limestone. From Racine.

Banded Agate. This superb specimen is typical of the concentric banding in most Lake Superior agates. Others, however, contain moss, onyx banding, eyes or plumes. From near Dresser Junction, in Polk County.

Limestone. A common sedimentary rock formed of calcium carbonate derived from ancient marine organisms, limestone originated in deeper water than the clastic rocks of the Paleozoic. Found abundantly in southern Wisconsin.

Shale. Also known as mudstone, shale is composed mainly of clay grains. From Bay Settlement, in Brown County.

Coquina. Comprised of organic shell fragments, coquina is a species of limestone. Some varieties can be cut and polished as gemstones. From Mineral Point, in Iowa County.

Sandstone. Most of Wisconsin's sandstones result from the deposition of sand grains on sea floors during the Paleozoic Era. This unusual variety from near Alma Center, in Jackson County, is called "Zebra Sandstone."

Meta-quartzite. This beautiful rock from Powers Bluff, near Arpin, in Wood County, was chert originally but has experienced a recrystallization through metamorphism.

Slate. A plately rock that can be split into sheets. From east of Black River Falls, in Jackson County.

Conglomerate. Composed of rounded gravel and sand lithified into a mass, conglomerate rocks are the most coarse grained of the state's sedimentary rocks. From south of Ashland, in Ashland County.

Lake Superior Agates. Ranking among the world's most beautiful agates, Lake Superior agates are found in a seemingly endless variety of patterns. From river gravel near LaCrosse, in LaCrosse County.

Banded Quartzite. A metamorphosed sandstone of Precambrian origin, this banded quartzite is an exceedingly durable rock. From the Seven Sisters, in northeastern Adams County.

Chert. Nodules of chert were formed commonly by the deposition of water soluble quartz in cavities in limestone and dolomite. From south of Madison.

71

Syenite. A common igneous rock in Marathon County, west of Wausau, syenite is similar to granite but contains less than 5% quartz.

Rhyolite. This fine-grained igneous rock formed from lava about 1½ billion years ago. From south of Junction City, in Portage County.

Granite. This granite contains large crystals of orthoclase feldspar as well as quartz and biotite. From east of Marshfield, in Wood County.

Gneiss. Among the oldest rocks outcropping in Wisconsin, gneiss is a coarsely banded metamorphic rock. From north of Milladore, in Wood County.

Gneiss. With a marble cake pattern, this ancient gneiss is found west of Stevens Point, in Portage County.

Andesite Porphyry. Crystals of feldspar impart an interesting pattern to this andesite porphyry. From east of Bloomer, in Chippewa County.

Red Granite. The official rock of Wisconsin, red granite is quarried near Wausau, in Marathon County.

Ophite. Freckles of augite appear in this specimen of greenish altered diabase, known as ophite, a common rock in the glacial alluvium of northern Wisconsin.

Black Granite. A form of gabbro, quarried near Mellen, in Ashland County, and marketed as "black granite."

Trap Rock. Pyroxene crystals pepper this specimen of basalt from Dresser Junction in Polk County. It is marketed as trap rock.

Quartzite. A typical specimen of the maroon or mahogany-colored quartzite composing the Baraboo Range, in Sauk County.

Diorite Breccia. Another visibly crystalline igneous rock, this specimen is composed of fragments of diorite cemented into a mass. From near Turtle Lake, in Barron County.

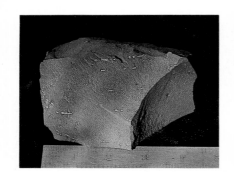

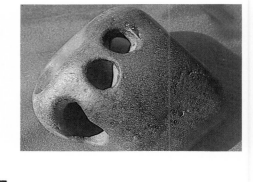

Jaspilite. This specimen of jaspilite shows uneven weathering between the jasper and hematite layers. From near Hurley, in Iron County.

Pipestone Carving. Because of its soft and smooth texture, pipestone is a highly suitable material for carving. Prehistoric Indians used it for fashioning pipes and ornaments. Pipestone from Barron County.

Specular Hematite. A principal ore of iron, specular hematite consists of tiny metallic flakes. From Florence in Florence County.

Needle Ore. Bladed crystals, sometimes more than a foot in length, produce this spectacular variety of hematite known as "needle ore." From Hurley, in Iron County.

Kidney Ore. Globular masses of hematite. From Montreal, in Iron County.

Concretions. This mushroom cluster and sculpture of an impish little girl were assembled from shale concretions found at Waverly Beach, in Ashland County.

Taconite Pellets. These taconite pellets are concentrated from iron ore at the Jackson County Iron Mine, near Black River Falls, in Jackson County.

Kaolinite. Quarried by Stone Age Indians, this form of pipestone crops up east of Rice Lake, in Barron County.

Marcasite. Resembling a turtle, this odd form of marcasite results from cavity-filling of subsurface rock by mineral-laden groundwater. From Shullsburg, in Lafayette County.

Water Sculptured Andesite. Water has augered holes, resembling those in a bowling ball, through this cobble of andesite. From near Bancroft, in Portage County.

Limonite. A field name for a mixture of various hydrous iron oxides, limonite is soft and earthy but never crystalline. From Florence, in Florence County.

Concretions. Sandstone concretions are found in a great variety of shapes near Arcadia, in Trempealeau County.

75

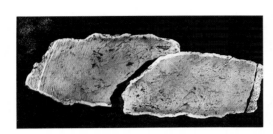

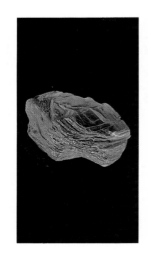

Amygdaloid. The gas cavities in the basalt have been filled with epidote. From Spooner in Washburn County.

Black Granite. Showing just one of the many colors and combinations of colors found in Wisconsin's abundant granites. From western Portage County.

Serpentine. A multicolored variety from near Rudolph, in Wood County. Note rind on outside from prolonged weathering.

Marcasite. The crystals appear almost brushed on the surface of this marcasite "skull." From Shullsburg, in Lafayette County.

Brochantite. Another copper mineral, brochantite somewhat resembles malachite but has distinctive crystals — slender, vitreous and showing striations. From Esofea, in Vernon County.

Asbestos. A form of chrysotile serpentine, found associated with soapstone. From north of Milladore, in Wood County.

Milk Quartz. A common seam filler in Precambrian bedrock in northern Wisconsin.

Iron Incrusted Sandstone. A showy specimen from east of Black River Falls, in Jackson County. The incrustation is mostly hematite and limonite.

Selenite. A variety of gypsum occurring as colorless crystals. From Calumet County.

Soapstone. This serene madonna is typical of the fine results obtained from soapstone as a carving material. Soapstone from north of Milladore, in Wood County.

Amethyst. These purple crystals of amethyst formed as cavity fillers in dolomitic bedrock. From south of Sparta, in Monroe County.

Conglomerate. This cobble of conglomerate is a form of breccia because the rock fragments composing it are angular. From near Tomahawk, in Lincoln County.

Table for Identification of Some Minerals Found in Wisconsin

(arranged in order of increasing hardness)

NAME	CHEMICAL COMPOSITION	HARDNESS	COLOR
Soapstone (Talc)	$Mg_3Si_4O_{10}(OH)_2$	1	gray, white, silver, light green
Gypsum- (Selenite)	$CaSO_42H_2O$	2	colorless, white, gray
Serpentine	$(Mg, Fe)_2Si_2O_4(OH)_4$	2.5	shades of green
Kaolinite	$Al_4Si_4O_{10}(OH)_8$	1-2.5	white, light gray
Muscovite	$KAl_2AlSi_3O_{10}(OH)_2$	2-2.5	colorless, light tan gray tint
Copper	Cu	2.5-3	orange-brown
Biotite	$K(Mg, Fe)_3(AlSi_3O_{10}(OH)_2$	2.5-3	black, dark brown
Silver	Ag	2.5-3	silver
Galena	PbS	2.5	shiny gray
Antigorite	$(Mg, Fe)_3Si_2O_5(OH)_4$	2.5	green
Gold	Au	2.5-3	gold
Asbestos (Chrysotile)	$Mg_3Si_2O_5(OH)_4$	2.5	shades of green
Calcite	$CaCO_3$	3	colorless, white, brown, blue
Bornite	Cu_5FeS_4	3	brownish bronze, purple, blue, black

78

EXPLANATION OF TABLE

Chemical Elements appearing in formulas shown:

ELEMENT	SYMBOL	ELEMENT	SYMBOL	ELEMENT	SYMBOL
Aluminum	Al	Fluorine	F	Phosphorus	P
Beryllium	Be	Gold	Au	Potassium	K
Calcium	Ca	Hydrogen	H	Silicon	Si
Carbon	C	Iron	Fe	Silver	Ag
Chlorine	Cl	Lead	Pb	Sodium	Na
Cobalt	Co	Magnesium	Mg	Sulfur	S
Copper	Cu	Oxygen	O	Zinc	Zn

Abbreviations for Crystal Systems

IS-isometric	HX-hexagonal	RO-hexagonal
TE-tetragonal	MO-monoclinic	(rhombohedral)
OR-orthorhombic	TR-triclinic	AM-amorphous

Parentheses ( ) around figures shown for hardness or specific gravity signify that such property is variable; however, the figure shown is an average value.

LUSTER	SPECIFIC GRAVITY	CLEAVAGE	STREAK	CRYSTAL SYSTEM	SPECIAL PROPERTY
pearly	2.7-2.8	1-perfect	none	MO	feels soapy, pulverizes to talcum powder
vitreous, pearly	2.3	1-perfect	none	MO	
greasy or waxy	2.2-2.7	none	light green, colorless	MO	
earthy	2.6	none	none	MO	sticks to tongue
vitreous, pearly	2.7-3.1	1-perfect	none	MO	peels in sheets
metallic	8.9	none	red	IS	corrodes green
pearly, vitreous	2.8-3.2	1-perfect	none	MO	peels in sheets
metallic	10.5	none	silver	IS	
metallic	7.5	3-perfect	gray	IS	
greasy	2.62	none	none	MO	
metallic	15-19.3	none	gold	IS	
silky	2.4	none	none	MO	frays into fibers
vitreous, pearly	2.72	3-perfect	none	RO	double image (Iceland Spar), effervesces in cold dilute acid
metallic	5.07	none	grayish black	IS	(peacock ore)

NAME	CHEMICAL COMPOSITION	HARDNESS	COLOR
Dolomite	$CaMg(CO_3)_2$	3.5-4	white, gray, variable
Chalcopyrite	$CuFeS_2$	3.5-4	brassy yellow
Sphalerite	ZnS	3.5-4	yellow, brown, black
Malachite	$Cu_2(CO_3)(OH)_2$	3.5-4	green
Fluorite	CaF_2	4	light green, yellow, green, bluish-white, purple
Smithsonite	$ZnCO_3$	5	white, blue, variable
Apatite	$Ca_3(PO_4)(F, Cl, OH)$	5	white, green, brown, red
Goethite	$HFeO_2$	5-5.5	black, brown
Limonite	$FeO(OH)$	5.5	brown, black, yellow
Augite	$(Ca, Na)(Mg, Fe, Al)(Si, Al)_2O_6$	5-6	green to black
Hornblende	$(Ca, Na)_{2-3}(Mg, Fe, Al)_5 Si_8O_{22}(OH_2)$	5-6	black-greenish
Actinolite	$Ca_2(Mg, Fe)_5Si_8O_{22}(OH)_2$	5-6	white, light green
Hematite	Fe_2O_3	5.5-6.5	grayish to reddish black
Hematite-Specular	Fe_2O_3	5.5-6.5	grayish black
Hematite-Oolitic	Fe_2O_3	5.5-6.5	brick red, reddish brown
Magnetite	$FeFe_2O_4$	6	black
Feldspar (Orthoclase)	$KAlSi_3O_8$	6	white-grayish, salmon
Feldspar (Albite)	$NaAlSi_3O_8$	6	colorless, white, gray
Pyrite	FeS_2	6-6.5	brassy yellow
Marcasite	FeS_2	6.5	brassy yellow

80

LUSTER	SPECIFIC GRAVITY	CLEAVAGE	STREAK	CRYSTAL SYSTEM	SPECIAL PROPERTY
vitreous	2.85	none	none	RO	effervesces in dilute acid if freshly scratched
metallic	4.2	none	green, black	TE	frequently tarnished on old surface
resinous, pearly	4.0	6-good	white, yellow, brown	IS	sulfur smell when scratched vigorously
vitreous, dull	3.9-4.0	none	pale green	MO	
vitreous	3.2	4-good	none	IS	sometimes breaks in octahedral fragments
vitreous	4.4	none	none	RO	
glassy	3.2	1-poor	none	HX	
earthy	5-5.5	none	yellow	OR	
earthy, dull	3.6-4	none	brown	AM	
vitreous	3.3	wedge-shape	none	MO	
vitreous	3.2	2-good at right angles	none	MO	
vitreous	3.1	2-good in individual crystals	none	MO	needlelike fans
metallic	5.3	none	reddish-brown	RO	
metallic	5.3	none	reddish-brown	RO	
earthy	5.3	none	reddish-brown	RO	tiny rounded masses the size of pinheads
metallic	5.2	none	black	IS	attracted to a magnet
vitreous, pearly	2.5-2.8	2-perfect	none	MO	fragments look like dominoes
vitreous, pearly	2.6	2-good	none	TR	fragments look like dominoes.
metallic	5.02	none	black, greenish	IS	(fool's gold)
metallic	4.89	none	black	OR	sometimes appears as cock's combs

NAME	CHEMICAL COMPOSITION	HARDNESS	COLOR
Epidote	$Ca_2(Al, Fe)_3Si_3O_{12}(OH)$	6-7	pistachio green, yellow, green, blackish
Jade (Nephrite)	$Ca_2(Mg, Fe)_5Si_8O_{22}(OH)_2$	6.5-7	greenish-white
Olivine	$(Mg, Fe)_2SiO_4$	6.5-7	olive to grayish green, brown
Garnet (almandite)	$Fe_3Al_2(SiO_4)_3$	6.5-7.5	red, brown, pink, green
Crystal Quartz	SiO_2	7	colorless or milk-white
Flint	SiO_2	(7)	black, gray, brown
Chert	SiO_2	(7)	white, various tints
Amethyst	SiO_2	7	purple
Jasper	SiO_2	(7)	red, brown, variable
Agate	SiO_2	(7)	red, brown, yellow, gray, black, green
Staurolite	$Fe_2Al_9O_6(SiO_4)_4 (O,OH)_2$	7-7.5	reddish brown to black
Beryl	$Be_3Al_2Si_6O_{18}$	7.5-8	pink, yellow, green and variable colors
Corundum	Al_2O_3	9	gray, brownish pink, ruby red, blue
Diamond	C	10	variable tints usually colorless

LUSTER	SPECIFIC GRAVITY	CLEAVAGE	STREAK	CRYSTAL SYSTEM	SPECIAL PROPERTY
vitreous	3.4	1-good	none	MO	
vitreous	(3.15)	2-good	none	MO	actually mineral composite, usually has a "rind" on outside
vitreous	3.2-3.4	none	pale green, white	OR	granular mass
vitreous to resinous	3.5-4.3	none	none	IS	
vitreous, pearly	2.7	none	none	RO	"the ubiquitous mineral"
dull, greasy	(2.7)	none	none	RO	white chalky coating, spoon-shape fracture, sparks when struck with iron
dull, greasy	(2.7)	none	none	RO	spoon-shape fracture
vitreous, pearly	2.7	none	none	RO	
dull, greasy	(2.7)	none	none	RO	
dull, waxy, greasy	(2.7)	none	none	RO	usually banded
vitreous, resinous	3.7	not prominent	none	RO OR	sometimes forms crosses (twinned prismatic XL's)
vitreous	2.8	none	none	HX	
vitreous	4.0	none	none	RO	barrel shaped
vitreous	3.5	1-good	none	IS	

IV
A Legacy of the Mountains, Oceans and Glaciers

The rocks of Wisconsin provide evidence for reconstructing the state's long geologic history — from the beginning of the earth to the present. Knowledge of the past helps us understand our present-day environment.

Early Millennia

The early chapters in Wisconsin's geologic history, like that of the earth everywhere, are largely undeciphered. Clues to much of what took place during the long span covered by the Precambrian Era are lost. The great happenings of the early millennia, occurring during the period from about five to three billion years ago, will always be shrouded in some mystery. However, geologists continue to probe into the rock record and are gradually learning more about very old occurrences.

Two universally accepted principles in geology are that there is very little in the changing earth that is permanent and that the earth processes responsible for these changes have operated throughout the past essentially in the same way and at the same rate as those of the present. Thus by looking to more recent events and making comparisons as to what could have been, we can infer some things about the state's early geologic history.

In the early millennia, infant Wisconsin probably experienced several periods of great uplift when forces operating from within the earth produced violent upheavals and severe folding and faulting of the crust, with mountains thrusting up and towering toward the skies. Each episode of crustal deformation must have been followed by a gradual wearing down of the land forms created by the uplift. We can assume that, during the unfathomed past, there were such periods of great deformation of the crust and great erosion of the surface because this has been the pattern of events in the state (and, moreover, all around the earth) as far back as clues exist in the rock record.

Plate tectonics, discussed in Chapter I, is a modern study of the

84

chief architectural features of the earth's crust. The whole concept unifies a number of major observations, including those of continental drift, sea floor spreading, mid-oceanic ridges, mountain ranges, volcanic zones, earthquakes and faulting. There is little doubt that plate tectonics as it becomes better understood and more universally applied by geologists will be used to explain both recent and remote events in the earth's history. Perhaps then, we may learn more about the succession of events that took place during Wisconsin's earliest geologic eras.

The oldest known rocks on earth crop up in Soviet Antarctica and have been radiometrically dated at an age of 4 billion years. An almost stationary icecap at Antarctica provides insulation from weathering and erosion. This is more favorable for the preservation of primordial surface rocks than the conditions at a less stable, mid-continental land region like Wisconsin, with seasonal changes over the years and climatic changes over the ages.

Despite the diligent searching of geologists, no rocks have been found anywhere around the world that are associated with approximately the first billion years of the earth's existence. Thus, about one-fifth of the earth's geologic history is unsupported as yet by any evidence in the rock record of occurences taking place on our globe. What about Wisconsin? The oldest rocks radiometrically dated so far in the Badger State register an age of 1.94 billion years.

In the exploration of space, we are gaining some knowledge about the earth's early years through a study of very old rocks brought back from the moon. Lunar rocks have been radiometrically dated at ages older than any rocks found on earth. We are also collecting information from sister planets through unmanned landing craft such as the Soviet Union's Venus 9 and 10 probe of Venus and the United States' Viking 1 and 2 probe of Mars. These explorations show that the crust of both Venus and Mars is composed of rocks that may be similar to those of the earth's original crust. Hopefully, rock samples available in the future from sister planets will produce convincing proof about the origin of the solar system and, inferentially, of the earth. We may then know more about how things were when Wisconsin was very young.

Pangaea

A growing number of geologists subscribe to the theory that originally all the present-day continents were joined together forming one supercontinent, called Pangaea. This colossal continent is believed to have started to break up about 200 million years ago, with detached segments drifting around the earth in several directions. The present-day continents actually fit together like the pieces in a jigsaw puzzle suggesting the shape of Pangaea. Continental drift on a global scale is an accepted hypothesis among many geologists. The theory of plate tectonics provides an answer for this phenomenon. With the earth's crust comprised of a series of plates that float upon denser plastic rocks

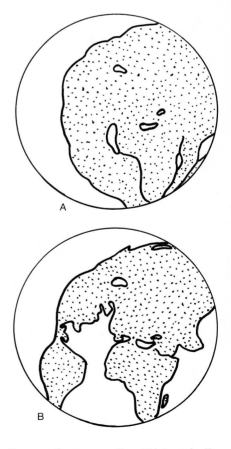

Pangaea, the supercontinent (A.), gradually pulled apart and, through continental drift (B.), the continents eventually moved to their present-day positions (not shown).

85

lying below, the lateral movement of continents occupying portions of such plates is not difficult to accept nor understand.

If Pangaea was a reality, it offers an explanation for the distribution of ancient plant and animal species whose fossils are now found in widely separated parts of the world. It also explains the extent of many of the widespread geologic occurrences of the past that simultaneously influenced almost all land masses. Wisconsin then would have been located within the vast interior of this supercontinent until well into the Mesozoic Era.

Precambrian Events

Wisconsin's geologic history during the Precambrian is a complex and often controversial subject, best presented in professional papers for professional audiences. However, several major episodes of the Precambrian will be commented upon before we leave the subject because they not only are fairly well described by geologists but also provide valuable insights into our understanding why Wisconsin appears the way it does today. An historian once said, "Knowledge of the past is important only if it leads to an understanding of the present."

Ages of Mountain Building

Perhaps the most dramatic chapters in the geologic history of Wisconsin are the several Ages of Mountain Building. Mountains are described as the external reflections of massive tectonic movements occurring within the earth. Thus, mountain building involves dynamic activities taking place both at and below the surface. The most recent episode of mountain building in Wisconsin (the Killarney Revolution) occurred during the late Precambrian.

Although the following account of events taking place during Wisconsin's Ages of Mountain Building may be somewhat fanciful, it is based upon generally accepted theories about how mountains develop during periods of violent crustal deformation.

During the various Ages of Mountain Building in Wisconsin, volcanoes pushed up, spewing fiery dust, ash and lava. Violent and beautiful, they covered the land in places with molten raw material that surged up from the restless interior of the earth. Bubbling and boiling, white-hot lava gushed through vents and fissures in the crust like thick pea soup spilled from a pot and spread an ooze of molten rock over all surface features in its path. Occasionally, earthquakes sent tremors through the land.

Underground, magma, welling up from the same sources that fed the volcanoes, invaded rocks below the surface. Domes of steaming viscous rock collected under thin sections of the crust. Layers of older rock near the surface bulged, wrinkled and folded, sometimes buckling and even becoming corrugated by compression. Along lines of weakness, the outer shell stretched, sometimes to the breaking point, and then fractured along faults and joints. Frequently, these fractures were injected with hot fluid rock surging toward the surface.

Wisconsin's Precambrian mountains, almost certainly, were without vegetation. Plant life, during the Precambrian Era, was primitive and existed in the seas. Land-dwelling plants, most likely, emerged later, during the Paleozoic Era. This highly stylized drawing is not intended to show how the ancient mountains actually looked. No doubt, they resembled some of our present-day mountains.

As these several tectonic forces interacted, mountains started to build, rising slowly as the land heaved and folded. Over a long period of time, peak after peak pushed up until majestic ranges stretched toward the skies.

During some of the Ages of Mountain Building the ancient mountains may have rivaled the greatest ranges of the present-day world in size and grandeur.

The mountains rose in various ways depending upon whether faulting, folding, volcanism or a combination of these forces provided the thrust for their vertical development. No doubt, some were so immense in size that mountain glaciers undercut their flanks, leaving sharp, jagged peaks. Some, smaller in size, pushed up as volcanic cones or domes. Sometimes massive upheavals caused extremely ancient rocks to reach upward as faulted and folded peaks. The original horizontal bedding of older rocks comprising the mountains frequently became tilted or set on edge, resulting in diagonal or vertical bedding. Occasionally, erosion, coupled with a rapid uplifting of the land, sculpted massive domes from bedrock that resembled huge inverted bowls. These mountains of different origin sometimes rose side by side.

Today, very little remains of Wisconsin's great mountain ranges of the past. With the youngest more than 600 million years old, the state's ancient mountains, although existing now only as stumps in a few scattered places, are among the oldest mountain remnants found anywhere on earth. By comparison, most of the world's present-day mountains are mere youngsters. The Adirondacks, Green Mountains, Catskills and Great Smokies pushed up with an upheaval of the earth's crust not quite 230 million years ago. At the same time, the Urals of Russia rose. The Rocky Mountains, along with the Andes of South America, thrust up about 70 million years ago, while the Himalayas began their spectacular rise in Asia. The Cascade Range pushed up about 15 million years ago, when the earth's surface was again deformed. During the same period, the Alps rose and the Himalayas towered even closer toward the skies, becoming the

The Rocky Mountains (this view is of Red Mountain Pass, Colorado) are Johnnies-come-lately compared to Wisconsin's ancient mountains.

87

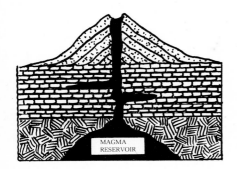

Profile of a volcano showing cone, vent and magma reservoir

MAGMA RESERVOIR

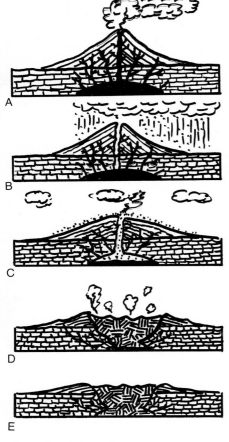

A

B

C

D

E

Stages in caldera collapse

Rib Mountain and part of Wausau Pluton

highest peaks of the present-day world.

Only a fragmentary record of the Ages of Mountain Building in Wisconsin remains in the form of scattered outcroppings of Precambrian rock. Thus, the wrinkled old rocks of the Precambrian persist to this day, seemingly immovable and imperturbable, despite the unrelenting violence of weather and erosion for more than a half billion years.

The Bygone "Rib Mountain Volcano"

An example of a remnant of an ancient mountain is Rib Mountain, still towering near Wausau, in Marathon County. Rib Mountain forms part of a large ring of exposed rocks referred to by geologists as the Wausau Pluton, which probably represents the roots of an ancient volcano.

The Wausau Pluton (17 x 8 miles) is elliptical in lateral shape and lies almost side by side with the smaller doughnut-shaped Stettin Pluton (5 x 3½ miles) located to the northwest. The Stettin Pluton has a more concentric structure and is believed, also, to represent the roots of a volcano.

When the "Rib Mountain Volcano" burst through the outer crust, the older rocks lying near the surface, although themselves not of volcanic origin, formed part of the rim around the volcano's vent and caldera. The caldera is the large underground pot-bellied chamber of a volcano, situated directly below the vent where magma collects before being erupted as lava. The so-called roots of a volcano are composed of a diverse rock assemblage underlying the caldera. The part of a volcano visible at the surface is called the cone. The cone builds up from an accumulation of lava, typically as a round-based tapering mass.

After subsiding, the Rib Mountain Volcano apparently suffered a collapse of its caldera, with rocks from its upper parts sinking into the cavity remaining from its original caldera. Caldera collapse usually results from a withdrawal of magma from deep underneath the volcanic cone. This weakens the caldera because of the removal of the structural support provided by the magma.

The Rib Mountain Volcano was active before the collapse of its caldera, erupting fiery lava, ash and gas, perhaps during the period when the central Wisconsin volcanic belt developed. At about the same time, the syenite, now found at the surface in many places in the vicinity of Rib Mountain, is believed as a molten material to have invaded older rock layers underground. Thermal activities typically occur simultaneously both above and below the surface. Since then, erosion has taken its toll. Most features of the Rib Mountain Volcano have been obliterated and most of the older rocks originally covering the syenite have been worn away.

Orogenies

A period of deformation of the earth's crust resulting in the building of mountains is called an orogeny. During the Precambrian Era, a succession of orogenies took place in Wisconsin, with

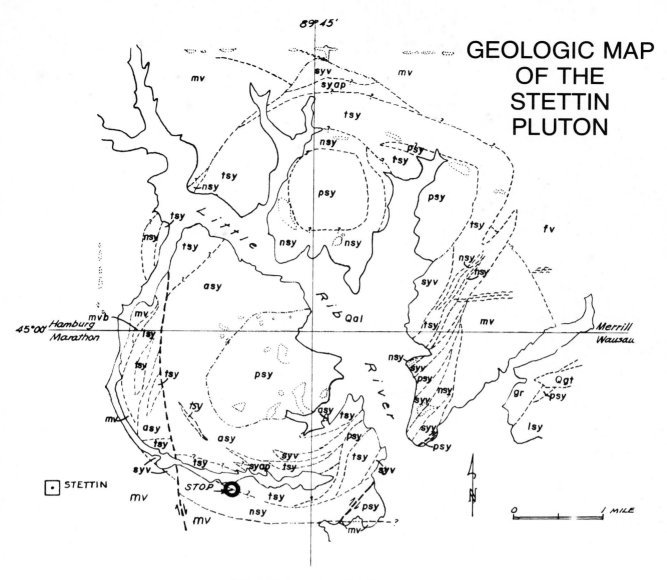

GEOLOGIC MAP OF THE STETTIN PLUTON

EXPLANATION

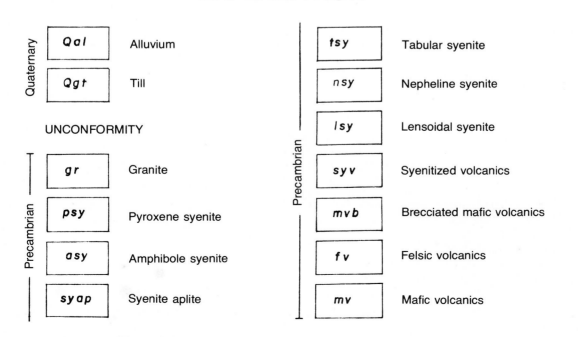

Quaternary
- Qal — Alluvium
- Qgt — Till

UNCONFORMITY

Precambrian
- gr — Granite
- psy — Pyroxene syenite
- asy — Amphibole syenite
- syap — Syenite aplite

Precambrian
- tsy — Tabular syenite
- nsy — Nepheline syenite
- lsy — Lensoidal syenite
- syv — Syenitized volcanics
- mvb — Brecciated mafic volcanics
- fv — Felsic volcanics
- mv — Mafic volcanics

89

each spaced hundreds of millions of years apart. Little is known about the earliest periods of mountain building, but ancient rocks still cropping up today provide solid evidence of several major orogenies, extending from the mid-Precambrian to the

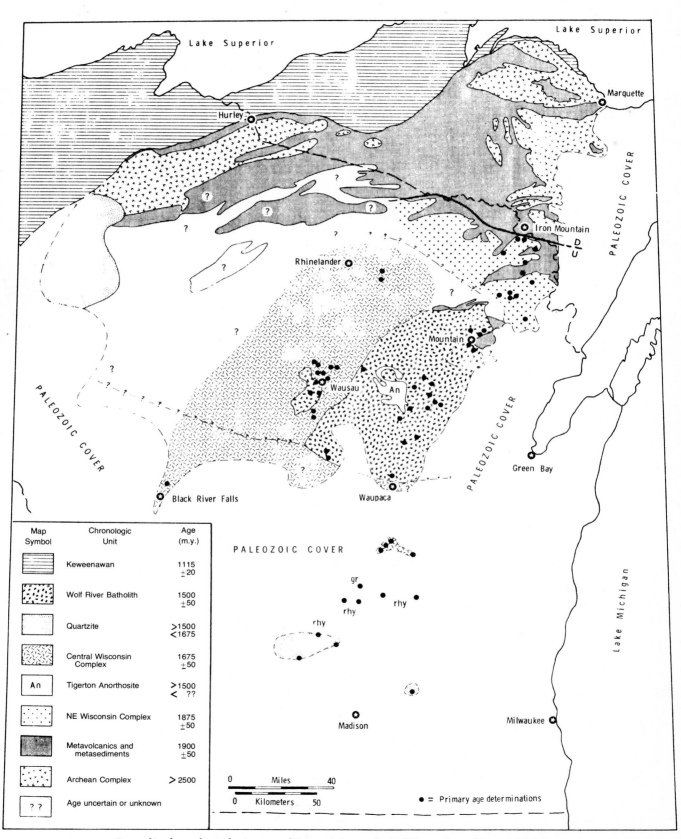

Generalized geochronologic map of Precambrian rocks in Wisconsin and Upper Michigan.

90

Paleozoic. Among these is the Penokean Orogeny, occurring about 1.85 billion years ago and producing the iron-rich mountains around Hurley in northern Wisconsin. The iron formations, of course, preexisted the dislocation of the crust responsible for the mountains. Even earlier, the state may have experienced other episodes of crustal deformation — folding, faulting, metamorphism and volcanism — during the Algoman Orogeny, about 2.7 billion years ago, and the Mortonian Event, about 3.5 billion years ago, which are known from rocks exposed in neighboring Minnesota. The Morton gneiss and Montevideo gneiss found in southwestern Minnesota, associated with the Mortonian Event, are the oldest rocks known on the North American continent. These remarkably old rocks were radiometrically dated in 1970 at an age of 3.55 billion years.

An excellent place for a field trip to study rocks of the Penokean Orogeny is the central and western Gogebic region in Wisconsin and Upper Michigan. A guidebook for such a field trip, designed for persons knowledgeable in geology, is published by the U.S. Geological Survey. It provides for visits to localities specially selected to give a general idea of "Precambrian X rock strata" and their relationships to older and younger rocks. In addition, the guidebook briefly describes several kinds of well-exposed volcanic rocks at easy-to-get-to places.

An interim scheme for subdivision of Precambrian time has been adopted by the U.S. Geological Survey:

Precambrian Z — base of Cambrian to 800 m.y. (formerly considered late Precambrian)
Precambrian Y — 800 m.y. to 1,600 m.y. (formerly considered late Precambrian)
Precambrian X — 1,600 m.y. to 2,500 m.y. (formerly considered middle Precambrian)
Precambrian W — older than 2,500 m.y. (formerly considered early Precambrian)

Iron Formations

During the Middle Precambrian, an ancient sea covered at least part of northern Wisconsin. Sediments that accumulated on the floor of the sea were the source of the present-day iron formations of the Gogebic Range. The iron formations consist of alternating bands of chert and silicon-bearing iron. The most iron-rich of these deposits were mined extensively until recent years. Some geologists believe that tiny organisms now extinct actually deposited the iron through a complicated biochemical process. Banded iron formations, like those of the Gogebic, are unique and occur only in rocks between 3.4 and 1.8 billion years of age. Geologists doubt that similar iron deposits will ever occur again because of the extinction of the organisms responsible for their deposition.

Keweenawan Period

The last period of the Precambrian is called the Keweenawan. Rocks, deposited during the early stages of the Keweenawan Period, are mostly conglomerates and sandstones now cropping up in northern Wisconsin in the vicinity of Lake Superior. The product of years of erosion and sedimentation like the iron formations that preceded them — they built up to an incredible thickness, estimated at 17,500 feet.

The deposition of these sedimentary rocks, during the Middle Keweenawan Period, was interrupted by outpourings of basalt and felsite lava that originated on both sides of a preexisting downwarp (in the area that is now occupied in part by Lake Superior).

Large volumes of lava flowed overland or, possibly, under water if the area was then still submerged below the sea. Eruption followed eruption. Once started, the flows poured out sporadically, layer upon layer, until hundreds accumulated. An estimated 300 flows, with an average thickness of 43 feet each, eventually mantled the land from the tip of Upper Michigan, across Wisconsin, as far south as St. Croix Falls, and well into Minnesota. The overburden of extruded igneous rock reached a thickness of more than 20,000 feet. The lava apparently gushed out of cracks (fissures) in the earth's crust. The flows were too great in lateral extent and thickness to have been the outpourings of conventional volcanoes. Today, some sedimentary rocks are found interbedded with the lava deposits.

During the Keweenawan Period, a huge intrusion of gabbro formed in northwestern Wisconsin, near what is now the city of Superior, and in adjoining Minnesota from magma forcing itself into older crustal rocks. This extensive mass of gabbro ranks among the largest intrusions of gabbro in the world and is known as the Duluth Complex, because it crops up near Duluth, Minnesota. From there, it extends northeastward in a vast sheet, dipping under Lake Superior. Keweenawan lava flows directly underlie as well as overlie the complex; thus, we can infer that the gabbro was implaced in very late Precambrian time.

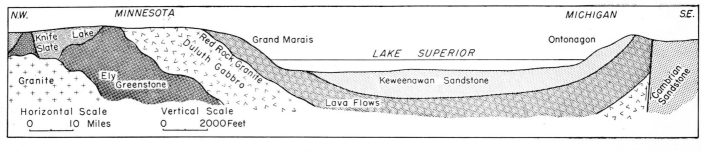

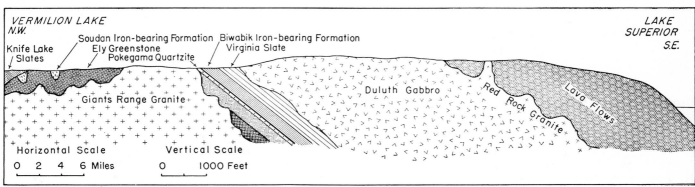

Top, cross section of Lake Superior basin showing the Duluth Gabbro. Bottom, cross section from Lake Vermilion to Lake Superior showing the detail of the Duluth Gabbro and associated formations.

92

Gabbro of Middle Keweenawan age, in the form of a major laccolith, is exposed at Mellen, in Iron County, but is not believed to be of the same vintage as the Duluth Gabbro.

Near the end of the Keweenawan Period, sandstones were deposited in northern Wisconsin that are seen today at the surface along the shoreline of Lake Superior. These Lake Superior sandstones are of two sequences — the Oronto Group and the younger Bayfield Group. Generally, they can be distinguished when observed on the landscape. The Oronto sandstones display sharp tilting and folding from deformation while the Bayfield sandstones are nearly flat-lying and undeformed.

The upper Keweenawan basalts and sedimentary rocks are part of a well-known mid-continent anomaly, an area distinguished by gravity highs and lows. This extends from Lake Superior to Kansas. Thus, basement rocks in Kansas and Nebraska are correlated with those cropping up in northern Wisconsin.

Hills bordering Lake Superior near Bayfield, in Bayfield County, are composed of Keweenawan-age sandstone.

Precambrian Rocks

Precambrian rocks are commonly referred to as crystalline rocks. These old-timers consist mostly of complex igneous and metamorphic rocks.

Northern Wisconsin is divided into ten areas for the purpose of studying Precambrian rocks of that region. The principal rocks found in each area, as reported by the U.S. Geological Survey, are as follows:

• Keweenawan Area — ancient sedimentary and older volcanic rocks, the former consisting of sandstone and conglomerate of late Precambrian age and the latter of massive basalt and andesite flows of Middle Keweenawan age.

• Gogebic Range — sedimentary rocks, including the Ironwood Iron Formation, of mid-Precambrian age, resting on metabasalt and granite of early Precambrian age, cut by intrusive igneous rocks of late Precambrian age.

• Barron, Butternut-Conover, Rhinelander, Florence and the Mountain-Amberg Areas — metasedimentary rocks and granite, mostly, of middle Precambrian age, some quartzite of late Precambrian age and greenstone probably of both early and middle Precambrian age.

• Black River Falls, Wausau-Wisconsin Rapids and Tigerton Areas — mainly a complex of extrusive and intrusive igneous rocks, with some metasedimentary rocks present locally, mostly of middle Precambrian age. Two granite units have been radiometrically dated at 1.43 and 1.6 million years old but relative dates of nearby rocks are not known.

The oldest Precambrian rocks in Wisconsin are referred to as the basal group consisting mostly of gneiss and schist. Gnarled and persisting, they have endured, with true grit, through hundreds of millions of years of lashing by the elements. These rocks have been found to be as much as 1.94 billion years old and about a billion years younger than similar rocks of the Canadian shield.

The basal rocks form the floor upon which ancient sedimen-

93

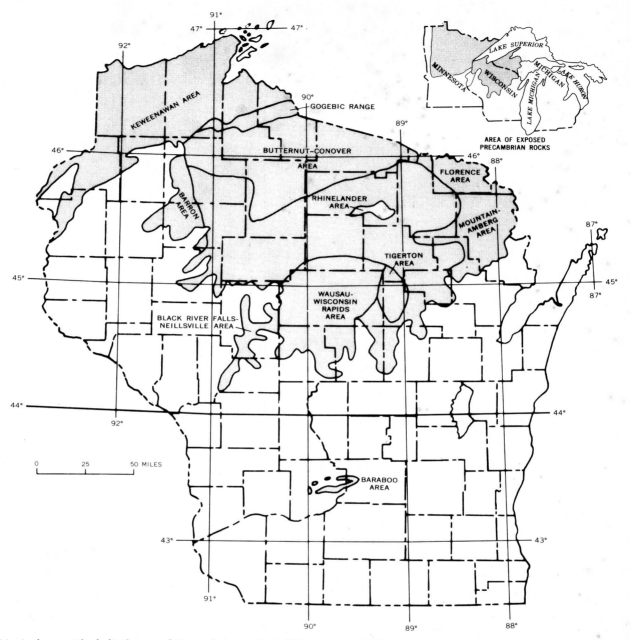

Principal areas (shaded) of exposed Precambrian rocks in Wisconsin. Unshaded areas are underlain mainly by Paleozoic rocks.

tary rocks were deposited during the mid-Precambrian. The original sandstone, shale and limestone of these sedimentary formations has long since been transformed by metamorphism into quartzite, slate and marble. These altered rocks are called metasedimentary rocks and include the iron formations of northern Wisconsin which were originally deposited as sediments on ancient ocean floors.

During the last Ages of Mountain Building, the basal rocks and metasediments were invaded underground by igneous rocks that welled up intermittently as magma from reservoirs deeper in the crust. At the same time, volcanic rocks, in many places, erupted and flowed as lava covering older rocks.

The intrusive igneous rocks gathered and solidified underground in bodies called plutons. Sometimes these intrusive

94

masses were exceedingly large and were emplaced and cooled slowly several thousand feet below the surface, covering many square miles and cutting across older rocks. They typically form the core of most of the world's mountain systems. These large bodies of rock are called batholiths. In some instances, they were exposed later at the surface in Wisconsin when overlying rocks had become completely eroded away. Other intrusive bodies, smaller in size, are called sills and laccoliths. A sill is a sheet-like intrusion. A laccolith is a flat-based, dome-like intrusion which arches the overlying older rock. The cross-section of a multiple laccolith sometimes resembles a cedar tree.

The igneous intrusive rocks found in Wisconsin consist mostly of granite, diorite, gabbro, syenite, monzonite and peridotite.

The extrusive igneous rocks deposited on the surface in Wisconsin, most commonly, were rhyolite, andesite and basalt. Extensive flows of basalt occurred during the late Precambrian, as described previously, in the upper northwestern portion of the state. Earlier, at least two large volcanic belts developed and extended through central Wisconsin, with outpourings of basalt, andesite and rhyolite.

A great amount of sandstone with some shale and conglomerate was deposited near the close of the Precambrian Era, as discussed earlier, in an immense trough which is now the basin of Lake Superior. These sedimentary rocks are referred to as the Oronto and Bayfield Groups and include the whimsically named Nonesuch Shale that reaches into Upper Michigan. The shale locally contains copper.

Sill

Simple Laccolith

Multiple Laccolith (Cedar-tree)

Wolf River Batholith

A huge batholith has been traced in the rocks underlying much of northeastern Wisconsin. Geologists call this extensive body of rock the Wolf River Batholith. Representing a major feature of the Precambrian terrain, the batholith covers an area of at least 3,600 square miles. Composed mostly of reddish quartz monzonite (a coarse-grained igneous rock) and granite, 1,450 to 1,500 million years in age, it has textural, mineralogical, chemical and structural characteristics similar in every respect to those of the classic Rapakivi Massifs. The Rapakivi Massifs are large bodies of intrusive igneous rock cropping up as structurally

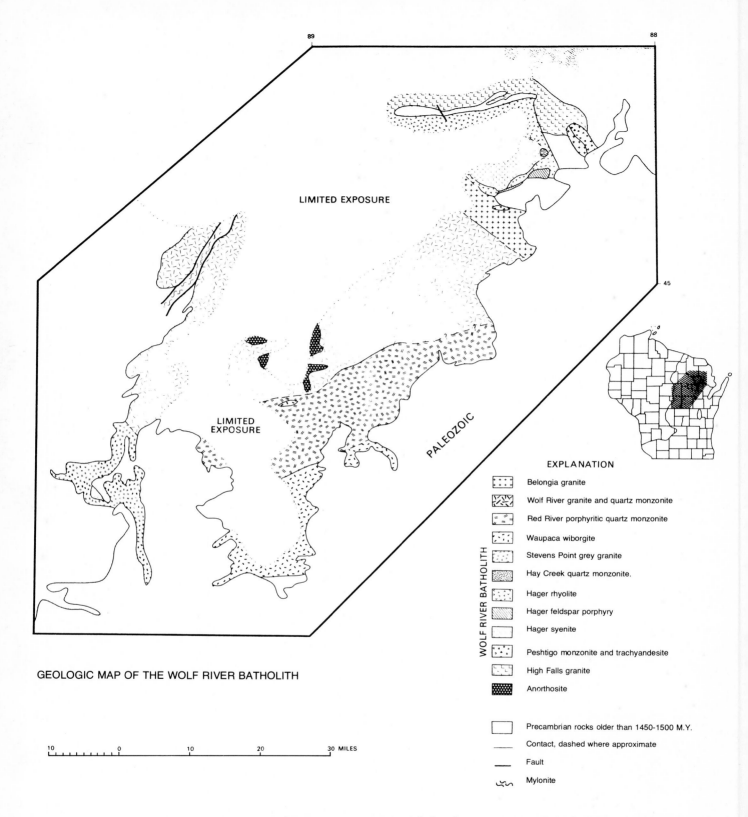

LIMITED EXPOSURE

LIMITED EXPOSURE

PALEOZOIC

GEOLOGIC MAP OF THE WOLF RIVER BATHOLITH

EXPLANATION

	Belongia granite
	Wolf River granite and quartz monzonite
	Red River porphyritic quartz monzonite
	Waupaca wiborgite
	Stevens Point grey granite
	Hay Creek quartz monzonite.
	Hager rhyolite
	Hager feldspar porphyry
	Hager syenite
	Peshtigo monzonite and trachyandesite
	High Falls granite
	Anorthosite

WOLF RIVER BATHOLITH

	Precambrian rocks older than 1450-1500 M.Y.
	Contact, dashed where approximate
	Fault
	Mylonite

10 0 10 20 30 MILES

resistant masses in uplifted areas in Finland. They are believed to represent the cores of ancient mountains. The distinctive texture of the granites comprising the massifs is referred to as ''Rapakivi texture'' and has become a prototype for describing the textures in similar granites around the world. In typical specimens, large flesh-colored potassic feldspars occur as rounded crystals (a few centimeters in diameter), mantled with white sodic plagioclase, with both feldspars embedded in a matrix of normal granite

96

texture made up chiefly of quartz and darker colored minerals.

As a formation, the Wolf River Batholith is the product of the youngest known plutonic event and the last major thermal event occurring in the state, except for the Keweenawan activity to the north.

Geochronology Of Precambrian Rocks

Geochronology is the measurement of time intervals on a geologic scale. It represents the absolute dating of rocks to establish the duration of geologic events in years before the present.

The geochronology of Wisconsin's Precambrian rocks is a subject of great interest for modern geologists.

A 1973 special paper published by the Wisconsin Geological and Natural History Survey entitled *Chronology of Precambrian Rocks in Wisconsin* by W.R. Van Schmus summarizes what is presently known about the ages of the state's Precambrian rocks and suggests some exciting correlations between these ancient rocks and others on the North American continent:

"Geochronologic data for Precambrian rocks in Wisconsin have existed for more than a decade, but until recently the data were limited to analyses of separate minerals and were widely distributed, so that exact interpretation of primary formational ages and delineation of chronologic provinces was not possible.

"Several major discrete igneous, metamorphic or sedimentary periods or events can now be recognized in Wisconsin and Upper Michigan. The 2,500 m.y. (million years) and older rocks represent the southern edge of the Superior Province of the Canadian Shield. The 1,850 to 1,900 m.y. old rocks represent a major period of sedimentation, volcanism, and orogeny and is considered by the author to represent the so-called 'Penokean Orogeny' in the area. The 1,650 to 1,700 m.y. old rocks can be correlated roughly with rocks of similar age in the Rockies and the Southwest, although exact correlations will need to await further data. In any case, it appears that rocks with ages of 1,650 to 1,750 m.y. comprise a major structural belt from Arizona to Wisconsin. The 1,500 m.y. old complex correlates well in age, lithologic character, and tectonic setting with 1,450 to 1,500 m.y.

Part of ancient Gogebic (Penokee) Range, west of Hurley, in Iron County.

97

old plutons throughout the Southwest and volcanic and plutonic rocks in Missouri. These rocks probably are part of another structural province south of and partially overlapping the 1,650 to 1,750 m.y. old rocks.

"In summary, it now appears that the various chronologic units recognized in Wisconsin can be related to other rocks throughout North America, and these correlations may ultimately provide the framework upon which we can determine the detailed evolution of the continent during Precambrian times."

1. Northeastern Wisconsin Complex: — Age (m.y.)

	Age (m.y.)
Quinnisec Fm. (rhyolite)	1905 ± 25 m.y.
Hoskin Lake granite	1890 ± 15
Dunbar gneiss	1880 ± 15
Newingham granodiorite	
"Amberg pink granite"	1800 ± 15
(Athelstane quartz monzonite)	
Marinette quartz diorite	1930 ± 50
Athelstane quartz monzonite	
Hoskin Lake Granite	1810 ± 50
Overall composite estimate:	1875 ± 50

2. Central Wisconsin Complex:

Baraboo rhyolite	1640 ± 40 m.y.
So. Wisconsin rhyolites	1665 ± 40
Wausau-Monice volcanics	1640 ± 40
Waushara Co. granites	1645 ± 70
Wausau area granites	1600 ± 85
Jackson Co. granites	1690
Overall composite estimate:	1675 ± 50

3. Wolf River Batholith:

Wolf River-Red River	$1450 \pm$ m.y.
quartz monsonites	
Belongia granite	1500 ± 20
Wolf River batholith combined	
Wolf River quartz monsonite	
Red River quartz monsonite	
Hager complex	
Belongia granite	
Waupaca wiborgite granite	1460 ± 25
Big Falls med-gr. granite	
Stevens Point gray granite	
Wausau syenite complex	
Stetin syenite complex	
Hogarty hornblends granite	
Overall composite estimate:	1500 ± 50

Ages of chronologic units in Wisconsin.

The Emergence Of Life

Fossils provide us with a glimpse of creatures that lived throughout the long succession of geologic periods since life first came into existence approximately three billion years ago. By comparing fossils of known relative ages, we can date the rock stratum in which the fossils formed. The oldest fossils found are associated with metasedimentary rocks of Precambrian origin. Fossils of more recent age than the oldest show a pattern of life progressing from simple one-cell organisms to increasingly more complex and diversified forms.

Typical marine fossils

98

Many of the sedimentary rocks deposited in Wisconsin, since the onset of the Cambrian Period, yield abundant marine fossils. The fossil content of these rocks is helpful in correlating their stratigraphy. Stratigraphy is the branch of geology which deals with the study of stratified or layered rocks. Stratigraphy, of course, is closely linked with geologic time. The stratigraphic features of rocks serve as a calendar dating their time of deposition.

We shall discuss the fossils of Wisconsin in Chapter IX.

The Development Of The Peneplain

Each of the Ages of Mountain Building in Wisconsin took a long time to develop. Like the mountains, each reached a pinnacle and then began to subside.

The ancient Precambrian peneplain

When the Killarney Revolution ended, the last of the state's mountains began to be worn down. Even before the final peak finished its skyward rise, weathering and erosion began, slowly but surely, carving away at the mountains' flanks. Gradually the mountains were reduced in size. Threading valleys between the waning mountains, rivers carried away pebbles, sand, silt and clay in their long journey to the seas. At the same time, underground water as a covert agent of erosion was hard at work dissolving and transporting minerals in solution for redeposit elsewhere.

One of the Blue Hills, looking east

With the forces of diastrophism and volcanism seeming to hibernate like sleeping giants, weathering and erosion slowly took their toll. Peak after peak was cut down to low relief and left to decay. Eventually, the last of the majestic mountains was almost leveled and the land took on a new look.

By the close of the Precambrian Era, most of Wisconsin was worn down to a vast nearly flat plain, known as peneplain. The land extended from one horizon to the other as a generally low undulating expanse. The bases of the leveled mountains joined like the patches in a quilt forming the almost featureless peneplain which was punctuated, only here and there, by low hills of highly resistant rock that had withstood the erosive forces. These isolated remnants of the ancient mountains are called monadnocks. Examples of monadnocks surviving today are Rib Mountain in Marathon County, the Blue Hills in Barron County, the Baraboo Range in Sauk County and Powers Bluff in Wood County.

The Baraboo Range, looking north

Thus the stage was set for a new era in Wisconsin's geologic history.

Paleozoic Era

About 600 million years ago, the Precambrian Era ended and the Paleozoic Era began with the opening of the Cambrian Period. For the next 255 million years, Wisconsin experienced a number of submergences beneath the sea.

The Paleozoic Era is characterized by Professor Richard M. Pearl of Colorado College:

"With the opening of the Paleozoic Era, geologic history as-

Powers Bluff, looking east

99

sumes a character that can be interpreted with some confidence. In general, the rocks have been less buried, metamorphosed, and eroded, the fossils are more numerous, and correlation is more definite — in extreme instances the difference between the Paleozoic and the Precambrian is like that between a well-printed book in our own language and a fragmentary manuscript written in a strange tongue."

Tectonic forces lurking below the crust make adjustments from time to time in the earth's outer shell. During the Paleozoic Era, the tectonic events taking place in Wisconsin were a recurring series of uplifts and downdrops of the crust (Wisconsin Dome) causing periodic fluctuations of the land elevation in relationship to sea level. The state sank below sea level twice during the Cambrian Period and three more times during the Ordovician Period, apparently remaining submerged during the Silurian Period and not emerging until near the close of the Devonian Period. Each time Wisconsin dropped below sea level, the seas transgressed by migrating inland or landward along advancing shorelines. Conversely, each time the state rose above sea level, the seas regressed by migrating seaward. Rivers draining the land, during this transgressive-regressive cycle, carried sediments which were deposited in shallow waters on broad depositional shelves along the fluctuating coastline of prehistoric Wisconsin.

Emptying loads of waterborne materials at deltas along shorelines, rivers pursued their ageless practice of meticulously sorting and depositing suspended sediments. First coarse mineral particles were unloaded near the shorelines, then smaller particles farther off shore and finally very small specks of silt and clay near the coral reefs that built up on the fringes of the ocean depths. Sediments deposited near the shorelines were abraded, reworked, and re-sorted, time and again, by waves that rolled in and receded with each passing wind. Shell fragments and flotsam captured by the action of the waves were pounded into tiny bits and mixed with sand along beaches marking the edge of the sea. Shore currents swept, sorted and redeposited sediments in the shallows bordering the coastline.

Through a succession of many years of sedimentation, sedimentary beds were laid down to great thickness, layer upon layer. Then they were compacted, cemented and turned into stone through a process called lithification. Sand was lithified to sandstone, silt to siltstone, clay to shale and shell deposits to limestone and dolomite.

As the seas continued to invade further inland, the ancient peneplain of Wisconsin gradually became buried under a blanket of sedimentary rocks. At first, the stumps of the old mountains rose defiantly as islands in the sea. Waves lapped at their bases on island shorelines. But, as the sedimentary rocks built up and sea levels continued to rise, the last of the islands sank slowly below the sea. The oceans then ruled supremely over the state. Marine animals and plants thrived

100

PALEOZOIC STRATIGRAPHIC NOMENCLATURE FOR WISCONSIN

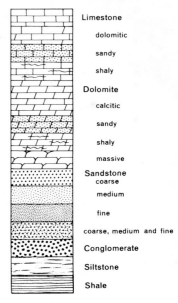

KEY TO SYMBOLS

Limestone
- dolomitic
- sandy
- shaly

Dolomite
- calcitic
- sandy
- shaly
- massive

Sandstone
- coarse
- medium
- fine
- coarse, medium and fine

Conglomerate

Siltstone

Shale

△	chert
▲	oolitic chert
⊙	oolites
⌒	openings (vugs, etc.)
⊥	dolomitic
~	silty
xxx	bentonite
G	glauconite
P	pyrite
M	mica
F	feldspar
Ph	phosphate pellets
⩔	pentamerus
⌒⌒	Receptaculites
∧	Prasopora
⌾	algae
ſ	burrows
⋰	conglomeratic
?	questionable relationship

*New names proposed (informal).
†Name being considered for adoption.

in communities on ocean floors where Precambrian mountains had once reached toward the skies. The Paleozoic was then in full swing reshaping in a new way the surface features of the buried land. Rocks that survive in great abundance to this day were formed then as a legacy of the oceans.

101

Lithotopes

A lithotope is a body of sedimentary rock composed of a common lithified material. Four major lithotopes are present in the rocks deposited in Wisconsin during the Cambrian and Ordovician periods. These are: (1) a thick-bedded, medium- to coarse-grained, well-sorted sandstone (quartzarenite), (2) a medium- to thin-bedded, reworked quartzarenite, (3) a thin-bedded, clayey (argillaceous) sandstone or shale, (4) a carbonate (usually dolomite but sometimes limestone) formed along offshore coral reefs.

The lithotopes correspond to the migration of the depositional shelf during the transgressive-regressive cycle of the seas, with the coarse-grained sandstones originating as shallow water deposits along the shorelines and the carbonate rocks forming as deeper water deposits on coral reefs farther from the shorelines.

A lithological cycle is a recurring sequence of sedimentary layers consisting of several lithotopes arranged in the same order. Each time the state's lands emerged above or were submerged below the level of the seas, the same lithotopes formed. The lithologic cycle went full circle twice during the Cambrian and then three more times during the Ordovician Period.

The coarse-grained sandstone lithotope, the basal unit of the cycle, is represented by the Mount Simon, Galesville, Jordan, New Richmond and Saint Peter sandstone formations. Fossils are rare or absent in these rocks.

The reworked quartzarenite lithotope includes the upper Mount Simon sandstone, the Ironton, the lower Stockton Hill member and the lower part of the Glenwood Formation. Fossils are locally common, especially in the upper part of the rocks.

The clayey sandstone or shale lithotope is represented by the Eau Claire Sandstone, the Lone Rock Formation, lower parts of the Stockton Hill Member, the upper New Richmond Sandstone and the Harmony Hill members of the Glenwood Formation. Fossils are plentiful in these rocks consisting of fragmented brachiopods, trilobite molds and casts and many burrows and trails.

The carbonate lithotope includes the Bonnetine Dolomite, Saint Lawrence Dolomite, the upper part of the Stockton Hill Member, Willow River Dolomite and the Sinnipee Group. In these rocks, fossils are more diversified and plentiful than in those of the other three lithotopes. Biohermal (coral) reefs are present in most of the carbonates. Animals and plants living in the sea deposited calcium carbonate and built reefs which have been transformed since into dolomite, a magnesium-rich limestone.

Deposits that built up in the sea when the land was submerged were worked on by erosion later when becoming elevated above sea level. Frequently, these deposits were only partially worn down but, sometimes, they were completely stripped away. Sediments laid down during periods of regression of the seas were more prone to devastation by the erosive action of streams and rivers draining the coastlines than were deposits made during periods of transgression.

The Passing Of The Paleozoic

At the close of the Ordovician Period — about 425 million years ago — and in the succeeding Silurian and Devonian Periods, Wisconsin remained submerged below the sea. During this long period of submergence, thick deposits of sedimentary rocks formed on sea floors. No rocks crop up in the state today that are younger than those laid down during the Devonian Period. The youngest cropping up is the Kenwood Shale along Lake Michigan in southeastern Wisconsin.

The deposition of sedimentary rocks came to an end in Wisconsin as far as known when the seas finally receded at the close of the Devonian. No evidence can be found as to what happened to the state from then until the dawn of the Ice Age, except for the reshaping of the surface by erosion.

This missing chapter in the rock record, including the Age of the Dinosaurs, makes an interpretation of much of Wisconsin's geologic history after the Devonian a matter of conjecture. But by looking to neighboring states with bedrock of younger origin, we may infer that Wisconsin at the close of the Devonian (perhaps about 345 million years ago) began a period of gentle uplift that has continued to the present.

Wherever the rocks of the Paleozoic still survive as bedrock, sculpturing by water, wind and ice is manifest in a variety of landforms — uplands, lowlands, escarpments, hills and valleys. We shall discuss these landforms in Chapter VI.

After The Paleozoic

During the vast span of time since the seas finally receded near the end of the Devonian, the land surface of Wisconsin has been extensively carved and manicured by rain, wind and running water. The tireless forces of weathering and erosion have gradually peeled off many of the rocks of the Paleozoic. Most of the northern portions of the state have been stripped of the thick sedimentary mantle that formerly covered them and the buried Precambrian peneplain has again been exposed. In other areas of the state, only the tops of ancient mountain stumps have been exhumed. These rise as inliers above a surrounding carpet of marine sediments. The rocks of the Silurian and Devonian Periods remain only in a few places, mostly in the southwestern and eastern portions of the state, while the rocks of the Cambrian and Ordovician Periods cover most of the rest of southern Wisconsin.

Underground water and, possibly, gas have been active agents for millions of years in redepositing the mineral content of the rocks of the Paleozoic. The lead and zinc deposits in the southwestern corner of the state are believed to have been concentrated by such hydrothermal activity.

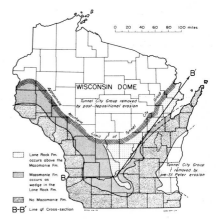
Areal distribution of the Tunnel City Group in Wisconsin

Paleogeology of the Pre-St. Peter erosion surface in southern and eastern Wisconsin.

Profile of an inlier

103

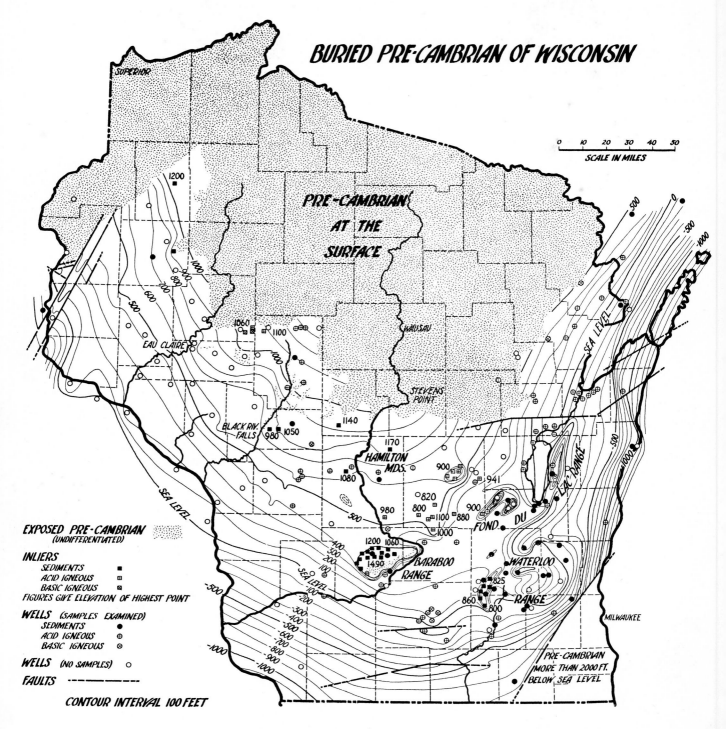

BURIED PRE-CAMBRIAN OF WISCONSIN

EXPOSED PRE-CAMBRIAN
(UNDIFFERENTIATED)

INLIERS
SEDIMENTS ■
ACID IGNEOUS ⊞
BASIC IGNEOUS ▨
FIGURES GIVE ELEVATION OF HIGHEST POINT

WELLS (SAMPLES EXAMINED)
SEDIMENTS ●
ACID IGNEOUS ⊕
BASIC IGNEOUS ⊗

WELLS (NO SAMPLES) ○

FAULTS -------

CONTOUR INTERVAL 100 FEET

At the present, where the sedimentary rocks of the Paleozoic continue to cover the surface, they still entomb the Precambrian rocks underneath a thick overburden. In the southeastern corner of the state where the surface lies high above sea level, the uppermost buried Precambrian rocks rest more than 2,000 feet below sea level. Well cores reveal the presence of these ancient rocks at such spectacular depths showing the amazing thickness of the overlying sedimentary strata. When one considers that the rocks of the Paleozoic were laid down in the sea, particle upon particle, the amount of time and sedimentation necessary for such an accumulation of marine materials seems almost incredible.

104

Latest Chapters In Wisconsin's Geologic History

The final major events leading to the present in Wisconsin's geologic history occurred during the last three million years when the state was exposed to the Ice Age. Glaciers made an invasion from the north and dynamically sculptured the land surface, planing off hilltops and filling in valleys. They left glacial debris, as a wall-to-wall carpet of unconsolidated rocks and soil, over all of the state, except in the central and southwestern portions, called the Driftless Area. It is only in the Driftless Area that we can see Wisconsin as it probably looked before the Ice Age. In the next chapter, we shall discuss the glaciers and the events of the Ice Age in more detail because of their great impact on Wisconsin today.

About 12,000 years ago the glaciers were running out of time and approaching a final retreat. Prehistoric people began to settle in Wisconsin. From this small beginning, the migration into the state has gone on continually until today 4,417,933 people reside within its boundaries. By changing things over the centuries to suit their needs, people have modified most lands and waterways. They have moved great quantities of earth materials and made countless changes in topography. To do the job more efficiently, they have come to use tools and machines like air hammers, bulldozers and power shovels. In fact, they have become more active than the agents of erosion in altering the features of the surface. Thus people, collectively, have developed into a significant geologic force.

An Unending Story

Through five billion years of change, Wisconsin has evolved into the beautiful and diversified land we see today. And, as time goes by in the long perspective of geology, the story of the state's changing countenance continues on unendingly. Doubtlessly, whatever is in store for Wisconsin in the future will be just as exciting as the events of the past.

Bearing a remarkable resemblance to a glacial kame, this hill at Oconomowoc in Waukesha County is a man-made mound, developed for a ski slope.

These piles of tailings near New Diggings in Lafayette County, offer mute testimony of lead and zinc mining in the past.

V
Giants of Ice

Unconsolidated rocks at the surface in Wisconsin were reshuffled by the glaciers during the Ice Age, representing one of the most dramatic chapters in the state's geologic history. Many present-day landforms are the handiwork of the glaciers.

The Ice Age Begins

Glaciers are the most spectacular of the geologic forces that sculptured the present-day surface features of Wisconsin. Glaciers are king-sized masses of moving ice that put a crunch on the land. Although less important than rivers in overall erosion, they are, nonetheless, responsible for having dynamically modified many of the state's landforms. Unleashing awesome power each time they advanced or retreated, the glaciers shuffled and rearranged the topographical features of the land, serving both as wrecking crews for old landforms and as master builders for new landforms. Today, you can see the mark of the glaciers upon the landscape in most parts of the state.

The glaciers were spawned at the dawn of the Ice Age more than a million years ago. It all started when the average annual temperature of the earth fell slightly. Perhaps the total loss of heat was no more than a few degrees. But even that small differ-

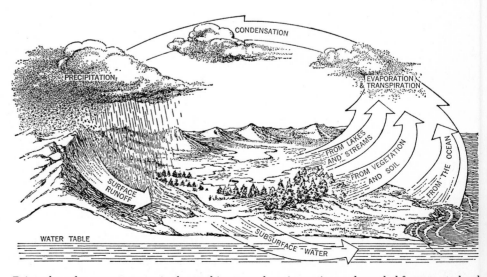

Driven by solar energy, water in the earth's atmosphere is continuously cycled from sea to land and back to sea in the hydrologic cycle.

106

ence in temperature was sufficient to upset the delicate balance by which the hydrologic cycle had kept the climates of the earth relatively stable for hundreds of millions of years.

The hydrologic cycle is the natural process by which a constant volume of water is evaporated from the oceans, formed into clouds, carried by winds, distributed through precipitation to every part of the earth and then returned by drainage to the oceans. Every drop in the earth's immense water supply moves in time through the cycle. It is estimated that, through this perpetual cycle of evaporation, condensation and precipitation, 95,000 cubic miles of water circulate each year between earth and sky. Climates are dependent upon the smooth operation of the hydrologic cycle just as it is essential to weather from day to day and season to season. Some climatologists hold that an average annual temperature drop of only 7.2° F. can unbalance the cycle and usher in a glacial epoch.

At the onset of the Ice Age, the snows that fell in certain areas in both the northern and southern hemispheres in the winter did not melt fully the next summer. Each year thereafter more snow built up. Eventually, the growing accumulation of snow became recrystallized to ice. The recrystallization resulted from the pressure of overlying snow transforming the light and loosely compacted snow at the base of the accumulation into small ice crystals. These tiny crystals of ice are called firn. As more snow and ice were added, pressure became more intense and the small crystals of ice became larger. As pressure further increased from more and more gathering snow, the grains of ice joined together. Becoming compacted, the interlocking grains in time turned into a solid mass of glistening ice. Over a succession of many years of accumulation, substantial bodies of ice developed.

The frigid ice bodies profoundly influenced climates around the world. Polar and tropical air masses met and intermixed over new areas. Cold blasts raked lands where only warm winds had blown before. The snowline and permafrost line, marking the boundary of the zone of permanently frozen subsoil, slowly advanced toward the equator. Climates everywhere began to change. And the ice accumulation gradually increased in size, both vertically and laterally, forming thick sheets over extensive areas. The world entered the Pleistocene Epoch. The Ice Age was underway!

Glacial Ice: A Rock

Ice, as we previously mentioned, is classified as a mineral and snow is regarded as a sediment in semisolid form. Fresh snow contains a large proportion of air and has a very low specific gravity, around 0.05 to 0.10. As snow converts to firn, much of the air is squeezed out of the compacted mass, which actually is a sedimentary rock with a specific gravity of about 0.80. Through further compaction and recrystallization, the mass transforms into glacial ice, which is a metamorphic rock with a specific gravity of about 0.90. The processes by which glacial ice develops are somewhat like the lithification of sand grains into

Small unnamed glacier west of Alsek River in St. Elias Mountains, Yukon Territory, Canada.

sandstone and sandstone's subsequent conversion through metamorphism into quartzite.

Other Periods Of Glaciation

The Pleistocene Epoch is at least the third time the world experienced a period of major glaciation. The other ice ages occurred about 700 and 275 million years ago. The younger of these is better known and took place in Africa, India and Australia, far from the present poles.

Perhaps the earth experienced other large-scale glaciations earlier than those known. Earth science detectives are still sifting through clues in the rock record trying to determine how many times ice ages occurred. As new facts are learned, our knowledge of the earth's geologic history constantly expands.

Glaciers

During the Pleistocene, increasing quantities of the earth's precipitation were stored as ice. Like restless giants, glaciers formed as the ice built up to great heights. During warmer seasons, some of the ice melted. During colder seasons, the glaciers grew in size. Finally, they began to move slowly downslope and along the path of least resistance with a mission that would make geologic history.

A mass of ice a few hundred feet thick behaves as a very viscous liquid. It is capable of flowing much like tar. Both rivers and glaciers flow downslope, drawn by gravity from higher to lower elevations. In moving, both seek the level of the sea. Yet these masses of flowing ice are spectacular agents of erosion. Unlike rivers, glaciers are capable of eroding below base level (the level of the water body toward which they flow) and of moving upslope to the extent that they are pushed forward by pressure from behind.

With a vertical development sometimes of more than 10,000 feet, the glaciers were real heavy weights. The plateau-like ice masses weighed as much as 18 trillion pounds per square mile (18 followed by 12 zeros), exerting a pressure on the land surface over which they moved of as much as 600,000 pounds per square foot. With such incredible power, they were capable of kneading soil and mauling almost any landform rising in their path.

The North American Ice Sheet

In North America, the initial center of ice accumulation developed in the Hudson Bay region of Canada. Glaciers moved out from this gathering ground in all directions. Over years of slow accumulation, the growing ice sheet gradually became continental in size. Geologists have named this ice mass the Laurentide Ice Sheet (after the Laurentide Hills, rising along the St. Lawrence River, in Canada). Although the ice advanced generally southward after it invaded the United States, it traveled northward, westward and eastward at the same time in Canada. But in no sense, contrary to popular notion, did the Pleistocene result from ice masses moving southward from the North Pole.

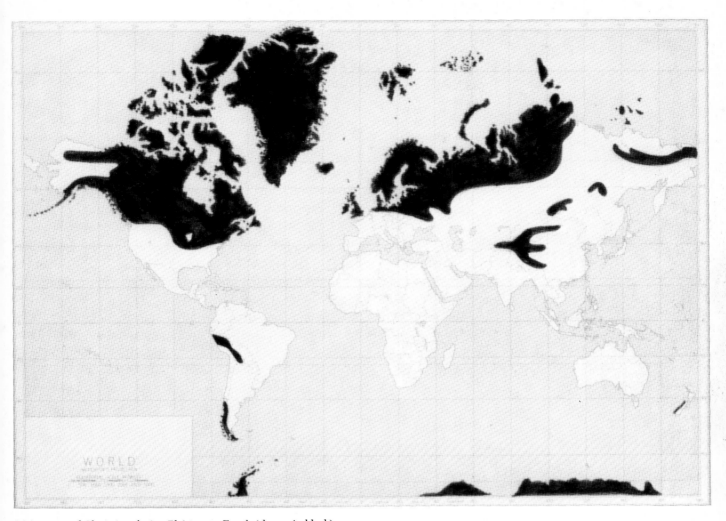

Major areas of Glaciation during Pleistocene Epoch (shown in black).

Each year, the glaciers grew in size during the winter but melted some in the summer. They inched forward the year around, picking up their pace during the warmer seasons. The sheet of ice spread outward in all directions like a great lava flow moving generally toward the equator. In time, much of North America was covered with a heavy over-burden of ice, reaching a thickness of as much as two miles. The regions invaded by the glaciers appeared as a featureless white table-land with the ice completely burying all surface features. Places as far south as St. Louis were blanketed by the icy mass. The glaciers encroached to within 650 miles of the Gulf of Mexico. Their southern-most advance coincided approximately with the present-day courses of the Ohio and Missouri Rivers.

Sometimes the melt over a period of warm climate was enough to cause the glaciers to shrink in size and then they receded slowly back in the direction from which they had come.

The glaciers, fed by the center of accumulation of the ice, advanced as long tongues of ice protruding in front of the main mass of the continental sheet. The tongues of ice are called lobes. Sometimes the lobes were thousands of feet thick.

QUATERNARY PERIOD

Began years
before the
present

		Began years before the present
Holocene Epoch	Recent Age	10,000
Pleistocene Epoch	(Glacial & Interglacial Stages) * Wisconsin	70,000
	Sangamonian	205,000
	Illinoian	305,000
	Yarmouthian	615,000
	Kansan	715,000
	Aftonian	915,000
	Nebraskan	1,000,000+

* There is no general agreement among glacial geologists as to the duration of the various Glacial and Interglacial Stages.

110

Glacial And Interglacial Stages

The continental ice sheet made four major advances during the Pleistocene Epoch. Each advance was separated by a prolonged recession of the glaciers representing an interglacial period of warmer climate. The interglacial periods were characterized by the deactivation of the glaciers after they had retreated, weakened and wasted away. (Some climatologists believe that the great Ice Age is still ongoing and that we live in an interglacial period.) The advances of the glaciers, in each case, marked their return to vitality with a renewal of ice accumulation. The advances are referred to as glacial stages. The four major glacial stages are called the Nebraskan, Kansan, Illinoian and Wisconsin. Each is named after the state in which the greatest evidence of a particular stage of glaciation is found, usually where parts of the advance halted and left terminal moraines. The last glacial stage is called the Wisconsin because it was in this state where it was first studied in detail. In other parts of the world, corresponding glacial advances occurred at each stage. In Europe, the glacial stage equivalent to the Wisconsin is named the Würm Stage.

The duration of the various glacial and interglacial stages is the subject of differences of opinion among glacial geologists. There are no exact dates for events so long ago. The dates assigned have to be approximate.

A growing number of geologists share the belief that the Ice Age started at a much earlier time than previously thought. They place the dawn of Pleistocene glaciation at two, or possibly, three million years before the present. As more information is gathered and correlated, the illusive inception of the Ice Age seems to reach farther and farther back into the geologic past. Unfortunately, radiocarbon dating is an effective tool in establishing the age of glacial activities for only the last 40,000 to 50,000 years and other methods must be used to ascertain the age of earlier events.

In describing the various glacial and interglacial stages, we shall refer to the duration of each as generally cited in geology textbooks. However, research now in progress suggests that most of the stages probably lasted longer than previously thought.

The Nebraskan Glacial Stage began about one million years ago and continued for 100,000 years. The most extensive mantle of drift associated with this stage was spread over Missouri.

The Aftonian Interglacial Stage came next and lasted for 200,000 years, with gumbotil (a dark, sticky subsoil formed by prolonged weathering of drift) developing to a depth of eight feet.

The Kansan Glacial Stage followed, lasting for 100,000 years, with the thickest drift deposited in Iowa.

The next interglacial stage was the Yarmouthian, continuing for 310,000 years, with gumbotil forming eleven feet thick.

The Illinoian Glacial Stage followed for 100,000 years with the heaviest loads of silt and clay dumped in Illinois.

Next came the Sangamonian Interglacial Stage, lasting for

135,000 years, with gumbotil developing from 4 to 6 feet in depth.

Lastly, the Wisconsin Glacial Stage began about 70,000 years ago, representing the final major advance of the continental ice sheet, and ended when the glaciers made a final retreat about 10,000 years ago.

We shall discuss the Wisconsin Stage glacial activities in most detail because of their great impact upon the state's present-day topography, watercourses, soils and land uses. The glacial deposits of the Wisconsin Stage, found in many places throughout the northeastern states, lie on top of the moraines left by the glaciers of the earlier stages. Wherever they cover the same area, the Wisconsin Stage deposits being uppermost are the most completely visible.

During their four major advances, the glaciers, with brute power almost beyond imagination, rounded off the corners of the Appalachian Mountains, gouged out basins for the Great Lakes and moved incredible quantities of earth and rock to form the New England Hills. The ice sheet at its greatest extent held as captive a huge amount of the earth's water supply — more than double that frozen in present day glaciers. Among the side effects of this was that ocean levels fell 400 to 500 feet. About 2½ million square miles of land in North America, ordinarily submerged, were exposed along the east and gulf coasts. Similarly, vast areas emerged as dry land along the west coast. The Bering Straits became a land bridge connecting Alaska and Asia. The British Isles and Europe likewise became connected.

After the close of the Pleistocene, the water released from the melting glaciers returned to the seas. Oceans rose close to their former levels, engulfing again most of the land that had been added to the continents during the periods of glaciation. But more importantly, the hydrologic cycle regained its former equilibrium and the world's climates resumed a level of stability.

Faunal Migration

The Ice Age land bridge at the Bering Straits together with surrounding parts of Siberia and Alaska exposed by the lowering of the seas, as a geographical area, is called Beringia. This land connection became an intercontinental passageway in Pleistocene times for many species of land animals that migrated between the Old and New World. Among the animals traveling over this migration route, in one direction or the other during various intervals of decreased glacial activity, were horses, camels, pig-like peccaries, moose, musk oxen, elk, wolverines, prong horns, arctic fox, reindeer, great sloths, ermine, voles, elephant-like mastodons and woolly mammoths, great dire wolves, giant bison, terrifying sabor-tooth tigers, scimetar cats, short-faced bears and a great variety of birds. The wild animals were on the move in search of food, pushed — from place to place — by changing climatic conditions that fluctuated with the advance or retreat of the ice masses. Many of these creatures found their way eventually to prehistoric Wisconsin. The most famous

The 12-foot-tall, eight-ton wooly mammoth was one of Wisconsin's giant Ice Age creatures.

111

migrant of all was *Homo sapiens* (early human), the hunter and food gatherer — who made the journey from Asia to the New World about 20,000 to 30,000 years ago. Immigrating in small bands, these early people brought dogs with them as well as the knowledge of flint knapping and using fire. They are believed to have traveled down an ice-free corridor, extending southward from Alaska along the east side of the Rocky Mountains, to unglaciated lands in southwestern Canada, where the Americas lay before them as a virgin wilderness — a vast, beautiful and unsullied domain.

All of us are descendants of early people who emerged around the world as a species during the Ice Age. The drama of the spreading ice masses and human evolution was enacted simultaneously on earth during the Pleistocene.

Gwen Schultz, a University of Wisconsin-Madison geography professor and an acknowledged authority on the Ice Age, in her book, *Ice Age Lost*, comments on our glacially-oriented origins:

"The Ice Age world was not static, but rife with conflict and adjustment. We have been brainwashed to think it was entirely unfriendly and austere, but this was a stimulating, challenging time, an evolutionary catalyst which improved the minds, physiques and skills of Early People, for they were compelled to improvise and adapt at a relatively fast pace if they would escape extinction and maintain an advantage over ever-present rivals. Around the world our Ice Age ancestors walked, commixing into one breed, and winning out over sundry competitors in all climates. We are descendants of those champions. There are glacial genes in us all."

Wisconsin Stage Of Glaciation

The Wisconsin Stage of glaciation began about 30,000 years ago. Like burly giants — flexing their muscles, going forth and spoiling to take things apart, the glaciers lumbered into Wisconsin from both the northeast and northwest. Lobes of ice along the border of the continental ice sheet advanced on five major fronts. One lobe moved through the area now occupied by Lake Michigan, scooping out an immense basin to a depth of nearly 1,000 feet. A smaller lobe dredged out the bay of Green Bay and continued southward rearranging the landscape to form Lake Winnebago, the Horicon Marsh and the hills around Madison. Another excavated the hole which is now Lake Superior. The fourth, called the Chippewa Lobe, worked over the terrain now drained by the Chippewa and Black Rivers in northwest-central Wisconsin. The fifth, called the Wisconsin Valley Lobe moved into the watershed of the Upper Wisconsin River from the northeast, rearranging the topography of that highland area. None of the lobes moved into the Driftless Area in the central and southwestern portion of the state. This area alone was left unravished.

The Wisconsin Stage of glaciation covered a period of about 60,000 years and is divided into five substages, representing the time intervals of the major advances of the glaciers, which, in the order of the earliest to the latest, are: 1. the Altonion, 2. the

Extent of Wisconsin stage glaciation of North America.

112

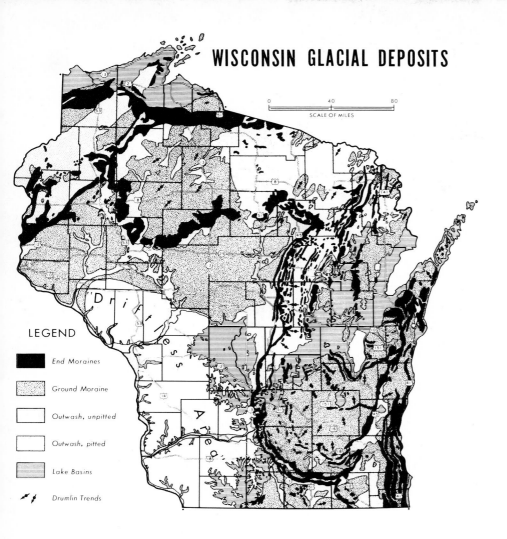

WISCONSIN GLACIAL DEPOSITS

SCALE OF MILES
0   40   80

LEGEND

End Moraines

Ground Moraine

Outwash, unpitted

Outwash, pitted

Lake Basins

Drumlin Trends

Glacial relics

Farmdalian, 3. the Woodfordian, 4. the Twocreekan, 5. the Valderan. The substages are separated by "interstadial periods", representing temporary pauses in the advances of the ice sheet.

The glaciers left their mark on Wisconsin to an extent unmatched anywhere else in North America. With Herculean strength they eroded the stumps of Precambrian mountains, smoothed off the crest of hills, toppled sandstone outliers, filled in valleys, tumbled and ground huge blocks of dislodged rock into boulders, cobbles and pebbles and scooped up and redeposited countless billions of cubic yards of earth. Wherever they went, the glaciers left an awesome amount of debris in their wake. The litter, deposited over three-fourths of the state and in all but the Driftless Area, is called glacial drift. It consists of a mixture of rocks and soil, in most instances a mish-mash of materials of different degrees of weathering, churned into a heterogeneous mass which now mantles the land. Rocks and soil transported from as far away as Canada and Upper Michigan are common ingredients in the drift. Today, rocks left behind by the glaciers are found piled along fence rows where fields have been cleared. There you are apt to come upon an assortment of youthful light-colored rocks, older brick red rocks and somber dark rocks of ancient origin. Float copper from the Keweenaw Peninsula of Upper Michigan is found occasionally in southeastern

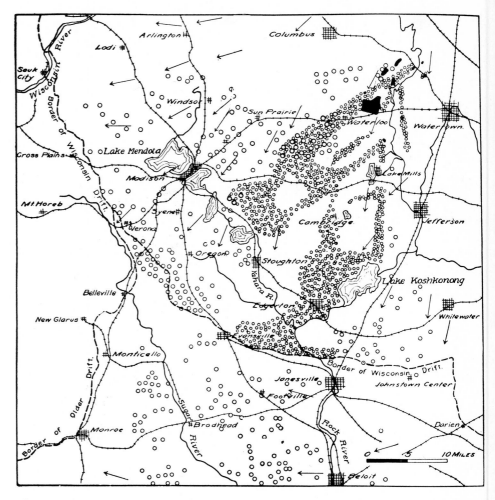

The Waterloo boulder train. Quartzite ledges shown in black, boulder train by circles, and directions of glacial movement by arrows.

Wisconsin in drift laid down by the Green Bay and Lake Michigan lobes.

Sometimes when the ice sheet was on the move, even the highly resistant crystalline rock forming the stumps of Precambrian mountains that had withstood hundreds of millions of years of erosion fell prey to the glaciers and succumbed, at least partially, to their irresistable power. An example of this is the boulder train found near Powers Bluff, at Arpin, in Wood County. Quartzite boulders plucked from this mound were moved overland by the glaciers southeastward for several miles and left in a pronounced fan-shaped pattern, called a train. Larger boulders are found at the surface closest to the mound and smaller ones progressively farther away.

A much larger boulder train extends southwestward for more than 60 miles from the quartzsite ledges near Waterloo, in Jefferson County. Lying in a fan-shaped pattern, the boulder train increases in width from a narrow band at Waterloo to about 20 miles between Sun Prairie and Lake Mills and about 50 miles between Madison and Whitewater. The dark quartzsite boulders scattered about the surface in this region are easy to recognize because the bedrock, in contrast, consists mostly of light-colored dolomite and sandstone.

114

Landscapes showing the handiwork of the glaciers in the North Kettle Moraine Area.

Kettle Moraine Scenic Drive

A recommended trip to see the sculpturing of the state by the glaciers is the Kettle Moraine Scenic Drive, in southeastern Wisconsin, which winds through a wonderland of forests and glacial forms. A booklet "A Trip on Glacial Geology In The North Kettle Moraine Area", by George Gaenslen, is published and distributed by the Milwaukee Public Museum, 800 West Wells Street, Milwaukee, Wisconsin 53233. This guidebook identifies and explains many glacial formations on a round trip between Menomonee Falls and Fond du Lac that takes, at least, a full day. It provides an informative and rewarding journey through an out-of-door art gallery featuring the masterpieces of the glaciers.

Ice Age National Scientific Reserve

The Ice Age National Scientific Reserve has been established in Wisconsin to preserve representative landforms created by the glaciers during the Wisconsin Stage of glaciation. Covering 32,500 acres, the reserve consists of nine separate units extending from Manitowoc County in the east to Polk County in the west. Each unit is designed through interpretive centers proposed for the future to tell part of the dramatic story of the advance and retreat of the ice sheet. The units are:

- Two Creeks Unit — an interglacial forest buried by the Valderan Ice Sheet.

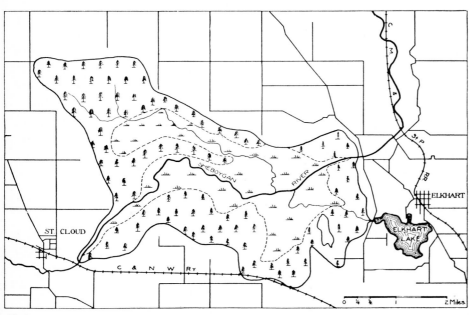

Sheboygan Marsh, a filled-in lake.

115

Devils Lake nestled among the hills of the Baraboo Range.

Shoreline of Lake Michigan at the Two Creeks Unit.

The St. Croix River gorge at the Interstate Unit.

- The Sheboygan Marsh Unit — a great postglacial marsh with its very own kind of wilderness.
- The Kettle Moraine Unit — a showcase of striking glacial forms in the interlobate kettle moraine area, including both the North and South Kettle Moraine Forests.
- Campbellsport Unit — rolling countryside with drumlins and other spectacular glacial landforms.
- The Cross Plains Unit — clearly defined end moraines marking the boundary between glaciated lands and the Driftless Area.
- The Devils Lake Unit — a glacially formed lake in an area where the advancing glaciers encountered the formidable Baraboo Range.
- The Mill Bluff Unit — castlelike sandstone outliers that escaped glacial destruction in the Driftless Area and now peer over the vast bed of old Glacial Lake Wisconsin.
- The Bloomer Moraine Unit — glacial lakes and rugged moraines in a northwoods setting.
- The Interstate Unit — a deep river gorge with numerous potholes carved out of lava rock by glacial meltwaters.

Ice Age Trail

An Ice Age trail, winding for 600 miles through the state, is proposed for designation as a national recreational trail. The serpentine trail will some day link all nine units of the Ice Age National Scientific Reserve. The trail extends through a rich variety of glacial topography from the Sheboygan Marsh in eastern Wisconsin, near Lake Michigan, to Interstate Park in northwestern Wisconsin, on the Minnesota border. Areas crossed by the trail represent the full range of glacial topography.

Glacial Topographical Forms

When the glaciers finally retreated from Wisconsin about 10,000 years ago, they left a rich variety of topographical forms. Landscape features built by the ice and its meltwater tell much about how the ice advanced and receded. These striking landforms, many of which are earmarked for inclusion in the Ice Age National Scientific Reserve of Wisconsin, are truly a legacy of the

116

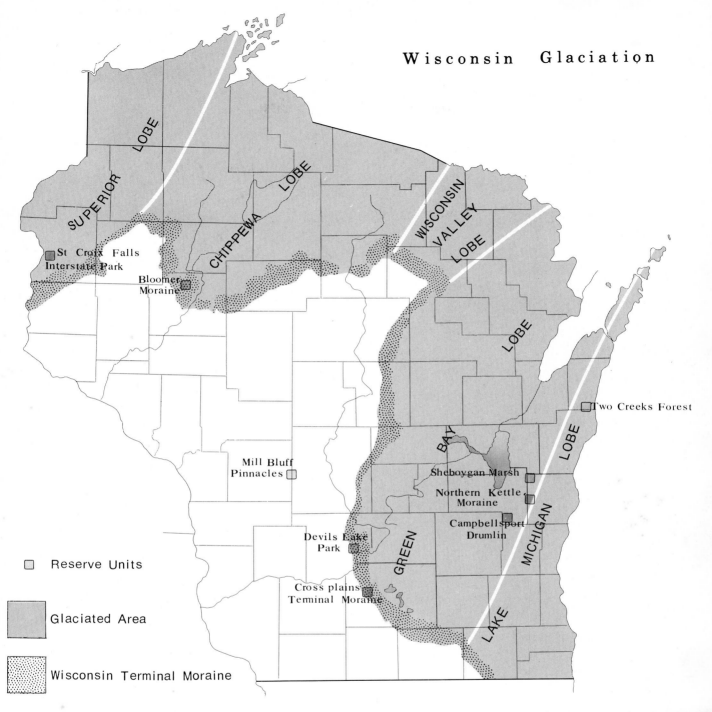

Wisconsin Glaciation

SUPERIOR LOBE

CHIPPEWA LOBE

WISCONSIN VALLEY LOBE

GREEN BAY LOBE

LAKE MICHIGAN LOBE

St Croix Falls Interstate Park

Bloomer Moraine

Mill Bluff Pinnacles

Devils Lake Park

Cross plains Terminal Moraine

Sheboygan Marsh

Northern Kettle Moraine

Campbellsport Drumlin

Two Creeks Forest

☐ Reserve Units

▨ Glaciated Area

⸬ Wisconsin Terminal Moraine

glaciers. Among these are ground moraine, terminal moraines, recessional moraines, kames, kettles, drumlins, eskers and crevasse fills.

Drift And Till

Drift is the name used for all types of glacially deposited debris. Till refers to ice-deposited sediments associated with glaciation but does not include materials deposited by meltwater.

Drift is either stratified or nonstratified. Stratified drift was deposited in beds by the meltwater of the glaciers. The bedding is the result of sorting of the drift during deposition.

Nonstratified till, south of Delafield in Waukesha County.

117

Rock fragments and soil were packed off generally for long distances by glacial ice and meltwater and, in the process, were churned, tumbled, abraded and sorted. Coarse heavy boulders and cobbles were deposited first, lighter pebbles next, and fine sands, silts and clays last. When currents in runoff water carrying sediments were constant in velocity and direction, the beds of deposited material tended to be parallel. However, with changes in the velocity and direction of such currents, the beds sometimes became wedge-shaped forming cross-bedded strata.

Nonstratified drift or till resulted when sorting or bedding of deposited materials was absent.

Ground Moraine

Ground moraine south of Merrill in Lincoln County.

The drift deposited under the ice, now spread upon the surface as if worked upon by an army of giant earthmoving machines, is called ground moraine. It covers most of the glaciated portions of the state, typically with a blanket less than 20 feet thick but varying from a few inches to more than 100 feet. Generally consisting of unassorted drift, the ground moraine produces several forms of topography. In places, only a thin veneer of ground moraine was laid down, with numerous bare rock ledges left relatively undisturbed. Elsewhere, a thick deposit of ground moraine completely buries the former land surface. The terrain in an area with a thick deposit is usually hummocky, giving no clue to the original lay of the land.

Most of a glacier's work was done at the base of the ice; it was there that the greatest amount of erosion of the surface and deposition of drift took place. Actually, glaciers "plucked" rocks and soils from the surface areas over which they moved. These materials were engulfed by the ice on the underside of the glaciers, then snatched up in large frozen masses, churned, separated and passed toward the front of the glaciers. In the process, ground moraine was deposited underneath the ice masses in folds on a large scale, somewhat resembling a wrinkled bedspread before it is smoothed.

Terminal Moraines

An enormous amount of unconsolidated rocks and soil was transported by the ice sheet as it moved slowly through Wisconsin. This material was carried as if on a giant conveyor belt to the snout of a glacier at the front of an advancing lobe, where it piled up to form end or terminal moraines. Thus, the farthest advance of each lobe before it started receding is marked by terminal moraines, which are characteristically curved because the snouts of the glaciers in most cases were curved.

Terminal moraines appear as ridgelike accumulations of drift formed along the downstream margin of a snout. Sometimes the front of a lobe remained stationary for a long period due to the glacier's melting back at exactly the same rate that it was being pushed forward. The glacier then waited with the impatience of a bull poised to charge. This condition resulted in the building up of substantial terminal moraines as a long procession of materials was moved to the snout for deposit, piling up battlements of debris like the front line of a fortified field.

The terminal moraines of the North Kettle Moraine appear as pronounced ridges peppered with loose rocks that consist of about 90% sedimentary rocks, mostly limestone and dolomite of local origin, associated with enough transported soil to fill a big part of the Grand Canyon.

You can see a good example of a terminal moraine deposited along the side of a glacial lobe on Highway 73, just east of Plainfield, in Waushara County, where the level sandy bed of old Glacial Lake Wisconsin gives way abruptly to rugged, rolling terrain, resulting from a series of irregular ridges, strewn with boulders of many sizes.

An example of a beautiful little city poised atop the ridges of a terminal moraine is Neillsville, in Clark County.

Recessional Moraines

Recessional moraines are similar to terminal moraines but mark the edge of a melting glacier as it retreated or receded from its line of farthest advance. Recessional moraines were formed whenever the ice front made a temporary halt in its general retreat. They appear on the landscape as a series of giant rock gardens, with an amazing assortment of rocks and soils.

Stagnate-Ice Moraines

Stagnate-ice or dead-ice moraines were produced, typically like those in the Interlobe Kettle Moraine Area, when the ice mass became stagnate in the process of melting and unloaded great quantities of debris as it receded northward. Most stagnate-ice moraines were deposited at the end of the Late Woodfordian Substage, about 13,000 years ago. Even during deglaciation, the glaciers were hard at work building many

The sheer ice cliff at the terminus of Nunatuk Glacier, Alaska. There was once a similar cliff at each end of Devils Lake, Wisconsin.

The terminal moraine at the southeastern end of the Devils Lake Gap. It occupies the site of a former ice cliff much like that shown in the upper picture.

This stagnate ice cliff on the southeast margin of the Malaspina Glacier in Alaska is covered with soil and vegetation. Note fractures in the ice.

119

Holy Hill

The well-known Dundee Kame in Fond du Lac County.

Kame at Slinger in Washington County.

Esker in North Kettle Moraine State Park.

striking landforms such as kames, eskers and crevasse-fills. This was the time, too, when most kettles were formed as blocks of ice, buried by the retreating glaciers, thawed and left depressions in the ground moraine or outwash plains. We shall discuss each of these glacial landforms in detail.

Kames

Kames are mounds or conical-shaped hills that were formed of sand and gravel at the periphery of a stagnate ice sheet. They result from sediments deposited by streams running off or swirling down drains in the ice mass. If you take a fistful of sand and let it trickle down, you produce a miniature cone resembling a kame.

Kames are classified as delta or moulin kames. Delta kames originated in bays along the ice sheet. Delta kames consist generally of stratified or cross-bedded sediments. Moulin kames, now looking like giant chocolate drops set upon the ground, were fashioned by torrents of water that flushed down shafts or wells in the ice sheets. Moulin deposits contain an amazing intermixture of materials ranging from silt to boulders.

Holy Hill, rising south of Hartford, in Washington County, is an immense moulin kame, one of the highest in southeastern Wisconsin. A twin-spired church crowning the summit of this beautiful eminence resembles a medieval castle. A visit here offers a panoramic view of the striking landforms of the Interlobate Moraine.

Some kames in the North Kettle Moraine area are so large that ski runs have been built on their slopes.

Kames, looming abrupty above rolling ground moraine, can be seen along Highway 53 between New Auburn and Cameron in northwestern Wisconsin.

Eskers

Eskers are long irregular snakelike ridges that result from large deposits of stratified sand and gravel dumped by streams flowing through channels or tunnels underneath the ice mass. Usually eskers lie parallel to the direction of movement of the glaciers. They generally appear as a series of sinuous segmented crests rather than as continuous ridges, somewhat resembling a string of giant elongated beads of varying sizes lying upon the ground. Their crests are usually knobby and hummocky but sometimes gently undulatory. They are rarely level for any great distance. In southeastern Wisconsin, eskers typically range in height from five or ten feet to as much as 40 feet and may extend laterally for as much as twelve miles. The Parnell Esker, located east and north of Dundee, just east of the Sheboygan County line, is a representative esker ridge, reaching from 5 to 35 feet in height and stretching through the countryside for about four miles. Eskers form humpback ridges in many places north of Bloomer, in Chippewa County. (The landscapes of this well-

120

known Ice Age area contain many other striking glacial forms.)

Crevasse Fills

Another kind of ridge of glacial origin, crevasse fills generally occur in areas where eskers are uncommon. Shorter than eskers, more serpentine in appearance and usually less than a quarter mile in length, crevasse fills go in any direction and do not necessarily point in the direction that the ice mass moved. Their narrow crests are continuous and horizontal, rarely showing any knobs or hummocks. Crevasse fills developed where meltwater stood on top of a stagnate ice sheet and flushed and filled sediments into deep factures (crevasses) in the brittle ice sheet. Usually fine sands were thus deposited. St. Augustine Road, south of Holy Hill in Washington County, follows the narrow ribbon-like crest of a crevasse fill, with very steep flanks descending 40 to 50 feet to swampy terrain below.

Crevasse Fill near Holy Hill

Kettles

A kettle is a depression in the drift of varied size, sometimes bigger than a football stadium, resulting from a buried block of ice which remained when a glacier receded. Later when the block of ice melted, a hollow was left in the surface, called a kettle hole. Some of these depressions eventually became filled with water producing kettle lakes.

Many of the jewel-like lakes of northern Wisconsin are kettle lakes, providing recreation each year for millions of resident and out-of-state tourists. These beautiful bodies of sparkling fresh water are among the states's most popular natural resources.

The Greenbush Kettle, in western Sheboygan County, is an especially deep and picturesque kettle.

Drumlins against the skyline in Campbellsport area in Fond du Lac County.

Drumlins

Drumlins are streamlined, elliptical hillocks of glacial drift. They have the shape typically of an inverted spoon-bowl, with the long axis lying in the direction of the flow of the glacier. Some drumlins, more elongated in shape, resemble giant cigars cast upon the ground. The steeper end (stoss end) of a drumlin always faces toward the direction from which the ice came while the other end (the lee end), longer and more gentle in slope, points toward the direction which the ice advanced.

Drumlins were formed as ground moraine was deposited, presumably, on the underside of an advancing glacier; and they vary considerably in size. Although representing obvious accumulations of till, the exact mechanics of their formation is not yet understood. Some are as much as a half mile long and a quarter mile wide, with elevations up to 70 feet. Most are smaller. When these elliptical hills are numerous in an area, they are referred to as a drumlin swarm. A typical drumlin swarm resembling a school of earthen porpoises can be seen along Highway 175 north of Theresa, in Dodge County.

121

The drumlin field of southeastern Wisconsin, peppered with an estimated 1,400 drumlins, is world-famous. Numerous drumlins border the freeway (Highway I-94) between Milwaukee and Madison. Drumlins also occur abundantly in the northeastern and northwestern portions of the state, where they trend toward the southwest.

Outwash Plains

Near the end of the Ice Age when the glaciers finally wasted away, meltwater draining from the receding ice mass energetically reworked moraines formed by earlier glacial activity and, in the process, washed out, transported and deposited great quantities of sediments. Materials thus deposited are known as outwash. Usually, outwash was spread out downslope of end moraines in broad fan-shaped beds, called outwash plains. Outwash plains are composed of stratified sediments because of the sorting action of streams flowing from both atop and underneath the glacier, with coarser materials deposited closer to the ice mass and finer materials farther away. Much of the stratified drift in outwash plains is cross-bedded as the result of changes in stream courses as the glaciers gradually melted and shrank backward. The topography of outwash deposits generally resembles that of rolling ground moraine, making identification difficult unless a check is made for the presence of stratified gravel beds. As one might assume, many of Wisconsin's gravel pits are located in outwash plains.

Outwash plains are classified as pitted or unpitted. Pitting results from the burial of ice blocks when the outwash was deposited, with the ice blocks subsequently melting and leaving pits or depressions in the surface. Other pitting results from the

This pit was once occupied by a loose block of ice.

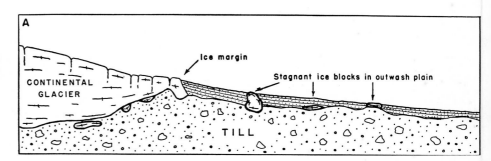

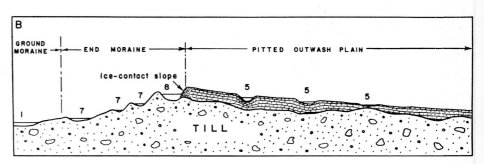

Diagrams showing origin of several different kinds of glacial lakes. The numbers indicate the lake type: (1) basin formed by the irregular deposition of till; (5) ice-block basins in an outwash plain; (7) ice-block basins in till; (8) ice-block basin in till and outwash.

burial of preexisting ponds and streams which were covered with outwash while in a frozen state and later melted, substantially indenting the surface. Pits formed from buried ponds appear as large bowls like those near Sarona, in Washburn County; but pits formed from buried streams appear as long sinuous hollows like those northeast of Rice Lake, in Barron County. Both types of pits tend to be steep-sided.

In areas where the water table lies close to the surface, most of the pits in an outwash plain are occupied by small lakes or swamps; however, in areas where the water table is low, many of the pits contain fairly dry soil and support upland vegetation.

In the higher elevations of northern Wisconsin, pits — unoccupied by lakes or swamps — commonly produce localized frost pockets due to poor air drainage and low nocturnal temperatures that have a noticeable effect on plant species. As a consequence of fewer frost-free days, the frost pockets experience a much shorter growing season than surrounding highlands.

Erratic Boulders

Erratic boulders offer telltale evidence of glaciation. The term is applied to boulders, some of which are very large (in rare cases as big as automobiles), found out of context with local bedrocks. Erratic boulders were transported for varying distances before being littered about by the glaciers. Some represent an odyssey of rocks from far away places, having been unwitting passengers of the glaciers for hundreds of miles. In some instances, erratic boulders may be traced back to their places of origin, thus indicating the path of the glaciers.

Some erratic boulders are large natural monuments. One found in the town of Marion, in Waushara County, is 110 feet in circumference and stands 13½ feet high. Others, fully as large, are seen near Pelican Lake, in Oconto County. Sometimes erratic boulders are found in areas otherwise free of moraine such as in the bed of a dried up glacial lake. In those cases, the boulders probably were carried on blocks of ice that had broken off and floated away from the main ice mass. The occurrence of these alien boulders was baffling to early geologists who were unable to account for their presence until it was determined that they had been ice rafted.

Striations

Many of the rocks carried by the glaciers became scratched or striated from abrasion during transport. The sharp edges of harder rocks scraped the exteriors of softer rocks. Sometimes bedrocks over which glaciers passed show striations marking the direction the ice mass moved. The centers where the glaciers originally gathered may be extrapolated by recording the regional trend of striations in bedrocks.

Lag Concentrates

Lag concentrates occur when an accumulation of cobbles and boulders appears at the surface of a moraine, overlying clays and

Erratic boulders near Amherst in Portage County.

Granite boulder near Shawano in Shawano County, showing striations, marked with arrow.

Lag concentrates near Mosinee in Marathon County.

123

clay-mixtures beneath. This is the result of erosion of the clay fraction of the till before it becomes protected by an overgrowth of vegetation.

Hilltops From Ice-Walled Lakes

A number of flat-topped hills west of New Auburn, in Chippewa County, have an interesting Ice Age history. These mesa-like mounds of sand and gravel are the remains of ice-walled lakes that once stood atop the ice sheet as it mantled the land. The lakes resulted from an impondment of meltwater in huge tub-like depressions or basins in the ice mass, without any outlets — except overflowing — that permitted the water to drain away. Unlike the conditions present when kames formed, there was no way for the basins to be flushed by waters draining out of their bottoms. Thus the basins became partially filled with glacial sediments as well as water. When the ice sheet finally melted, the flat hilltops (once the sedimentary materials in the bottoms of the ice-walled lakes) settled through the ice and remained as elevated casts, prominently rising above the level of the ground moraine.

Today, when you view these unusual landforms, you have the unique experience of looking upward at lake bottoms.

Nunataks

Nunataks (the word is of Eskimo origin) are bedrock masses which protruded through the top of the glacial ice sheet. Nunataks are generally found where the ice was thinnest, near the margin of the sheet. Good examples of these unusual landforms, composed of Cambrian-age sandstone, can be seen near Neillsville in Clark County. Three miles west of that city on Highway 10, a roadside sign in the Clark County Moraine Park (a Wisconsin Registered Landmark) reads as follows:

"Most of the topographical features to be seen here can probably be attributed to deposits or moraines left when the glaciers receded. The castellated hills or mounds northwest of Neillsville are of greater geological significance and interest, however. These are believed to be nunataks — hills which projected through the ice sheet so that their tops were left untouched by the glaciers."

Closeup of sandstone pinnacles on the flank of the Nanatak shown below.

Nanatak northwest of Neillsville in Clark County.

124

Icebergs

Icebergs were chunks of ice that became detached from the main ice mass and floated on glacial rivers or lakes, often carrying quantities of rocks and soil as passengers. Sometimes icebergs became grounded and partially buried and were left to melt and drop their loads of unassorted rocks and soil, which are now found out of context with the evenly sorted sediments that otherwise accumulated on the river or lake bottoms.

Rock Flour

The meltwater of the glaciers was colored white due to the presence of fine mineral fragments carried in suspension, called rock flour. This powder-like substance resulted from the abrasive action of the glaciers on earth materials over which they passed. During the glacial summertime each year when the glaciers melted, rock flour precipitated out of meltwater collecting as a coating on deposited sediments. A layer of coated sediments contrasts noticeably with those deposited during the following wintertime, which have virtually no coating of rock flour. Summertime sediments also tend to be coarser. Thus, successive layers of sediments are distinguishable by grain size and color variation. The successive layers are called varves.

Varves like rings in a cross section of a tree show clearly the seasons during which sediments were deposited. By counting varves in a sedimentary bed, geologists can calculate the number of years over which the sedimentation took place.

Interlobate Moraine

An interlobate moraine is a distinctive topographic feature, made up of hills and depressions, lying along the line of junction of two separate glacial lobes. A world-famous interlobate moraine was formed between the Green Bay and Lake Michigan lobes as they converged in southeastern Wisconsin, in the area now comprising the Northern Kettle Moraine State Forest. The resulting topography has been referred to as kame-and-kettle or knob-and-pothole topography. Each lobe concentrated glacial activity between the lobes, resulting in many striking landforms, such as the moulin kames found northeast of Dundee, in Fond du Lac County.

The interlobate moraine in southeastern Wisconsin developed during the Woodfordian Substage, between 22,000 and 13,000 radiocarbon years ago. It was described by T.C. Chamberlin, a pioneer glacial geologist, as the "master topographic feature of the whole series of glacial deposits in eastern Wisconsin". It consists of drift dumped between the two lobes of ice as they "butted" against each other. Later, at the time of the final stagnation and destruction of the ice masses, with the slowly developing demise of the glaciers, more drift was heaped upon the moraine along this junction. The light gray gravel deposited in the interlobate moraine contrasts noticeably today with the reddish-brown and light yellowish-brown sand till of the ground moraine; each is noticeable in plowed fields.

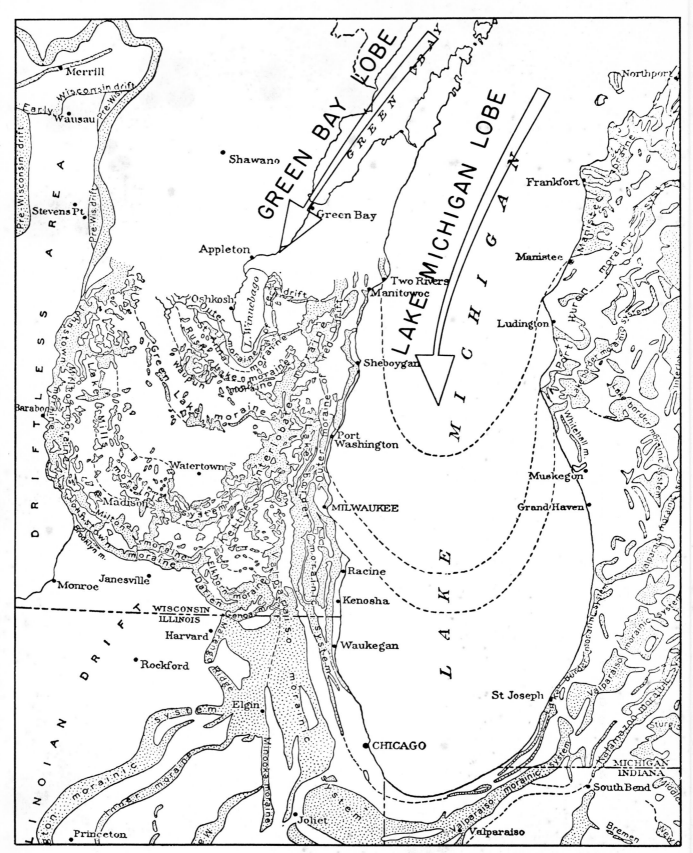

Relation of moraines of Lake Michigan and Green Bay lobes.

Valderan Substage

The last productive period of the glaciers before their demise is called the Valderan Substage. Named after the village of Valders,

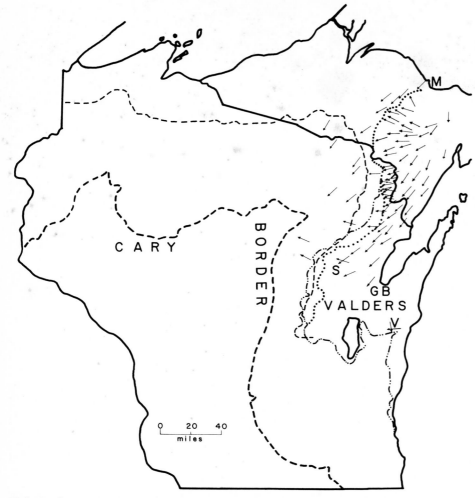

Relationship of Valderan striae to late Woodfordian (Cary) striae in northeastern Wisconsin and part of Upper Michigan.

in Manitowoc County, it is defined as "the youngest time-stratigraphic subdivision of the Wisconsin Stage". Drift of Valderan Age was deposited sometime between 12,500 to 11,000 years ago but the exact interval of this substage has not been accurately dated. The Valders ice sheet was rather thin and thus its activities were weak and short-lived.

Buried Forest

A buried forest has been discovered at Two Creeks in Manitowoc County, about 10 miles north of Two Rivers along the shoreline of Lake Michigan, and has been identified as an "interstadial forest bed". Remains of trees originally comprising the forest — spruce, tamarack and hemlock — have been radiocarbon dated at 11,840 years before the present. The most mature tree found had 142 growth rings. Other relics unearthed at the site were mosses, plants, insects, pollen, fungi and microfossils, including seven species of land mollusks. A number of buried logs had ragged, splintered ends — the result of glacial harvesting. Several logs and stumps lay pointing significantly toward the southwest, the direction of the Valderan ice flow.

The buried forest serves as a recording clock registering the date of the last advance of the glaciers in Wisconsin, thus estab-

Log from Two Creeks buried forest on display at Point Beach Power Plant in Manitowoc County.

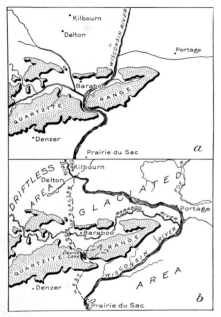

Ice Age change in watercourse of Wisconsin River.

lishing the time at one place of the Valderan Substage. The period of deglaciation represented by the time interval of the forest before succumbing to the glaciers is called Twocreekan.

The fossil forest of Two Creeks has been set aside by the Nature Conservancy for future inclusion in the Ice Age National Scientific Reserve of Wisconsin. Sample collecting and digging at the site are prohibited.

Another buried forest, radiocarbon dated at about 11,800 years before the present, has been found north of Appleton. The forest-bed is similar to that of Two Creeks and consists of a compact layer — three inches to one foot in thickness — of logs, leaves, twigs and peat. It was studied through test borings drilled into a surface deposit of glacial till.

The End Of The Ice Age

Near the end of the Pleistocene in Wisconsin as the climates warmed, the glaciers began to wane. Like tired aged giants, the glaciers were approaching death. The mass of ice, no longer fed from the center of accumulation, lost vitality and became stagnate receding slowly to the north. Gradually melting and turning into slush, the glaciers made a final retreat from Wisconsin, which extended over an unknown number of years. Their fluctuating withdrawal was much like their earlier advances, except in reverse. Dumping loads of rocks and soil while wasting away, they continued to build landforms even in their very old age. But the end was near. At approximately 10,000 years before the present, the glaciers expired.

Changes In Watercourses

The action of the ice mass, both in advancing and retreating, had profoundly modified the state's landscape. Glacial deposition as well as glacial erosion had put a new look on the face of the land. In the process, the glaciers wherever they had transgressed had greatly influenced the pattern of local drainage. In places, the layout of entire drainage systems and waterways had been drastically altered. Many present-day rivers and streams originated during the period when the glaciers finally became stagnate and turned to slush. Great fractures forming then in the decaying ice mass became drainage courses developing into rivers and streams, many of which have survived to the present. In other instances, the glaciers had changed the courses of preexisting rivers, forcing them to cut new valleys. Typical of this occurrence is the change in course, during the Pleistocene, of the Wisconsin River in the vicinity of the Baraboo Range. Before the Ice Age, the river flowed through the Devils Lake watergap. But as a result of glacial diversion, it now makes a great bend to the east, passing near Portage and rejoining its former valley just west of Merrimac.

Near the end of the Ice Age, enormous volumes of meltwater flowed off the waning glaciers. Frequently, these waters draining along swollen river courses were powerful and spectacular agents of erosion. As an example, at St. Croix Falls, in Polk

County, rampaging meltwaters incised a 200-foot-deep gorge through solid basalt, leaving many potholes along the river floor. Likewise, the Dells of the Wisconsin River, in Sauk and Columbia Counties, were carved by torrents of water draining from the ice mass.

Glacial Lake Wisconsin

A great lake, known as Glacial Lake Wisconsin, was created, near the end of the Ice Age, when the waters of the Wisconsin River became dammed by ice and glacial rubble at the Baraboo Range. The impondment formed a gigantic, though rather shallow, lake that cover 1,800 square miles of central Wisconsin. By way of comparison, Lake Winnebago, the state's largest present-day inland lake, occupies about 215 square miles. Eventually this vast glacial lake established a drain through the Black River, which it joined east of Black River Falls.

Beachlines formed along the shores of the big lake. As waves reworked and resorted lacustrine sediments out in the lake, scattered mounds of rock — both outliers and inliers — rose as islands. Pronounced beachlines may still be seen on the flanks of Necedah Mound, a quartzite inlier at Necedah, in Juneau County, that loomed as a rocky isle in the old lake. Many sandstone mesas and buttes likewise developed into barren islands.

The flow of water in the Wisconsin River downstream of the lake was diverted for a long time until river currents feeding the lake finally cut a new channel through the Baraboo Range, completely draining the lake. Today, a vast plain of lake bottom sediments marks the bed of this great glacial lake.

Parts of the bed of the lake were devoid of vegetation for a long time after it dried up. Resulting in a sandy wasteland; at the same time, other parts with poor drainage developed into marshland. At first in the desert-like wasteland, winds whipped sand into

1916 sketch map of Glacial Lake Wisconsin. Some of the place names have been changed since then. Grand Rapids is now Wisconsin Rapids and Kilbourn is now Wisconsin Dells.

Bed of old Glacial Lake Wisconsin in Clark County.

129

dunes. But in these areas in time, grasses and other small plants took root and prairies gradually replaced the barren expanses. And finally the land developed a mixed marginal forest cover in the form that you see today, with some patches of prairie, scattered stands of trees and brush and a few sand dunes still remaining.

Deposits found on the floor of the dried-up lake are comprised of beds of various lacustrine sediments, sorted as to size somewhat in the direction that currents moved through the lake from the source of water supply to the outlet. As you proceed from east to west across the old lake bottom, the particle size of sediments generally decreases from coarse sand grains to tiny specks of clay and silt (commonly referred to as muck). At the present, where poor drainage conditions exist in beds of very fine-size sediments, swampy terrain replaces the drier surface of the sandy areas.

Another good example of a former glacial lake bed is found north and east of West Bend, in Washington County. Here you see two clearly defined levels of old Glacial Lake West Bend, the older level being about 20 feet higher. Just east of the intersection of Highways 45 and 1 in West Bend, a hill rises abruptly, which is composed of dune sand derived from beaches along the southwest shoreline of the old lake. Having been pounded by waves and whipped by winds, the quartz grains of the sand can be seen under a hand lens to have developed frosted exteriors.

Glacial Shorelines

During the Pleistocene, meltwaters of the glaciers filled and overflowed the basins of both Lake Michigan and Lake Superior. As immense quantities of water collected, shorelines migrated inland for many miles, far removed from the present day beaches of these great lakes. Today, the remains of some of the Ice Age shorelines may still be seen in the state, high and dry, south of Lake Superior and west of Lake Michigan.

Influence On Soils And Water

Wisconsin's soils were affected profoundly by the glaciers. The ice mass left behind, in the drift, an assortment of rocks of varying degrees of weathering that have become the parent material of many present-day soils. These soils represent a wide range of fertility. In places, farming is all but impossible. Elsewhere, there are many feet of rich soil parent materials.

In rearranging the lay of the land, the glaciers both removed old soils and laid down new soils. Much of the variability of Wisconsin's soils today result from the earth-moving activities of the glaciers.

Runoff water from the glaciers created mud flats and bars in many rivers from which winds picked up and redeposited silt-sized particles. This dust, during a PreWisconsin Stage of deglaciation, was laid down as a blanket of loess throughout the Driftless Area. The loess, a very rich soil, was deposited generally on relatively sterile bedrock surfaces.

Glacially deposited sand and gravel are presently the state's leading mineral commodities, used extensively as dug or as constituents in concrete for road building and many other purposes.

Glacial drift provides an excellent source for drinking water in many rural homes and smaller communities.

Along with determining topography, glacial drift is important, too, as a factor in the distribution from place to place of the state's vegetation and wildlife.

The Driftless Area

The Driftless Area of southwestern and central Wisconsin has long been a mecca for geologists, who have been fascinated by it as a unique region since it was first reported. As an island of drift-free land in a sea of glacial activity, it is unlike any place else in the world. After bypassing the Driftless Area, the glaciers joined forces to the south and completely surrounded the Driftless Area in a ring of ice.

The Driftless Area covers all or parts of 23 counties in the Western Upland, Central Plain and Northern Highland Provinces of Wisconsin. This isolated bastion of unglaciated land occupies nearly 15,000 square miles, an area about the size of Denmark. With 13,360 square miles lying in Wisconsin, the remainder reaches into northwestern Illinois, northeastern Iowa and southeastern Minnesota. Its northwestern boundary was marked by Prehistoric Indians with a large boulder known as the painted stone. The rock — situated near Red Rock, Minnesota, along the Mississippi River — was painted with stripes of bright red. This erratic boulder was a ceremonial object to the early Indians and had been singled out for veneration, perhaps, because it was the only dark colored crystalline boulder found in an area where the talus consists wholly of light colored sandstone and limestone. Unknowingly, its caretakers had established a monument marking the northwestern corner of the zone of transition between the Driftless Area and the drift-covered glaciated lands of the rest of Wisconsin and Minnesota.

Much north of the northernmost limits of the Driftless Area, the glaciers were confronted, as they lumbered along, by the deep basin of Lake Superior and by highlands with numerous hills and ridges of highly resistant Precambrian rock. These surface features lay as a formidable barrier, thwarting the flow directly southward of the advancing ice mass. In addition, the glaciers were blocked from swinging in from the east by the deep basins of Green Bay and Lake Michigan. Hemmed in, somewhat pinned down and channeled southward mainly to the east and west, the ice mass bypassed the Driftless Area, sparing it from potential ravaging. The path of the glaciers generally was around the contour rather than over the top of the Wisconsin Dome. As a result, the preglacial topography of the Driftless Area was preserved mostly intact and shows what the rest of Wisconsin probably looked like before it was modified by glaciation.

The Driftless Area, as the name implies, is free of the glacial

Sandstone formations unabraded by the glaciers in the Driftless Area.

Castle Rock near Camp Douglas, in Juneau County.

Mesa near Camp Douglas.

Butte near Camp Douglas.

litter found as ground cover in the rest of the state. It contains numerous sandstone outliers, which are virtually absent in the glaciated portion of the state. The outliers, in the form of crags, pinnacles, chimneys and towers, — are composed of fairly soft, low-resistant rock. Similarly, the Driftless Area contains numerous caves and sink holes and a few natural rock bridges. Absent, however, are lakes of glacial-origin found in profusion in most of the rest of the state.

The Driftless Area was first described in detail in 1885 by two University of Wisconsin geologists. T.C. Chamberlain (a former University of Wisconsin-Madison president) and R.D. Salisbury.

Recently, however, another former University of Wisconsin geologist, Professor Robert F. Black, has uncovered evidence suggesting that the Driftless Area may have been invaded by a very thin sheet of "clean, slow moving ice that did little work and left little obvious evidence of its former presence". He attributes such ice to an "older advance" than the Wisconsin Stage of glaciation. Other present-day geologists, however, reject this conclusion and refuse to concede that the Driftless Area is anything except what its name implies.

Further study of this very interesting area may provide conclusive proof, one way or the other, as to its actual geologic history during the Pleistocene.

Rebounding

In areas like Wisconsin exposed to the full impact of continental glaciation, the great weight of the ice sheet, as it covered the

This display, in relief, at the museum of the State Historical Society of Wisconsin, in Madison, illustrates how the ice sheet overburdened the land.

133

land with a mass of solid ice up to two miles thick, caused the underlying crust of the earth to be pressed downward. In some parts of North America, ice-loaded terrains sank as much as 1,000 feet. But after the glaciers finally melted and no longer overburdened the land, the crust rose slowly, returning toward its former position. The upward movement of terrains relieved of an ice burden is called rebound.

Some geologists believe that Wisconsin may still be in the process of rebounding from the glaciers.

As To The Future

At the present time, our larger glaciers — the ice sheets of Greenland and Antarctica — influence climates over wide areas. The state of health and behavior of these glaciers command worldwide attention because of their effect on sea level. As these glaciers grow and prosper, sea levels fall; as they melt and shrink, sea levels rise. Changes in either direction have a vital impact upon shoreline operations.

Glaciers currently cover about 10 percent of the earth's land mass and contain less than three percent of its total water supply. During the Pleistocene, glaciers covered nearly 30 percent of the land and held approximately eight percent of the water.

In Greenland, after 10,000 centuries of snow, the ice cap is presently 10,000 feet high.

If the ice of Greenland and Antarctica should melt, the level of the world's oceans would rise as much as an estimated 200 feet. This would result in disaster along all coastlines, drowning seaports and many of the world's major population centers. The oceans would advance inland on continental shelves, flooding vast areas and shrinking the size of the continents. Flat lying islands, like most of the West Indies, would disappear below the

Alaska's Blue Glacier.

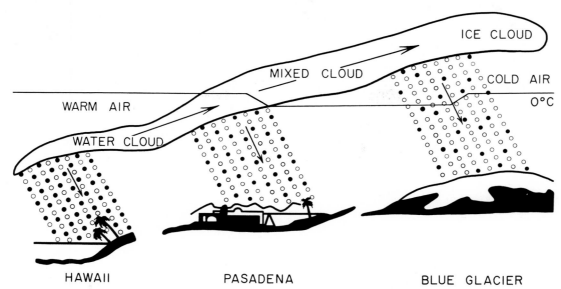

ICE CLOUD

MIXED CLOUD

WARM AIR

COLD AIR

0°C

WATER CLOUD

HAWAII   PASADENA   BLUE GLACIER

This illustration shows the influence of weather on glaciers . . . on a worldwide scale.

waters of the oceans. One science writer observed that a rise of 200 feet in the oceans' level "would be up to the Statue of Liberty's armpits".

The Wisconsin Geological and Natural History Survey reports: "Most scientists now believe that the cause of the Pleistocene 'Ice Age' was due to variations in the solar energy reaching the earth, but how these may have occurred is still a matter of conjecture. We are still in the Ice Age and it is anybody's guess whether future millenia will see the melting of the ice caps and the slow drowning of our coastal cities or the regrowth and once more the inexorable advance of the glaciers."

Overall, glaciers have been retreating in historic times as climates have gradually warmed, with the result in the last 90 years that mean sea level has risen about 7.5 centimeters. A recent study by the National Oceanic and Atmospheric Administration suggests that major changes in the world's climate could result from mankind's growing consumption of fuels such as oil, coal and gasoline. The burning of fuels in greater quantities in the future could raise the earth's average temperature and intensify rainfall because it increases the amount of carbon dioxide in the atmosphere. Carbon dioxide, the administration reports, acts "like a glass over a greenhouse and, the more carbon dioxide there is, the more glass there is over the greenhouse and superheating of the air inside". In time, this could raise the average temperature of the earth's surface . . . predictably, at a projected rate, as much as 5.3° F. by the year 2030. "Even so small a temperature change could have profound but undetermined effects upon conditions on earth."

Records show, however, that since 1940, overall world temperature has dropped 1° F. This temperature drop has had a noticeable affect on the world's weather, particularly on rainfall patterns in portions of the Northern Hemisphere. Likewise, it has coincided with the expansion to the south of a meteorological phenomenon known as the circum-polar vortex. The vortex is an

135

immense whirling system of cold air that covers the North Pole like a giant cap. The enlargement of the vortex is critical because the dynamics of weather in the Northern Hemisphere depend to a great extent upon the role of the vortex. Most climatologists are unwilling to speculate, however, whether this situation represents a foreboding of a shift toward another period of glaciation.

From time to time, various proposals have been made for modifying climate to control the behavior of glaciers in the Northern Hemisphere. One suggestion is to eliminate the ice pack of the Arctic Sea by spreading soot on the ice in the spring and summer in order to absorb solar energy and induce melting. Another is to divert the rivers that normally drain into the Arctic Sea from Russia and Canada as a means of lowering the flow of freshwater which has a greater tendency than saltwater to freeze. Some scientists, however, see perils in such experiments. The deputy chief of the climate project at the National Center for Atmospheric Research, Boulder, Colorado, recently warned, "A climate modification of this magnitude would change the equator to pole temperature gradient (range) and almost certainly lead to major climatic changes in other areas of the globe on a scale that is now uncertain . . . While there are a number of conceivable ways in which the climate could be modified, my fear is that our knowledge is inadequate to control, or even predict, the eventual outcome."

As to the future, we don't know whether we are backing off or proceeding toward another period of large-scale glaciation.

VI Wisconsin — The Beautiful Land

Rocks are the building blocks of Wisconsin's landforms. The beautiful landscapes seen throughout the state result largely from the influence of underlying rocks.

General Geomorphic Regions

When touring Wisconsin, you are impressed always with the great variety of beautiful scenery in every part of the state. Wisconsin has many facets. It seems like a land of a thousand different places. Engaging vistas unfold in the changing landscape as you travel a short distance down a road or go around a bend. Landforms are greatly diversified.

If you include as landscape elements not only landforms but also vegetation, Wisconsin's beautiful landscapes are even more diverse. The great diversity results from three factors that distinguish the state's scenery from that of any other area in the world

LANDFORMS OF WISC

SCALE OF MILES

List of High Points in Wisconsin

	Elevations
Tim's Hill, East of Ogema	1,952.9
Pearson Hill, East of Ogema	1,950.4
Rib Mt., Marathon Co.	1,940.76
Sugarbush Hill, near Laona	1,939.30
Mt. Whittlesey, near Mellen	1,872
Muskellunge Hill	1,860
Hill in Sec. 34, T.36N., R.12E	1,850
T.37N., R.8W. (Meteor)	1,770
Squirrel Hill	1,730+
Summit Lake Station	1,723
Blue Mnds., West Mnd.,	1,716
McCaslin Mt.	1,625
Point Sauk	1,620
Upper Mosinee Hill	1,610
Flambeau Ridge, Chippewa Co.	1,500
Powers Bluff	1,472
Platte Mnd., Lafayette Co.	1,430
Wadels Hill,	1,403
Ridge in Jackson Co. 3 mi. S. of Fairchild	1,391
Thunder Mt.	1,375
Highest Point in Trempealeau Co., NE¼, Sec. 2, T.20N., R.8W.	1,369
Bayfield Lookout Tower, Bayfield Co.	1,368
Bruce Mnd., Clark County	1,360
Ridge 5 mi. NE of Westby, Vernon Co.	1,340
Holy Hill, Washington Co.	1,335
Castle Rock, Monroe Co.	1,335
Friendship Mnd., Adams Co.	1,330
Ridge 4 mi. N of North Bend Jackson Co.	1,300
Silver Mnd., Jackson Co.	1,260
Gibralter, Columbia Co.	1,240
Lapham Hill, Waukesha Co.	1,233
Sinsinawa Mnd., Grant Co.	1,185
Grandfather Bluff, or Granddad, LaCrosse Co.	1,172
Petenwell Peak, Juneau Co.	1,125
Liberty Pole Hill, Green Co.	1,102
Observatory Hill, Marquette Co.	1,100
Necedah Mnd., Juneau Co.	1,100
Mt. Morris, Waushara Co.	1,100

— the unique geologic framework, the topographic influence of the glaciers and the climatic setting.

The effect of climate is noticeable by differences in vegetation. Where still in a native state, the northern portions are mainly dense coniferous forests and the southern portions mostly mixed hardwood stands.

In physical geography, Wisconsin is divided into two general geomorphic regions — the northern and southern. Each is determined by differences in underlying rocks and resulting topography.

Physiographic Divisions

The northern region is part of the Laurentian Upland and marks the southernmost extension of a vast complex of Precambrian rocks forming a shield under northern and eastern Canada. More than 600 million years old, this potpourri of igneous and metamorphic rocks represents the roots of ancient mountains that have been leveled by erosion. Here you find outcroppings of various kinds of crystalline rock such as basalt, rhyolite, metasediments, granite, granitic gneiss and schist. This region is separated into two divisions — the Northern Highland and the Lake Superior Lowland.

The southern region, in contrast, is part of the Central Plain, which extends southward along the drainage basin of the Mississippi River. This region is covered with flat-lying sedimentary

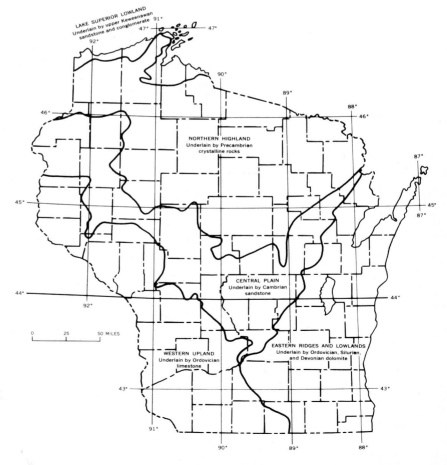

Physiographic divisions of Wisconsin and their relations to bedrock.

138

rocks of the Paleozoic Era, deposited during the Cambrian, Ordovician, Silurian and Devonian Periods. Here you find outcroppings of sandstone, shale, limestone and dolomite, formed in massive layers from sediments laid down on ancient ocean floors, from 600 to 300 million years ago. This region is separated into three divisions — the Western Upland, the Central Plain and the Eastern Ridges and Lowlands.

In each region, the physiographic divisions are determined largely by the kinds of rock underlying the surface. Each, however, is distinguishable by differences in topography, soils, land use, climate and vegetation.

Wisconsin Dome And Arch

The general inclination of the bedrock in Wisconsin, taking into account overall changes in elevation but discounting local topographical features, is referred to sometimes as the Wisconsin Dome. If we consider a dome to look like half a grapefruit with the flat side down, this description of the contour of the state's exterior is misleading because it hardly resembles a dome. More nearly, it has the appearance of an inverted, lopsided plate, with the long half facing to the south. Actually it resembles no common object that permits a meaningful comparison. However, the overall exterior does have a moderate slope to the east as well as to the west. Much north of center, it dips sharply to the north. It is inclined southward on its longest axis. The southward slope in the form of a huge convex mass of bedrock is called the Wisconsin Arch. A profile of this downslope to the south does resemble a giant arch so the term is aptly applied. The Wisconsin Dome probably formed in late Paleozoic time as the result of a gentle uplift that has continued to the present. The major river systems, commonly crossing geographical divisions, drain the state generally outward and downslope toward its boundaries.

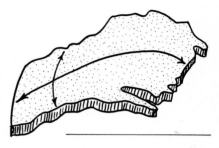

The Wisconsin Dome

Boundaries

If you look at a map, you will see that most of the state's boundaries are formed by rivers and lakes which serve as principal drains — Lake Michigan, Green Bay and the Brule and Menominee Rivers on the east, Lake Superior and the Montreal

River on the north and the St. Croix and Mississippi Rivers on the west. Only short sections of the northern and western boundaries and the entire southern boundary are designated by lines that do not follow waterways. Actually, some portions of the state within its legally defined boundaries are submerged below the waters of Lake Michigan and Lake Superior. The true boundaries of the state, established by imaginary lines, extend into the basins of these two Great Lakes. They enclose a total area whose shape is quite different from the one familiar to us. Our concept of the shape of the state is based on the total area of unsubmerged or dry land as depicted on most maps. For our purpose, we shall consider Wisconsin to look like we have always known it.

General Geographic Information

Before we take a closer look at each of Wisconsin's physiographic divisions, which sometimes are called provinces, let's share some general information about the state.

Wisconsin, the "Badger State", is situated near the headwaters of the Mississippi and St. Lawrence Rivers, two of North America's greatest inland waterways. It has a shoreline on Lake Michigan of 381 miles and on Lake Superior of 292 miles and is bordered inland by the states of Michigan, Minnesota, Iowa and Illinois.

Wisconsin occupies 56,154 square miles. Its elevation ranges from a maximum of 1,953 feet above sea level at Tim's Hill, east of Ogema in Price County, to a minimum of about 300 feet below sea level in some of the submerged lands of the state lying below the waters of Lake Michigan. The eastern coast of Wisconsin, with an elevation of 580 feet above sea level at the water's edge of Lake Michigan, is the state's lowest exposed land area. The state's approximate mean altitude is 1,050 feet above sea level.

Wisconsin lies between 42°30' and 47° north latitude, situated too far north of the Equator to be heated by the vertical rays of the sun. Yet it is located sufficiently south of the Arctic to escape polar extremes. The state has the distinction of lying exactly halfway between the Equator and the North Pole. No ocean encroaches closer than 900 to 1,000 miles. As a result, Wisconsin has a continental (temperate) climate, with very cold winters and rather hot summers, experiencing four seasons each year.

Average January temperatures in Wisconsin vary from 10° F. in the north to 22° F. in the southwestern corner. On rare occasions, freezing temperatures have been recorded in the state's cranberry bogs in July. But average July temperatures range from 66° F. in the north to 70° F. in the south. Record extremes are 114° F. in July, 1936, and −54° F. in January, 1922, at Danbury, in Burnett County. Yearly rainfall varies from 28 inches in the northwestern corner to 32 inches in the southern areas. The average annual snowfall ranges from 55 to 60 inches in the far north to about 30 inches in the south. Hurley, in Iron County, on the border with Upper Michigan, has recorded yearly snowfall in excess of 200 inches. Of the average annual precipitation of 31.4 inches, 1.5 billion gallons per day runs off the state as streamflow.

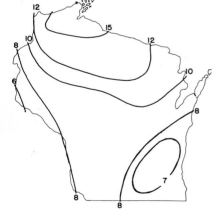

Average annual runoff in inches

Wisconsin has abundant water resources. Sugar Bush Hill in Forest County serves as a backdrop for this typical inland lake.

140

The word, Wisconsin, translated from its Indian origin, means "where the waters gather". This is especially fitting as the state is rich in water resources, having 1,138,374 acres of water areas, with more than 8,000 lakes, thick and extensive groundwater reservoirs, and more than 9,000 miles of streams.

Wisconsin's greatest distance east-west measures 295 miles and north-south 320 miles.

Drainage Systems

Wisconsin lies in two major drainage systems. About 30% of the state (about 17,500 square miles) drains through Lake Superior and Lake Michigan to the St. Lawrence River and thence to the Atlantic Ocean. The remaining 70% of the area (about 38,600 square miles) drains to the Mississippi River and thence to the Gulf of Mexico. The interior of the state is drained by seven principal river systems. These, with their approximate drainage areas, are: the Wisconsin, 11,715 square miles; the Chippewa-Flambeau, 9,519 square miles; the St. Croix, 4,206 square miles; the Black, 2,493 square miles; the Rock, including the Pecatonica, 5,569 square miles; the Fox-Wolf, 6,529 square miles; and the Illinois-Fox, 900 square miles. All of these principal rivers draining the interior originate within or along the boundaries of the state. The Mississippi River is the only Wisconsin river having its headwaters originating exclusively outside the state.

The Western Upland

Let's take a look at each of the state's geographical provinces.

The Western Upland encompasses the western and southwestern portions of Wisconsin. Hilly, rugged and verdant — the landscapes of the Western Upland are among the most picturesque in the state. Much of this area is devoted to dairy farming and the countryside almost everywhere suggests rural Americana. The scenery has been compared to that of the Rhine River basin in West Germany, a favorite of European travelers.

10 CFS
100 CFS
1,000 CFS
10,000 CFS
OVER 10,000 CFS
Width of river line indicates average flow

Average flow of the principal rivers

This remarkable photograph, showing a large protion of the Western Upland, was taken in February, 1974, from Skylab 4, a manned space vehicle that was launched on November 16, 1973, and recovered on February 8, 1974. The spacecraft traveled in orbit 270 miles (430 km) above the Earth and acquired photography, imagery and other data of selected areas between latitudes 50° N and 50° S. The data covered a number of scattered test sites to support Earth resources experiments.

The dendritic (tree-like) images in this picture represent forested areas along rivers and tributary streams. Note the Mississippi River in the lower left and its confluence with the Wisconsin River flowing from the right side. The lakes shown in the upper right are Petenwell Lake and Castle Rock Lake. Further details can be discerned by comparing this picture to a Wisconsin highway map.

Skylab spacecraft

141

View of part of Western Upland from top of Wild Cat Mountain in Vernon County.

The landforms of most of the Western Upland were spared from glacial ravaging. Crag west of Liberty Pole in Vernon County.

Typical escarpment near Sparta in Monroe County.

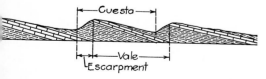

A series of cuestas and escarpments

This exaggerated profile shows how layers of sedimentary rock erode back, downslope of the Wisconsin Dome, with their trailing edges forming escarpments (E). Resistant segments of the layers remain as outlier hills (OL).

As a rough-hewn highland area, it is elevated about 100 to 200 feet above the Eastern Ridges and Lowlands to the southeast and about 200 to 350 feet above the Central Plain to the northeast. The most prominent topographic feature in the Western Upland is the rocky gorge of the Mississippi River, incised more than 500 feet below the crests of steeply rising bluffs to the east. The hard working Wisconsin River has cut a similar but less spectacular trench through this area, descending to a juncture with the Mississippi near Prairie du Chien.

Most of the Western Upland lies within the Driftless Area. Thus it preserves many landforms as they existed in Wisconsin in preglacial times. The green hills in the unglaciated portions of the Western Upland have been referred to as the Berkshires of Wisconsin.

This province is carpeted with the nearly flat-lying sedimentary rocks of the Paleozoic Era, predominately with those deposited during the Cambrian and Ordovician Periods.

The upland consists of a series of cuestas resulting from erosion of the uppermost layers of exposed sedimentary rocks. A cuesta is a ridge with a broad gentle slope on one side and a steep slope on the other, resembling a giant tilted step. The abrupt riser of the step is called an escarpment. The wide gently sloping top forms the rest of the cuesta. Cuesta is derived from the Spanish word for hill.

In a panoramic view, a series of cuestas looks like a broad-topped stairway or multileveled terrace slightly inclined from both the horizontal and vertical.

The escarpments along the cuestas in the Western Upland mark the trailing edges of exposed layers of resistant sedimentary rocks that are slowly retreating southward and westward under the onslaught of erosion. These strata, instead of lying horizontally as originally deposited, are tilted slightly from doming. They are wearing away downslope in such a fashion that the edge of each layer forms the step of an escarpment. The escarpments rise as segmented ridges with ragged edges, frayed by the action of weather and streams. In most places, valleys severly etch cuesta tops.

Principle escarpments occur on the edges of exposed strata of Prairie du Chein and Galena-Black River dolomite.

Ridged and furrowed, the Western Upland is a thoroughly dissected area where you find all the essential features of stream erosion and deposition. Underground water, a less ob-

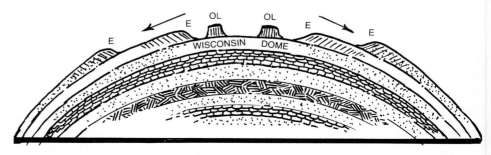

GEOLOGIC MAP OF WISCONSIN

1971

SCALE OF MILES
0   30   60

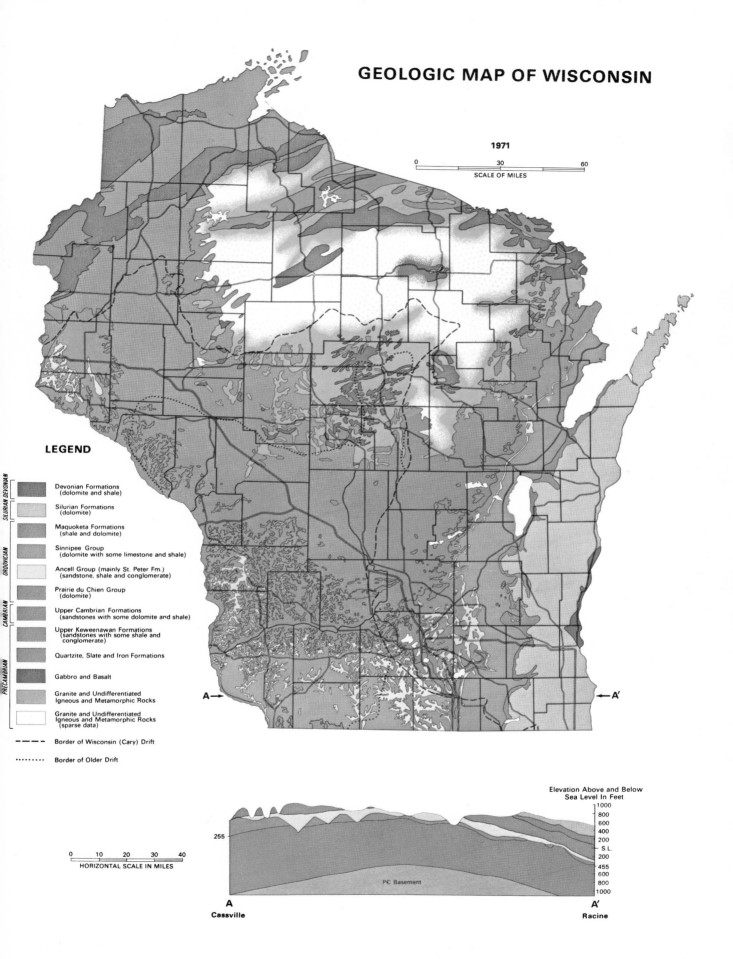

LEGEND

SILURIAN DEVONIAN
- Devonian Formations (dolomite and shale)
- Silurian Formations (dolomite)

ORDOVICIAN
- Maquoketa Formations (shale and dolomite)
- Sinnipee Group (dolomite with some limestone and shale)
- Ancell Group (mainly St. Peter Fm.) (sandstone, shale and conglomerate)
- Prairie du Chien Group (dolomite)

CAMBRIAN
- Upper Cambrian Formations (sandstones with some dolomite and shale)

PRECAMBRIAN
- Upper Keweenawan Formations (sandstones with some shale and conglomerate)
- Quartzite, Slate and Iron Formations
- Gabbro and Basalt
- Granite and Undifferentiated Igneous and Metamorphic Rocks
- Granite and Undifferentiated Igneous and Metamorphic Rocks (sparse data)

— — — Border of Wisconsin (Cary) Drift

·········· Border of Older Drift

HORIZONTAL SCALE IN MILES
0   10   20   30   40

Elevation Above and Below Sea Level In Feet

A — Cassville

A' — Racine

PC Basement

143

Distribution of prairies in southwestern Wisconsin

Typical scenery in Coulee Country.

vious agent of erosion, has played a major role in redepositing the mineral content of the rocks of this region.

Erosion of the surface has carved many hills, valleys, ridges and coulees in this province but has fashioned few hinderlands (broad expanses between valleys). The word coulee is the French designation for valley and is a colloquialism used throughout this region to describe tributary valleys that frequently become dry in summer. Much of the Western Upland is popularly known as Coulee Country, characterized by lush green, steeply pitched hills edging the coulees.

Rocky bluffs, castellated spurs and rock monuments abound in this province and answer a landscape photographer's dreams. Caves and sinkholes are found in many places. These subsurface cavities were produced by the solvent action of underground water along joints and faults in the sedimentary bedrock.

The general elevation of the Western Upland is 1,000 to 1,250 feet above sea level, with high and low spots at 1,450 and less than 700 feet. Some of the steep-sided valleys in this region penetrate deeply into surface rocks, producing marked relief below cuesta levels. Where the valleys lie deeply furrowed, the interfluves (ridges formed between valleys) are usually quite narrow.

The predominant structure of the bedrock in southern Wisconsin, inclined to the south while dipping both to the east and west, is called the Wisconsin Arch. Some Precambrian rocks crop up along the axis of the arch, poking through the flat-lying sedimentary strata that underlie the surface. These outcrops are called inliers because they lie within the boundaries of rockbeds of younger age. The best known of the inliers is the Baraboo Range, located in Columbia and Sauk Counties. The Baraboo Range consists of an elongate ring of gnarled old hills that rise to a maximum elevation of 700 to 800 feet above the level of the valley of the Wisconsin River. The hills are composed of massive pink, maroon and purple-colored quartzite, with a total thickness — much of which extends below the surface — of more than 4,000 feet, resting upon a basement of rhyolite. The quartzite is believed to be about 1½ billion years old and was formed from even more

Typical rock formations of the Western Upland.

Pinnacle southwest of Spring Green in Iowa County.

Enee Point at Govenor Dodge State Park in Iowa County.

Table rock near Readstown in Vernon County.

144

One of the old hills comprising the Baraboo Range.

ancient sandstone, originally existing in great purity and volume.

For more than half a century, the Baraboo Range has served as a geological laboratory, contributing to the education of thousands of students from at least 100 different colleges. A list of teachers and researchers who have been attracted to these hills would read like a "Who's Who" of American geologists.

Devils Lake State Park is nestled in the Baraboo Range. The park's Nature Center offers a variety of programs for nature lovers, with exhibits on the rocks, plants and animals of the area.

A roadside marker on Highway 12, five miles northwest of Sauk City, provides the following information about the Baraboo Range:

Devils Lake

"The rugged range of hills which can be seen to the north of here is among the oldest visible physical features on the earth. The hard quartzite rock that forms them was deposited as sand in a shallow sea which once covered this region. Although deposited horizontally, the layers were warped until they were tilted fifteen degrees at Devils Lake and vertically at Rock Springs. The gorges which may be seen at these places were eroded by rivers millions of years ago.

"The Wisconsin River once flowed through the Devils Lake Gorge. Glaciers brought debris which blocked the river, leaving the lake after melting.

"Exploration for iron ore began in 1887, and in 1900 ore was found and mining operations started. By 1925 the cost of mining had become too high to compete with other sources and mining in the district ceased after producing 643,030 tons of ore."

The caves of southwestern Wisconsin have an interesting geologic history. The result of hundreds of millions of years of preparation by interacting earth processes, they are natural cavities within the bedrock, with openings to the land sur-

Van Hise Rock, a well-known landmark of the Baraboo Range at Rock Springs in Sauk County.

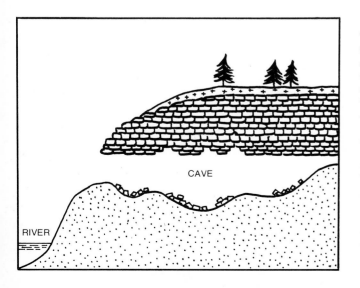

This sketch shows a section through a typical sandstone cave adjacent to a river gorge. The floor and walls of the cave were carved from fairly soft sandstone. The ceiling follows the underside of a layer of more resistant dolomite. The dolomite is concealed at the surface by a layer of sod supporting the growth of plants. Some fragments of dolomite have become detached from the ceiling and litter the cave floor.

Quartzsite wall at Rock Springs shows vertical stratification due to extreme tilting.

145

Quartzite talus at Devils Lake.

Wisconsin's oldest known rocks, near Mill Creek, in Portage County.

Rocks exposed at the surface are forever under attack by the agents of weathering and erosion. The siege is unending. It has been going on for eons without letup. Never has there been a longer nor more persistant effort to overcome resistance.

Composed of nature's most durable materials, rocks seem indestructible. They seem capable of resisting the attack. But, under the continuing onslaughts of water, wind and ice, they slowly yield. Thus, the "irresistable forces" gradually overwhelm the almost "immovable objects."

Ironically, out of this epic struggle comes great beauty. Wisconsin's beautiful and richly varied landforms result from the changing posture of its besieged bedrocks.

Early spring runoff at Eau Claire Dells, in Marathon County.

Exposed volcanic rock at Little Bull Falls, in Wood County.

Brownstone Falls at Copper Falls State Park.

Sandstone Knob at Mirror Lake State Park, in Sauk County.

Rainbow Falls, near Neopit, in Menominee County.

Sandstone sculpture, near Wisconsin Dells, in Sauk County.

Three Chimneys Rock, north
of Viroqua, in Vernon County.

147

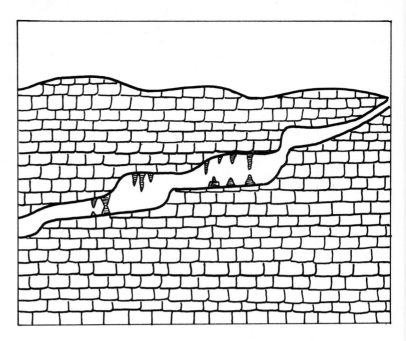

This sketch shows a section through a typical limestone cave. Note the speleothems. Unlike sandstone caves which were excavated largely by hydraulic action (surface water erosion) limestone caves were formed by chemical excavation. Three conditions are necessary for the development of a cave in limestone strata: (1) fractures must be present to provide channelways for the movement of groundwater (2) the groundwater must carry chemicals that are capable of dissolving the limestone (3) the water table, marking the uppermost level of the groundwater, must be gradually lowered over a long interval of time.

face. They range in size from small tunnels, just large enough for a person to crawl through, to extensive underground caverns with long interconnecting passageways and large chambers. All occur in the sedimentary rocks of the Paleozoic, either in beds of limestone (dolomite) or sandstone. The most sizable and difficult to locate are formed underground in limestone. Sandstone caves, in contrast, generally are small, easily accessible and form along fractures in vertical faces of Ordovician and Cambrian-age sandstone, marking the walls of deep river valleys, such as the Mississippi and Wisconsin. Most of the sandstone caves were produced during the Ice Age by stream erosion from the meltwaters of the glaciers draining in large volume from other areas of the state. The limestone caves, found mostly in Ordovician-age strata, were excavated along joints in the bedrock by the chemical action of naturally-occurring carbonic or sulphuric acid transported in solution by underground water.

The unusual geologic formations developing within caves are called speleothems. Speleothem formations result from a redepositing of dissolved limestone. These include stalactites, stalagmites and flowstone. All develop from an accumulation of calcium carbonate precipitated from underground water.

Stalactites appear as icicles of stone hanging from cave ceilings. Stalagmites are their counterparts rising from cave floors. Flowstone is the term applied to the thin sheet-like coating that ices cave walls. Columns develop when stalactites and stalagmites join, from floor to roof of caves, as pillars of stone. Some speleothems form in beautiful and complex shapes resembling animals, mythical objects, historical figures or architectural structures. Prehistoric Indians commonly occupied caves as places of shelter. Archeological diggings in some of Wisconsin's caves have uncovered remains of such early human occupancy.

Several of the caves of the Western Upland have been

Speleothem formations.

Flowstone in Cave of the Mounds.

Column and other speleothems in Cave of the Mounds.

Stalactites and stalagmites in Cave of the Mounds.

Small stalactites at Crystal Cave.

commercialized, providing a visitor with an opportunity to see the unique beauty and handicraft of nature otherwise hidden underground. Cave Of The Mounds and Crystal Cave — both commercial ventures — are popular tourist attractions; each has subterranean caverns with a variety of speleothem formations, including stalactites and stalagmites. The former is at Blue Mounds in Dane County, the latter at Spring Valley in Pierce County.

The commercialized Kickapoo Indian Caverns, located at Wauzeka in Crawford County at the confluence of the Kickapoo and Wisconsin Rivers, were occupied originally by Prehistoric Indians and later by early miners. The caverns contain a variety of speleothems as well as massive deposits of cave onyx.

Eagle Cave, situated on Highway 60 in southwestern Richland County, the first cave commercialized in Wisconsin, was discovered in 1849 when a hunter pursued a bear into a yawning hole in a hillside. The three chambers of the cave are lined with countless speleothems, including a 30 foot stalagmite.

Inexperienced persons, however, should not undertake exploration of noncommercialized caves because of the risk of in-

149

Nunatak near Neillsville, in Clark County.

Sunset on Lake Superior.

Longslide Falls, north of Pembine, in Marinette County.

Dells of the St. Croix River, in Polk County.

Dells of Wolf River, upstream from Keshena, Menominee County.

Little Manitou Falls at Pattison State Park, Douglas County.

Bear Trap Falls, in Menominee County

Wisconsin River, upstream from Merrill, in Lincoln County.

Enee Point at Governor Dodge State Park.

A typical tepee butte, near Blair, in Trempealeau County.

Wisconsin River at Wisconsin Rapids, in Wood County.

Old Glacial Lake Wisconsin bed, Jackson County.

Natural Bridge, southwest of Baraboo, in Sauk County.

151

jury involved and the likelihood of doing damage to speleothems and other irreplaceable cave features that are important for future scientific study.

Lake Pepin is the largest lake in the Western Upland and represents a striking example of an uncommon kind of lake known as a river lake. A river lake occurs at a place on a river where a tributary stream empties an excess of sediments, deposited as a delta, forming an obstruction or dam in the channel of the main stream; the water of the main stream impounded behind the dam spreads out into a lake. Lake Pepin has developed as a river lake on the Mississippi River where the Chippewa River drains into it, causing the Mississippi to expand over its floodplain. It is interesting to note that the Chippewa descends to its juncture with the Mississippi at a rate of nearly three feet per mile but the bed of the Mississippi in this area slopes no more than three inches per mile. The degree which a stream flows downslope is referred to as its gradient. The Chippewa, as the result of its greater gradient, is the swifter flowing and carries with it much coarse sand and gravel, which is dumped in the channel of the Mississippi where the two rivers meet. The slower moving Mississippi lacks the carrying capacity necessary to sweep up this heavy load of sediment and to continue to carry it downstream. Thus Old Man River, confronted by this barrier, is forced to back up, rise and spread out before flowing on. The backwaters of this natural dam reach about 30 miles upstream.

Another example of a river lake farther upstream is Lake St. Croix, formed by sediments deposited by the Mississippi across the mouth of the St. Croix River.

State parks in this province include the following, with a brief comment on the location and dominant features:

• Blue Mound, 1 mile NW of Blue Mounds on State Highway 151 and 18, highest point in the southern part of the state.

• Cadiz Springs, 6 miles west of Monroe on State Highway 11, springfed lakes.

• Devils Lake, 3 miles south of Baraboo on State Highway 123, bluffs and mountain scenery.

• Elroy-Sparta Trail, ½ mile northwest of Elroy or 2 miles SE of Sparta on State Highway 71, scenic hills and valleys and old railroad tunnels.

• First Capital, 3 miles north of Belmont on County Trunk G, first territorial capital.

• Governor Dodge, 3 miles north of Dodgeville on State Highway 23, rocky promonteries.

• Merrick, 1 miles north of Fountain City on State Highway 35, a river park, especially scenic in fall color.

• Mirror Lake, 1 mile SE of Lake Delton, lake scenery.

• Nelson Dewey, 1 mile west of Cassville on County Trunk VV, home of first governor of Wisconsin.

• New Glarus Woods, 1 mile south of New Glarus on State

Blue Mound, west of the village of Blue Mounds in Iowa County

Highway 69, wooded valleys and natural oakwoods.

• Perrot, 1 mile north of Trempealeau on State Highway 35, river scenery with wooded bluffs.

• Sugar River Trail, State Highway 69, 39, 11 and County Trunk E, 23-mile-long old railroad grade.

• Tower Hill, 3 miles south of Spring Green on State Highway 23, historic shot tower and river bluffs.

• Wildcat Mountain, 3 miles south of Ontario on State Highway 33, bluff lands.

• Willow River, northeast of Hudson along the Willow River, river scenery and three dams.

• Wyalusing, 12 miles south of Prairie du Chien on U.S. Highway 18, junction of Wisconsin and Mississippi Rivers.

• Yellowstone, 7 miles northwest of Argyle on County Trunk N, lake scenery and wooded valleys.

Among the well-known landforms of this region are the precipitous bluffs on the Mississippi River, Military Ridge, Blue Mound, the Black River Escarpment and the Kickapoo Valley. The lead and zinc mining, which contributed much to Wisconsin's early history and economy, developed in this area.

Where can you go in the Western Upland to savor the role it served in the state's history and see the beauty of its rugged terrain? The places are many and varied. Let's discuss a few, noteworthy because of their historical background or beautiful landforms and landscapes, typical of those found throughout the region. However, there are many other places of equal appeal and, doubtlessly, some of your favorites may be omitted because only a limited number can be selected for our purpose.

• Flaring up during the territorial period, the Black Hawk War of 1832 was fought among the hills and valleys of the Western Upland, in the southwest corner of the state. Identified now by historical markers, many vestiges of this unfortunate encounter between the early settlers and the Fox and Sauk Indians are found throughout the countryside.

• A real cliffhanger, the Dug Road winds from Glenhaven to a junction with Grant County Trunk A, south of Bagley. Dug out of a bluff overlooking the Mississippi River, this narrow four-mile stretch of gravel road is completely overhung in one place by an enormous shelf of sedimentary rock. On the surface the rock appears friable like clay; but it is stone-hard. The drive offers beautiful views looking down on the placid river.

• Perhaps the most impressive landforms in the Western Upland are the bold headlands edging the Mississippi River. Incised by plunging, steep-walled coulees, the towering bluffs overlook the river valley below. The sheer bluffs frequently dwarf little riverfront villages. Looking up and down the chasm forming the river valley from the vantage point of a vaulted bluff, you can see far peaks looming in the distance. Peering across the river, you can see other steep bluffs rising in misty blue on the Minnesota and Iowa side. The scope and beauty of this sweeping view are breathtaking. The sparkling river, resembling a broad blue ribbon, is segmented in long lazy stretches by a series of lock

The Dug Road

153

Abandoned "Black Granite" quarry, near Mellen, in Ashland County.

The Eagle Pitcher Mine (zinc), Shullsburg, in Lafayette County.

Mining and quarrying of mineral commodities are important industries in Wisconsin.

Entrance core from Cary Mine near Hurley.

Old shaft building at zinc mine, in Lafayette County.

Penokee Range, west of Hurley, in Iron County.

154

Digging of "rotten granite" in Marathon County.

Ruby Red Granite quarry, north of Wausau, in Marathon County.

Limestone quarry, south of Fond du Lac.

Limestone crushing operation at Sussex, in Waukesha County.

Red Granite quarry, northeast of Wausau.

Lannonstone quarry at Sussex, in Waukesha County.

Old Settlers' Outlook

House On The Rock

dams, punctuated here and there with green tree-covered islands. You are likely never to forget this view of Old Man River from the dizzy heights of the bluff.

• The Mississippi River floodplain is a complex of channels, lakes and marshes. The great river, today, is hardly in a natural condition. Dams for flood-control and navigation have created artificial impoundments and dredging has changed the location of channels. But Old Man River still keeps rolling on, with the basic features of its floodplain not being completely obscured. As in the past, the river still produces a beautiful setting along the boundary of southwestern Wisconsin.

• A scenic delight, the Great River Road (State Highway 35) skirts the east bank of the Mississippi River, permitting close-up viewing of the bluff headlands. Featured along this award winning drive are numerous rest areas, overlooking the sweeping expanse of the river valley. Maiden Rock, in Pierce County, rises as one of many prominent bluffs that tower above the widening of the river at Lake Pepin.

• Sight-seeing cruises along the Mississippi River are offered daily during the warmer season aboard the La Crosse Queen from the home port of La Crosse. The boat is described as "the great granddaughter of the majestic and graceful paddlewheelers that cruised the length of Ol' Man River back in the days of Mark Twain". The excursions provide a rare oppportunity to roll back history aboard a paddlewheeler and witness the awesome beauty of the river and the bluffs and coulees adorning its edge.

• Guided tours are offered of the historic St. John Mine at Potosi, on the Mississippi River, in Grant County. Initially known as Snake Cave, this lead mine was first developed in 1827 and was worked for more than 40 years. Visitors are shown through about 300 feet of diagonal shafts and inclined drifts. Stalactites cover portions of the roof of the original cave. Accumulations of cave onyx are also visible.

• Big sheltering hills stand up all around Glenhaven, in Grant County, stuffing the little village like a handkerchief into a small pocket at the Mississippi River's edge.

• The Old Settlers' Outlook is a scenic vista along the Great River Road (Highway 35) between Stoddard and Genoa, in Vernon County. From this vantage point, atop a 450-foot bluff bordering the Mississippi River, you can enjoy an inspiring view of three states — Wisconsin, Minnesota and Iowa — at a place where Pool 7 of the river spreads out into a flowage (nearly three miles wide) behind Lock No. 8 at Genoa. The overlook also provides a sweeping view of a coulee that incises the verdant ridge marking the eastern wall of the great river's gorge.

• The Badger Mine and Museum is located at Shullsburg, in Lafayette County. Visitors may explore the half mile underground passageway of the mine, first worked for lead ore in 1827. The museum contains much old mining paraphernalia.

• An interesting commercial venture, the House On The Rock is located on State Highway 23, between Spring Green and Dodgeville, in Iowa County. A sprawling multilevel house, con-

156

structed of local sandstone, seems to grow out of Deershelter Rock, a large chimney rock, overlooking the Wyoming Valley, 450 feet below. The architecture of the building is impressive. The furnishings are plush. Views of the hilly terrain on a tour of this attraction are spectacular.

• A seven-mile stretch of Highway 78 between Argyle and Blanchardville, in Lafayette County, offers road cuts that reveal in miniature some of the geologic features of Arizona's Grand Canyon. Both formations expose St. Peter sandstone and limestone of Ordovician age. The coloration of the rocks forming the walls of the Highway 78 "canyon" is most impressive.

• The Wisconsin Department of Natural Resources describes the 380-acre Yellowstone State Park:

"Scenic Yellowstone Lake, surrounded by a rolling landscape, is the only sizable lake in southwestern Wisconsin. It is located in northeastern Lafayette County, about seven miles southwest of Blanchardville and just off County Highway F. Gentle hills, valleys, open fields and woods characterize this area.

"Yellowstone Lake is 2½ miles long, and averages slightly more than ¼ mile wide. The lake covers approximately 455 acres and averages eight feet in depth; in the channel, depths of about 20 feet are common.

"This region of southwest Wisconsin was never covered by any of the four glaciers that once spread massive ice sheets across the northern United States and the Yellowstone River flows lazily through scenic unglaciated terrain.

"The entire Yellowstone area, consisting of the big lake, marsh, woodlands, croplands and public use areas, covers an expanse of 2,300 acres of state-owned land."

• A laughing stoneface juts out of the Paleozoic rock at the junction of County Highways N and NN, three miles southeast of Avoca, in Iowa County. No imagination is required to understand the reason for its name: Camel Head Rock.

• The Mississippi River's complex network of channels, sloughs, ponds, islands and lakes in the vicinity of Prairie du Chien is shown on a riverfront billboard in that city erected by the local Jaycees as a navigational aid. It graphically portrays the drainage labyrinth of this great river, which borders and drains much of western Wisconsin.

• Pendarvis — a unique complex of restored 125-year-old homes of Cornish miners — is located at Mineral Point, in Iowa County. It is open to the public from mid-May through September and tells the story of the immigrant Cornishmen who came to Mineral Point in the 1830's-1840's to mine lead.

• Scarlet apples add color every September to hilltop orchards on the ridges at Gay Mills, in Crawford County. Great numbers of people make an annual autum trek to Gays Mills to buy apples. Many come from distant places in Wisconsin, Illinois and Iowa.

• The feature attractions at Tower Hill State Park, located near Spring Green, in Iowa County, are a 120-foot vertical shot shaft bored through solid sandstone and a restored old smelting house. These oddities are the remnants of a once thriving indus-

Pendarvis

Kickapoo appleland at Gays Mills.

Eroded sandstone ledge at Governor Dodge State Park, in Iowa County.

Hikers' trail at Devils Lake State Park, in Sauk County.

Cambrian-age sandstone, in Jackson County.

Door Peninsula jutting into the water of Green Bay.

Baraboo Range, in Sauk County.

One of the inland lakes
in the Northern Highland Province.

try that supported the now vanished village of Helena. Here, at the summit of Tower Hill overlooking the Wisconsin River valley below, shot was manufactured before the Civil War from lead brought in from the mines of southwestern Wisconsin. The lead was dropped from a perforated ladle through the long shot shaft. As it landed in a cistern at the bottom, it cooled in little spheres of solid lead. The operation was active for about 30 years starting in the 1830s. The origin of the shaft is of interest. It was bored by a 23-year-old man, T.B. Shaunce, and just one assistant. They did the job entirely by hand, using only the simplest equipment. They also bored a horizontal tunnel at the base of the hill, intercepting the shaft at a perfect right angle. Lacking anything as sophisticated as a compass or surveyor's chain, Shaunce kept his bearing throughout the project by using a plumb and sighting over a row of lighted candles. Today, you can walk through the horizontal tunnel to where it meets the vertical shaft, peer upward and see a little patch of sky far above. No doubt, you will be impressed with this remarkable engineering feat accomplished — more than 140 years ago in just 187 days!

• A massive natural rock bridge crosses the Pine River, at Pier County Park, in Richland County, nine miles north of Richland Center on State Highway 80, permitting small boats to pass underneath. Composed of Paleozoic-age rock, it was carved over the centuries by the erosive action of the river.

• Bogus Bluff, once famed as a hideout of counterfeiters and still believed by some to conceal buried treasure, rises near Gotham, in Richland County.

• Elephant Trunk Rock, a spectacular sandstone sculpture, is located on Highway 58, two miles north of Ithaca. Point Jude, another Richland County landmark, is located on County JJ, three miles east of Gotham. This formation commemorates a frontier woman who is said to have jumped off the hill, about 1845, to escape hostile Indians. Whether she leaped to her death or to safety is not known. Some say that she held a baby in her arms.

• Rated by a national magazine as one of the 10 most unusual byways in the United States, County Trunk U winds through the lush pastoral countryside of Richland County.

The Shot Tower at Old Helena, 1833-1861

This is the entrance to the ninety-foot horizontal tunnel that connects with the bottom of the vertical shaft of the shot tower.

This is the top of the 120-foot shaft for the shot tower.

Tower Hill Shot Tunnel

Rock bridge at Pier County Park.

Elephant Trunk Rock

159

The Three Chimneys

Monument Rock

Looking at Grandad Bluff

Looking from Grandad Bluff.

160

• An unusual formation known as The Three Chimneys is found north of Viroqua, in Vernon County. Its name describes its general features. Another extraordinary formation is Monument Rock, near Liberty Pole, south of Viroqua, resembling a massive exclamation mark.

• A giant icicle hangs the year around in a tunnel near the bygone railroad town of Summit, in southern Monroe County. The big icicle measures as much as 11 feet in circumference in late summer. It reaches approximately 15 feet from tunnel floor to ceiling and is remembered by old-time-residents of the area "as the source of ice for making homemade ice cream during the summertime."

The underground deep freeze where this ice oddity is hidden away is part of a diagonal access shaft, carved out of solid sandstone in a hillside (more than a century ago) during the construction of Tunnel No. 3, formerly a ¾-mile-long railroad tunnel but now a feature attraction on the scenic Elroy-Sparta Trail. During the warm season each year, thousands of bicyclists pedal over this trail, maintained by the Wisconsin Department of Natural Resources along an abandoned railroad right-of-way that slices through the beautiful hill country, in the general area where the Kickapoo River flows.

Three tunnels along the trail, exposing a cross section of dolomite, limestone, shale and sandstone, permit close-up inspection of Ordovician-age strata. In the illumination of a flashlight, the tunnels' walls and ceilings glisten like ice from seeping water and flowstone.

• The countryside around New Glarus in Green County, with gently rolling hills, neatly parceled farms and unique Swiss-style buildings — usually with barns painted white — has been likened by many visitors to Switzerland, the homeland of many of its original settlers.

• Blue Mound, in western Dane County, is a huge tapering hill, rising to 1,716 feet and looming above the surrounding countryside. The early Indians believed that the blue haze sometimes crowning the hill is an aura of smoke from the pipe of their great god, Wakanda — the maker of the earth.

• An excellent view of coulee country is pointed out on a roadside marker at Rest Area No. 16, on Interstate Highway I-90, 15 miles east of West Salem, in La Crosse County.

• La Crosse County's towering Grandad Bluff has an elevation of 1,172 feet above sea level. Rising majestically above the Mississippi River Valley, this landmark can be seen from miles away.

• Mindora Cut, believed to be the second largest hand-hewn road cut in the U.S., was cleft by hand tools and horse-drawn equipment in 1907 and 1908. This man-made canyon, 74 feet deep and 25 feet wide, is located on Highway 108 north of West Salem, in La Crosse County. It exposes Paleozoic-age strata.

• Trempealeau, an old river town, is nestled among the towering bluffs and pyramid-shaped hills carved by erosion from the ridge bordering the Mississippi River. Its name is derived from the French "La Montagne qui trempe a l'eau" which translates

Mindora Cut

Maiden Rock

into "the mountain that soaks in the water". Nicholas Perrot spent the winter of 1685 here "at the foot of the mountain behind which was a great prairie abounding in wild beasts". According to his account, the wild beasts were buffalo, elk, deer, cougar and lynx. Today only the deer remain.

• Chimney Rock juts from the top of a hill off Highway 93, near Eleva, in Trempealeau County. This sandstone eminence resembles a giant chimney.

• Two streams — Wilson Creek and Mill Creek — join the Black River at North Bend, in the southwest corner of Jackson County. Wilson Creek plunges over a steep rock shelf producing an attractive little waterfall. Mill Creek flows through a miniature gorge and drops over a rock ledge creating a companion cascade.

• "Floating down the river on a Sunday afternoon" at Somerset, in St. Croix County, is a favorite summer pastime for thousands of young folks who float down the steeply descending Apple River on an assortment of inflated innertubes. The swift currents and short rapids provide a thrilling float trip.

• A seldom visited place to see a good example of stratification in an outcrop of limestone is a ridge on Bear Creek, about five miles east of Durand, in Pepin County. The ridge forms a wall for a sequestered hollow carved over the ages by the creek. Sometime ago, a man-made tunnel was constructed at the base of the ridge to divert surplus water from the creek during floodstage. But the creek has forsaken its old bed and now flows constantly through the tunnel.

• The story of Maiden Rock is told on a roadside marker at the city of the same name, in Pierce County.

"The story of Maiden Rock has several versions. One by Mary Eastman was published in 1848. She heard the story from an old Indian friend, Checkered Cloud, who firmly believed the event happened around 1700. A more roman-

161

Roadcut exposing St. Croixan sandstone on Highway 54 west of City Point in Jackson County.

Mill Bluff

tic version in verse was written by Margaret A. Persons. James Duane Doty accompanied the Henry Schoolcraft expedition into this area and on June 3, 1820, Doty wrote in his journal: 'It is told that many years since, a young and beautiful Sioux girl was much attached to a young Indian of the same band and who would have married her but for the interference of her relatives. They insisted upon her marrying another one whom she despised, and she contrived to avoid the connection for near a year. At length her relations, having sent away the young man she loved, on this point compelled her to marry the one they wished. It was evening, and she had not been united more than an hour, before they missed her from the lodge. Nothing could be found of her until morning, when they discovered her at the foot of this precipice, down which she probably precipitated herself.''

The Central Plain

The Central Plain is a level interior belt, shaped somewhat like a crescent, stretching across the midsection of the state. The floor of the Central Plain is composed mostly of flat-lying Cambrian-age sandstones, bordered on the northwest by Keweenawan-age lavas and on the northeast by Ordovician-age dolomites. The plain takes over, in the center of the state, where the Precambrian rocks of the exposed peneplain are first found buried en masse beneath layers of St. Croixan sandstone. Along the Wisconsin River, this zone of contact between the two types of bedrock is seen at the Nekoosa dam in Wood County. The westernmost margin of the Central Plain is marked by the forested valley of the Upper St. Croix River.

In the Central Plain, as the name implies, austere flat expanses and gently rolling surfaces are characteristic with typical elevations at no more than 750 to 850 feet above sea level. The even-

162

ness of the landscape is broken, only here and there, by pinnacles and hills. These, in most instances, are outliers resulting from the uneven erosion of the St. Croixan sandstone. (Outliers lie outside the boundaries of the otherwise intact layers of rock of which they are formed.) In several places, they are scattered about like a child's blocks on a family room floor.

Remaining as rear guards, the outliers are resistant segments, detached from the original layers of sandstone, which are retreating slowly southward under attack by weather and erosion. The outliers commonly wear a cap of dolomite, a harder and more resistant substance than the sandstone, which protects them from the elements. When the cap becomes lost, they wear down to conical hills and then rapidly fade away and merge into the plain.

Found in many shapes, the outliers rise abruptly above the plain as mounds, bluffs, mesas, buttes, crags, pillars and castellated hills. These white battlements add grandeur to an otherwise monotonously even tract in the center of the state which extends eastward to the terminal moraine of the Wisconsin Glacier and westward to the escarpments of the Western Upland.

Much of the Central Plain was glaciated and is covered with ground moraine. But some of it, lying adjacent to the Driftless Area, is overlain with glacial outwash pitted in some areas and unpitted in others. A large portion of the inner lowlands of this province is occupied by a vast dried up lake basin that formed near the end of the Ice Age.

Some travelers have spoken of parts of the Central Plain as "the beginning of the American West". This is a fitting description because landscapes with a pronounced western look unfold in the vicinity of Camp Douglas and Merrillan. Here, you come upon a very flat plain punctuated only with isolated rocky crags and hills, resembling castle ruins and grotesque sculptures. These highly stylized sandstone formations have a singular beauty, characteristic of the "big sky country" of some of the western states but lacking entirely anywhere farther east. These unique landforms rise occasionally as mesas and teepee buttes, in areas where jack pine and scrub oak share space in the prairie with several species of dwarf cacti, including the prickly pear.

The Buena Vista Marsh, in southern Portage and northern

A.

B.

C.

D.

Stages in the demise of an outlier.

Mesa near Camp Douglas

Tepee Butte near Blair in Trempealeau County

163

Butte along I-90-94 west of Camp Douglas

Castle Rock near Camp Douglas

Buena Vista Marsh

Cranberry Marsh at harvesttime near Cranmoor in Wood County

Adams County, presents a broad plain, almost as level as a lake sill, stretching out for miles. This area was reclaimed about 50 years ago from a post-glacial swamp through the installation of an elaborate network of drainage ditches. The banks of the ditches, hump-backed and tree-lined, produce the only noticeable relief to the evenness of the plain. Brook trout thrive in the sparkling waters of the ditches, attracting an army of fishermen every springtime. Bluegrass grows almost everywhere on this flat expanse supporting large herds of beef cattle. A common sight here is a cowboy on horseback crossing the range, perhaps, rounding up some strays that wandered from a herd. This area is one of the last communal dancing grounds in Wisconsin for the vanishing prairie chicken; in the springtime, the roosters, on the approach of hens, perform a mating ritual by dancing and making weird booming sounds.

Other portions of the Central Plain contain marshy terrain. An extensive swamp stretches almost the full distance from Wisconsin Rapids to Black River Falls and southward to Camp Douglas, providing some of the state's best aquatic waterfowl and big game habitat. This is a favorite region for duck and deer hunters. Cattails, leather leaf, partridge berry, sphagnum moss and wintergreen thrive in these muck and peat covered wetlands. Here the going is rough for most creatures but not for the long legged blue heron nor white tailed deer. This great swamp, peppered with potholes, covers about 300,000 acres and is more than twice as large as Milwaukee County. Much of it is devoted to the culture of cranberries, one of the state's unusual but important agricultural crops.

The glaciated parts of the Central Plain appear generally as flat but rolling terrain. The soft ripples and swells of glacial till are interspersed with small lakes. These areas exist in marked contrast to the extremely flat expanse found in a large portion of this province originally occupied by Glacial Lake Wisconsin. Sand dunes appear, here and there, in the shifting sands of this vast dried up lake bed on barren surfaces in parts of Adams and Juneau Counties.

Several scattered mounds of Precambrian rock poke up through the sedimentary bedrock in the Central Plain. These are fossil-like survivors of the ancient mountains of Wisconsin. They now rise prominently in the landscape because weathering and

164

This composite aerial photo shows the Lemonweir River meandering through the Central Plain. The small degree of gradient in the very level plain accounts for the river's aimless course. The settlement in the lower right is New Lisbon, the airport to the left center is Camp Douglas. The photo was taken in May, 1961, from an elevation of 9,000 feet above ground.

One of the Seven Sisters rising above the Central Plain.

Quartzite talus on face of one of the Seven Sisters.

One of the Seven Sisters being leveled for road materials. Soon there'll only be six.

The rapids of the Wisconsin River at Wisconsin Rapids are near the contact zone of the Paleozoic and Precambrian rocks.

erosion have stripped off the marine strata that buried them during the Paleozoic. The mounds are called inliers because they surface or lie within the boundaries of rock beds of younger origin. Examples of inliers are the Seven Sisters (Hamilton Hills) in northeast Adams County and Necedah Mound, at Necedah, in Juneau County. Both formations are composed of highly resistant green-banded quartzite of Huronian-age.

Little streams curl and wind through the Central Plain, in some places stumbling over beaver dams and flowing darkly under the shadows of overhanging trees. The lack of any great change in grade results in the slow flow of most rivers and streams crossing this province.

The Wisconsin River flows lethargically through the Central Plain after tumbling down the slope of the Northern Highland, where in some stretches it charges through rapids or drops over crystalline rock ledges producing falls. Called the hardest working river in the world, it is harnessed by dams along most of its long course. The river originates at Lac Vieux Desert in the northernmost part of Vilas County, travels for 300 miles — almost the full length of the state — and joins the Mississippi River near Prairie du Chien, in Crawford County. The backwaters from two hydroelectric dams in the Central Plain produce Lake Pentenwell, 23,040 acres in area, and Castle Rock Lake, 16,640 acres in area, before the river flows downstream through the world-famous gorge at Wisconsin Dells.

Hagman Falls County Park, west of Shawano in Shawano County, contains a stream with more gradient than characteristic of the Central Plain.

166

Roche A Cri, a prominent outlier, north of Friendship in Adams County.

Rabbit Rock, an outlier, near Big Flats in Adams County.

Saddle Mound west of City Point in Jackson County.

State parks in this province include the following, with a brief comment on the location and dominant features:
- Brunet Island, 1 mile north of Cornell on State Highway 27, river island park.
- Hartman Creek, 6 miles west of Waupaca on State Highway 54, lake scenery and pine plantation.
- Interstate, at St. Croix Falls on U.S. Highway 8, river gorge and rock bluffs.
- Lake Wissota, 5 miles east of Chippewa Falls on State Highway 29, then north on County K, lake scenery.
- Roche A Cri, 2 miles north of Friendship on State Highway 13, woodlands and rocky bluffs.
- Rocky Arbor, 1 mile northwest of Wisconsin Dells on U.S. Highway 12, rocky ledges and wooded valleys.

There are many beautiful scenic places in the Central Plain. The following are typical:
- Tour boating of the scenic dells at Wisconsin Dells has gone into its second century of operation, helping to draw annually almost two million tourists to this prosperous resort community. Sightseers on the boat trips, which leave every half hour during the warmer months, can relax and view the striking sandstone formations of both the Upper and Lower Dells with three ports of call at Cold Water Canyon, Stand Rock and Witches Gulch.

Ship Rock northeast of Friendship in Adams County.

167

Visor Rock

Stand Rock

• A roadside marker on Highway 16, a short distance west of the city, explains the origin of the dells. It reads:

"The Indians believed that many ages ago the Great Spirit, in the form of a snake, created the Dells when it forced its huge body through a narrow opening in the rocks. Geological studies, however, show that the Dells were formed some fifteen thousand years ago after a glacier turned the Wisconsin River into a new channel through the center of a sandstone plain. French-Canadian traders used their word 'dalles', meaning a trough or narrow passage, to describe this section of the Wisconsin River. Wind, weather and the river have combined to create the seven miles of chasms, cliffs, pillars and columns which form part of the many scenic features of the world-famous Dells."

• A trail for hikers follows the gorge carved out of bedrock by Perry Creek as it descends to a juncture with the Black River in the lush Black River State Forest in Jackson County. The stream cascades over a series of rock ledges. The dashing waters of the stream are dark brown in color because of the presence of humic acid coming from tamarack swamps within its watershed.

• Belle Mound, a sandstone outlier, is accessible off I-94, a few miles east of Black River Falls, at a scenic-view exit leading to a parking lot. A foot path zigzags to the top of the mound (elevation 1,154 feet above sea level) offering a view for many miles around. In the distance you can see the radiant green expanses of the Black River State Forest. Not far away are Castle, Silver, Squaw and Wildcat Mounds — all similar sandstone outliers, that once rose as islands when this area was covered by a vast shallow lake near the end of the Ice Age.

• A national award-winning roadway as a scenic drive, County Trunk K in Jackson County brings a traveler close to beautiful untrammeled woodland and clean wild waters.

• Had the glaciers not missed the Driftless Area, rock formations like the outlier found west of Alma Center in Jackson County would have been reduced to rubble by the glacial ice

Chimney Rock

Devil's Anvil

The dells of the Wisconsin River.

mass. An irregular sandstone pillar capped with a table rock, the outlier resembles a big dinosaur looking over the lay of the land. This rock oddity startles many motorists driving by on Highway 121.

• Black River State Forest in Jackson County has a wildlife observation tower, the only one of its kind in the state, from which you can look out over Dike 17 Flowage and see sandhill cranes, great blue herons, mallards and other birds as well as deer, beaver and a variety of wildlife. The flowage consists of a patchwork of ponds, marshes and lowland forests in the Ice Age bed of Old Glacial Lake Wisconsin.

• The Sandhill Game Farm, located in southwestern Wood County, is operated by the DNR as a wildlife demonstration area. Principally a marsh habitat of 9,510 acres, it is home for stilt-legged sandhill cranes, geese, swans, ducks, deer and numerous other species of wildlife. Typical of the many early-morning sounds ushering in an autumn day at this beautiful tract are the drumming of male ruffed grouse and the "weird and wonderful" call of sandhill cranes.

• A 110-ton boulder, along with many other huge erratics, are a featured attraction at the Boulder Lake Campgrounds in the Nicolet Forest, north of Keshena, in Menominee County. Self-guiding trails winding through the Boulder Lake Forest are popular with nature lovers.

• At Hamilton Falls, in northeastern Eau Claire County, the racing waters of the north fork of the Eau Claire River cascade over a rock ledge. This secluded beauty spot has public access.

• Devil's Punch Bowl is a beautiful little gorge located at roadside in a Dunn County park between Menomonie and Irvington. A streamlet of springwater trickles through this bowl-shaped hollow, dropping down the face of a rock wall and creating a diminutive waterfall.

• Chimney Bluffs, located two miles southwest of the village of Downsville in Dunn County, were made famous in Carol Ryrie Brink's Newberry Award book, *Caddie Woodlawn*. In the story, set more than 100 years ago, some of the principal characters

St. Croix Dalles

(Caddie and two companions as children) went to the bluffs to pick blueberries but were frightened away by a coiled rattlesnake, its tail buzzing. Two distinct castellated sandstone columns form Chimney Bluffs and have the unique feature of markedly changing profiles as you circle them. The column to the south has two window-like openings.

• A cataract called Clam Falls is found on the Clam River at the hamlet of Clam Falls in Polk County. The Clam River flows downstream into Upper Clam Lake and then into Clam Lake. Apparently, some early "name-giver" in this region had no aversion for clams.

• The Dalles of the St. Croix River at St. Croix Falls in Polk County contain some fantastic stone sculptures carved by the river — such as the Devil's Chair, Turk's Head and Old Man of the Dalles, as well as some unusual potholes — round pits augered by water in solid basalt, up to 60 feet in depth.

• Dozens of these potholes in the hard lava-rock floor of the St. Croix River were created by whirlpools from rampaging water flowing off the melting glaciers. Mineral particles carried in suspension by the water swirled around in whirlpools acting like a core drill and scouring the potholes to substantial depths. A spectacular egg-shaped hole, located atop a rock formation called the Old Man of the Dalles, is four feet across and eighteen feet deep. Sometimes large stones fell into potholes and became victims of the watery merry-go-round. Spinning about freely, they were ground into almost perfect spheres that closely resemble bowling balls.

At Interstate Park, Pothole Trail leads to dozens of these very interesting depressions, showing the great erosive power of the river while draining the glaciers.

• The Central Plain and parts of the Eastern Ridges and Lowland are "John Muir Country". John Muir (1838-1914) was one of America's greatest naturalists and authors. He spent most of his boyhood on a farm a few miles south of Montello in Marquette County. His deep-seated love for nature led him eventually to audiences in the highest offices. He became one of the nation's most persuasive apostles of the wilderness. Upon completing a four-year-course of study at Madison, Muir commented that "he left one university for another, the Wisconsin University for the University of the Wilderness".

He devoted his life to the cause of conservation. His main influence came through his books and articles about his personal experiences in the wilds. He tramped through many regions. His persistent letters (his writings are voluminous) persuaded Congress to pass the National Park Act in 1890. Thus, Muir has become renown as "the father of our national parks".

He once wrote, "John the Baptist was not more eager to get all his fellow sinners into the Jordan than I to baptize all of mine in the beauty of God's mountains . . . Any fool can destroy trees . . . If a war of the races should occur between the wild beasts and Lord Man, I would be tempted to sympathize with the bears."

Founder of Yosemite, savior of the magnificent sequoia red-

John Muir County Park off Highway 51 south of Westfield in Marquette County.

woods, guiding light of the national park movement and Sierra Club, pioneer ecologist, explorer, mountaineer, author and advisor to Presidents — few persons have had such a beneficial impact upon our country as this one-time Wisconsin farmboy.

The Eastern Ridges and Lowlands

The eastern portions of the state make up the Eastern Ridges and Lowlands and contain the state's greatest density of population. Most of Wisconsin's principle cities are located here, including metropolitan Milwaukee, Waukesha, Racine, Kenosha, Oshkosh, Appleton, Fond du Lac, Manitowoc, Sheboygan, Green Bay and Madison. More than 300 years ago, European immigrants started settling this region. As land was cleared, farms sprang up, then villages, and finally cities. The proximity to Lake Michigan, as well as the topography, fertile soil and favorable climate, makes the Eastern Ridges and Lowlands a suitable place for a large proportion of the people of the state. Urban areas are common but dairy farms throughout the countryside present a patchwork of fields, pastures and woodlots.

The Eastern Ridges and Lowlands take in all of the state between Lake Michigan and the Western Upland and Central Plain. The dominant topographical feature of this province is a plain and the only hilly places are ridges. Generally unspectacular in appearance, the topography results from a series of cuestas that developed from the uneven erosion of the uppermost sedimentary strata. The sedimentary bedrock carpets this region in alternate layers of weak and resistant rock. Moderately inclined, these rock layers have been carved by weather and streams over the ages into a belted plain. The plain consists of parallel strips of lowland and upland corresponding with the major weak and resistant rocks. The uplands coincide with the ridges of the cuestas and the lowlands with the broad vales formed between the ridges.

This region is underlain by Ordovician, Silurian and Devonian-age sedimentary rocks of which the dolomites are the most resistant and the shales the weakest. (The shales exposed along the walls of Lake Michigan generally have an abundant fossil content.)

Rising irregularily, the low-lying, step-like ridges of eastern Wisconsin are escarpments marking the exposed edges of the Prairie du Chien, Galena-Black River and Niagara dolomites. The ridges trend north-south, generally paralleling the coastline of

This spectacular Skylab photo shows a large portion of the Eastern Ridges and Lowlands. The dark area to the right is Lake Michigan. The largest shaded area landward along the coastline is Milwaukee, with the smaller shaded area below being Racine and Kenosha.

Lake Winnebago can be seen near the top right center. The lakes around Madison appear to the left center. The shaded areas a little to the right and below Madison are Janesville, Beloit and Rockford, Illinois. This photo was taken from 270 miles up in February, 1974, when the ground was covered with snow. Principle rivers can be seen winding through the area. Note, especially, the Rock River.

171

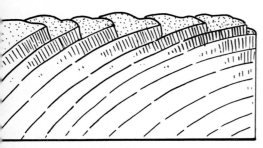

Tilted layers of bedrock erode unevenly at the surface.

Dolomite wall marking the Niagara Escarpment at High Cliff State Park on east shore of Lake Winnebago.

Lake Michigan, except that they curve southwestward and then westward in the southeastern corner of the state. These ridges lack the distinction of being very high and the lowlands along Lake Michigan, at 580 feet above sea level, are the lowest land areas in the state. The Niagara Escarpment produces the most prominent of the ridges. The greatest relief in this region reaches generally no more than 100 to 250 feet. The ridges usually are segmented and sometimes appear almost without any topographic features.

It is interesting to note that an escarpment marking the edge of the exposed strata of Niagara Dolomite, which bed of rock extends eastward from Wisconsin after dipping under Lake Michigan, forms the famous Niagara Falls on the boundary between New York State and Canada. Niagara Falls is located approximately 500 miles east of Wisconsin, demonstrating the great lateral extent of the Niagara Dolomite. Wherever exposed at the surface, this thick, continuous hard formation serves as a cuesta-maker, prominent locally as a topographic feature in the landscape. Traced inland from New York, it trends as a circuitous upland or ridge, except where buried by younger rock or glacial drift, westward and northward through the Province of Ontario to the peninsulas and islands between Georgion Bay and Lake Huron, westward through the upper peninsula of Michigan, southward through eastern Wisconsin, westward through Illinois, westward and northward through eastern Iowa and thence northwestward through the U.S. and Canada all the way to the Arctic Circle. In eastern Wisconsin, the Niagara Escarpment extends in segments for more than 230 miles, but nowhere is it so conspicuous in the landscape as just east of Lake Winnebago. It is here that high rising bluffs reveal the thickness of this great layer of dolomite, sliced off and laid bare by the glaciers during the Pleistocene.

If we were able to view Wisconsin from a spaceship far enough above the earth to see the full sweep of the land from Lake Michigan to the Mississippi River, we could trace the escarpments stretching through both the eastern and western portions of the state. We would observe that some of these step-like ridges, although segmented here and there, reach from one side of the state to the other, generally bowing to the south and following the contour of the Wisconsin Dome. We would notice that the series of cuestas in the Eastern Ridges and Lowlands, resembling giant terraces, connect and correspond with the series of cuestas on the "other side" of the dome in the Western Upland, also

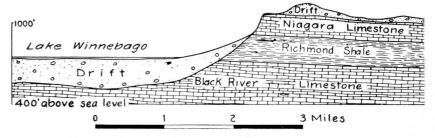

Cross-section of the Niagara escarpment near Fond du Lac.

172

resembling giant terraces. The escarpments with the most obvious continuity and completely crossing the state would be those marking the exposed edges of the Prairie du Chien and Galena-Black River dolomites. We would confirm, too, that the even more prominent Niagara Escarpment leaves the state and goes into Illinois.

The Eastern Ridges and Lowlands were extensively sculptured by glaciation during the Ice Age. The handicraft of the glaciers is seen almost everywhere in a great variety of topographic forms. Thousands of oval hills of glacial drift, called drumlins are found throughout eastern Wisconsin. Some of the drumlins rise as much as 140 feet above the plain, others as little as 5 feet. Many kettle holes dot the countryside.

Wisconsin is famous the world over for two of its glacial-geological features — the Driftless Area of the Western Upland and the drumlin fields of the Eastern Ridges and Lowlands.

The Eastern Ridges and Lowlands were entirely overridden by the Laurentide ice sheet. As a consequence, the surface is covered with a blanket of glacial drift. The two principal tongues of ice advancing through this region during the Wisconsin Stage of glaciation are called the Lake Michigan and Green Bay Lobes. Together, these ice masses resembled the shape of a huge mitten, with the Green Bay Lobe representing the thumb. A great amount of glacial erosion dredged the remarkably deep basin of Lake Michigan, a lesser amount gouged out Green Bay. Lake Michigan was deepened in places to as much as 900 feet; Green Bay to more than 140 feet.

The most beautiful landscapes in this province doubtlessly are those along the long sweeping coastline of Lake Michigan. Incidentally, Lake Michigan is the only one of the five Great Lakes that lies entirely within the United States. This vast body of fresh water — enclosed by the coasts of Wisconsin, Michigan, Illinois and Indiana — has a total surface area of 22,400 square miles and a maximum depth of 923 feet.

State parks in this province include the following, with a brief comment on the location and dominant features:

• Ahnapee Trail, ¾ mile north of Algoma or 1 mile south of Sturgeon Bay, 15 miles of old railroad grade.

• Aztalan, 4 miles east of Lake Mills on County Trunk B, ancient Indian Village.

• Big Foot Beach, one mile south of Lake Geneva on State Highways 12 and 120, a beach park.

• Cushing at Delafield on U.S. 30, historic monument.

• Harrington Beach, 10 miles north of Port Washington on State Highway 32, Lake Michigan shoreline and abandoned limestone quarry with lake.

• Heritage Hill, State Highway 57 on south side of Green Bay, a restored early American home.

• High Cliff, 9 miles east of Menasha on State Highway 114, wooded bluffs on Lake Winnebago.

• John M. Kohler, 4 miles south of Sheboygan on State Highway 141, lake scenery.

The dolomite forming escarpments in the Eastern Lowlands and Ridges is extensively quarried. These scenes are of quarries near Fond du Lac.

Esker at North Kettle Moraine State Forest

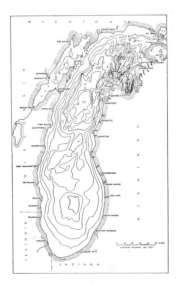

Contour map of bottom of Lake Michigan, based on U.S. Lake Survey

173

- Lake Kegonsa, 3 miles north of Stoughton on County Trunk N, a prairie park.
- Lizard Mound, 2 miles northeast of West Bend on State Highway 141, Prehistoric Indian mounds.
- Lost Dauphin, 5 miles southwest of De Pere on U.S. Highway 41 and County Trunk D, home of the Lost Dauphin of France.
- Newport, 2 miles southeast of Gill's Rock at the tip of Door County, lake scenery.
- Old Wade House, 6 miles west of Plymouth on State Highway 23, restored early American inn.
- Peninsula, at Fish Creek on State Highway 42, limestone bluffs on Green Bay.
- Pike Lake, 2 miles east of Hartford on State Highway 60, a glacial lake.
- Potawatomi, 2 miles northwest of Sturgeon Bay on State Highway 42, limestone bluffs.
- Rock Island, 50 miles northeast of Sturgeon Bay, island scenery.
- Terry Andrae, 4 miles south of Sheboygan on State Highway 141, Lake Michigan.

The principal landforms and places of interest in this province include the coastline of Lake Michigan, the Door County Penin-

A composite aerial photo of Madison. Note the chain of lakes of glacial origin. Photo taken November, 1974, from an elevation of 18,000 feet above ground.

Lake Mendota at Madison

174

Glacial landforms predominate throughout Wisconsin, in all but the Driftless Area.

Quartzite cliff at Devils Lake State Park, a well-known glacial area.

Famous Dundee Kame in Fond du Lac County.

Typical drumlin, near Theresa, in Dodge County.

South Kettle Moraine State Forest, in Walworth County.

Roadcut revealing cross section of a kame near Fond du Lac.

Holy Hill, a large kame, south of Hartford, in Washington County.

175

Landforms almost everywhere in this province remind a traveler of the former presence of the glaciers.

Kettle at Pike Lake in South Kettle Moraine State Forest.

Kame with kettle in top in North Kettle Moraine State Forest

sula, the Horicon Marsh, Lake Winnebago, the lakes around Madison, the escarpments previously discussed and the Upper and Lower Kettle Moraine Glacial Areas.

There are many places of interest in this province of which the following are typical:

• The capital city of Madison, second largest city in the state, is situated at a place originally called Taychopera by the Winnebago Indians, which means "four lakes". The beautiful lakes and hilly terrain around Madison are creations of the glaciers.

• Lake Geneva, a beautiful lake with many bays surrounded by soft green hills, is the center of one of Wisconsin's oldest resort areas. The rolling glacial terrain in this area appears as a quiltwork of farmlands, resorts and urban areas.

• Washington County has much engaging rural scenery. The land rolls in the characteristic domes and dips of the kettle moraine and a few high hills stand out like sentinels above the countryside.

• The Kettle Moraine region of the Eastern Lowlands and Ridges, with its dome-shaped hills and bowl-shaped valleys, is especially delightful to visit in fall, when there are hickory nuts and walnuts to gather and wild grapes to taste. Much of the area has poor, rocky soil unsuitable for farming and, as a result, supports an extensive hardwood forest cover.

• The Dundee Kame, near the village of Dundee, is in the heart of the North Kettle Moraine Forest in Fond du Lac County. Backroading in this area is full of many pleasant surprises. Everywhere the landscape reveals the former presence of the glaciers, whose sculpturing of the terrain has produced a vast out-of-door art gallery.

• Cedarburg Bog is described by an ecologist of the Wisconsin Department of Natural Resources:

"Cedarburg Bog in Ozaukee County fills a glacial lake basin left when ice sheets last retreated from southeast Wisconsin 12,000 years ago. With gradual filling, open water has been reduced to half a dozen small lakes, the largest being Mud Lake, about 200 acres in size, but only four feet in depth.

"The bog forest advanced on Mud Lake during the past century when water levels declined, perhaps due to clearing of uplands, but accentuated by the long drought period in the 1930s. However, increased precipitation and several man-made obstructions at the lake outlet resulted in return of higher levels in the late 1950s. The encroaching forest was drowned, leaving rampikes of dead tamarack, white cedar and black ash. The dams have now been removed and water levels will be allowed to fluctuate naturally as in the presettlement era.

"Mud Lake is shallow and freezes out in winter, preventing establishment of even hardy rough fish species. This favors a luxuriant growth of aquatic plants such as pickerel weed and water lily — habitat for waterfowl, wading birds and muskrats. Recreational use is limited by difficult access and, except for waterfowl hunters in the fall, the solitude is enjoyed by those interested in nature hikes and bird study."

However, the DNR expresses concern about the future of the Cedarburg Bog and other natural areas in Wisconsin:

"Preservation of the Cedarburg Bog Scientific Area in the face of southeastern Wisconsin urbanization is an awesome but necessary task. Cedarburg Bog and areas like it have survived thousands of years of climatic extremes including floods, droughts and wild fires, but they cannot survive continuing encroachments by man."

• Lake Winnebago, with shorelines in Winnebago, Calumet and Fond du Lac Counties, is the state's largest inland lake. Produced by glacial scouring, it has a length of 28 miles, a maximum width of 10.4 miles and a depth at the deepest part of its basin of only 21 feet. The steep dolomitic cliffs of the Niagara Escarpment rise as a retaining wall along the lake's eastern shore. The lake is fed by the waters of both the Wolf and Fox Rivers, which join forces between Lake Poygan and Lake Butte des Morts upstream and to the west.

Horicon Marsh, a swamp occupying the site of a former lake

• Fall is the season to see enormous flocks of wild geese at the Horicon Marsh. The geese stop over temporarily on their migratory flight southward, enroute from northern nesting areas to southern wintering grounds. When the "honkers" return, the marsh and skies above come alive with activity. More than two hundred thousand geese gather at the peak of the migration. Their plaintive voices combine in a chorus and the wetlands resound in a harmonious song of the wild. The best vantage point to see and hear this extravaganza is along Highway 49, west of Waupun, especially in early morning or late afternoon.

Geese on the wing above the Horicon Marsh

• A must to enjoy the full sweep of Lake Michigan is an early morning walk along one of the broad wave-washed beaches, such as those at Sheboygan and Kewaunee. The lakefront takes on the qualities of another world in the early light of dawn.

Geese on the pond at the Horicon Marsh

• The Lake Michigan smelt run begins about mid-April (the Lake Superior run about a week later) with hotspots at Kenosha, Racine, Jones Island off Milwaukee, Port Washington, the west shore of Door County and the Green Bay shoreline south of Marinette. The highly popular sport of catching smelt draws thousands of enthusiasts. The little fish average 8 to 9 inches in length, travel in large schools and crowd the shallows along the shoreline at nighttime.

• South of Sheboygan, Terry Andrae State Park is located on Lake Michigan with a long stretch of beach. Close to the water's edge are "singing sands," so-named because the quartz grains underfoot emit sighing and humming sounds.

• The Door County Peninsula juts into the waters of Green Bay and Lake Michigan like a giant finger. With beautiful scenery

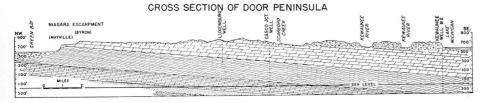

177

Saddle Mound, a prominent sandstone outlier, west of City Point, in Jackson County.

Table Rock also called Five Point Rock, near Readstown, in Vernon County.

Monument Rock, southwest of Viroqua.

Ship Rock, east of Friendship, in Adams County.

Sandstone Butte, southwest of Viroqua, in Vernon County.

Caves reveal nature's awesome beauty otherwise hidden underground.

Cave interior at Crystal Cave, near Spring Valley, in Pierce County.

Stalagtites on the ceiling of a cavern at Cave of the Mounds (near Blue Mounds, in Dane County.)

"Icicle" of stone at Cave of the Mounds.

Speleothem formations at Cave of the Mounds.

179

Peninsula State Park as seen from Eagle Harbor.

Sugarbush Hill

sometimes compared to that of New England, this narrow projection of land, surrounded on three sides by water, contains a pleasing mixture of topographical forms — jagged coastal cliffs, wave-washed beaches, rolling hills, boulder-strewn glacial moraines and windswept craggy sedimentary rock formations. Picturesque little fishing villages and resort towns are interspersed among hillside orchards and farmlands.

• Late May is cherry and apple blossom time on the Door County Peninsula. Blossom routes for viewing the 10,000 acres of orchards in bloom have been laid out on maps available from the Door County Chamber of Commerce. Cherry harvesting usually takes place in early August and thousands of visiting families pick their own cherries for home canning and freezing.

• A roadside marker identifies the landing place of Jean Nicolet, the first European to set foot in Wisconsin, at Red Banks, on Highway 57, 5 miles northeast of Green Bay in Brown County.

• A footpath descends along rugged limestone cliffs to the caves found at Maribel Caves County Park, just off Highway 41, between Denmark and Manitowoc, in Manitowoc County. Secluded in a dense pine-scented forest, the park offers a close-up view of a sizable vertical exposure of weathered Ordivician-age strata.

• There is an old Indian legend that straight stretches of the Fox River were dug by squaws using canoe paddles to shortcut what once were bends in the river. In historic time, the river has been harnessed for many industrial uses. But the upper reaches still attract thousands of fishermen each springtime during the annual walleye and whitebass spawn runs.

• Green Lake, in Green Lake County, is the oldest resort town west of Niagara Falls. In 1972, the resort community celebrated its 125th anniversary. Sailboating, lake trout fishing, scuba diving and ice fishing are among the popular recreational activities on the lake, which is 7½ miles long and 2½ miles wide. The town sits on the shores of Green Lake, the state's deepest inland lake, plunging to a depth of 237 feet.

The Northern Highland

The Northern Highland is the largest geographic division in Wisconsin, covering about 15,000 square miles. It is part of a great upland area, underlain with Precambrian rocks, that stretches northward into Canada all the way to Labrador and Hudson Bay. This region is gently arched with a strong southward slope. It is also inclined both east and west.

A roadside marker on U.S. Highway 8 near Crandon in Forest County contains a brief comment on the Northern Highland:

"Sugarbush Hill which you see across the valley is one of the highest points in the northern highland geological province. This province, which includes some 15,000 square miles in northern Wisconsin, is underlain by the crystalline rock of an ancient mountain range comparable to the Rockies, the peaks of which were ground down by glacial and other geological processes extending over almost infinite time. Because it is particularly suitable for the growing of timber, extensive forests of hardwoods and conifers cover most of its area. Within this forest region lies one of the greatest concentrations of lakes in the world, similar to that of Finland. Its cool climate and myriad of lakes make it an ideal summer vacationland.''

A bird's-eye view of the Northern Highland reveals a flat velvety surface of green, the color of forests, interspersed with spots and streaks of blue, the color of lakes, streams and rivers. This region is popularly called the Northwoods.

The Northern Highland is a land of extensive forest cover. ''The forest primeval'', referred to by Henry Wadsworth Longfellow in *The Song of Hiawatha,* served as the home for Stone Age Woodland Indians before Wisconsin became settled by European immigrants who brought with them an Industrial Age civilization. In the days of the frontier, the majestic stands of virgin timber lured an army of loggers and lumberjacks who invaded the northern forests with axes and crosscut saws. Although the great white pines of the forests were regarded as limitless, they couldn't resist civilization's insatiable appetite for lumber. Soon lumber mills added efficiency to a burgeoning industry and, as giant trees fell, the cry of ''Timber'' rang throughout the pinewoods. In time, most of the northwoods were clear-cut. Fires raging out of control completed the toll. Today, only a handful of virgin white pine stands remain as isolated survivors of the original forests. One such stand is at Lucius Woods, near Solon Springs, in Douglas County. But charred stumps of the great trees, in many places, still serve as silent reminders of the magnificence of the pinewoods of old.

Despite the final loss of the great trees to axes, saws and fires, less than a century ago, the northern forests are resurging in a remarkable comeback and, today, many varieties of second growth evergreens and hardwoods thrive. Now aspen, paper birch, white pine, red pine, tamarack, sugar maple and other forest species share space with wild Christmas trees.

The Northern Highland is the state's leading vacationland, the domain of the legendary Paul Bunyan, the great lumberjack. Like a magnet, it draws legions of vacationers, hunters, fishermen, nature lovers, campers, rockhounds, snowmobilers, skiers, canoeists, motorboaters, landscape artists and camera buffs.

Sixteen counties in northwestern Wisconsin comprise the Indianhead Country, one of the state's concentrated vacation areas. Another intensified tourist area is centered around Minocqua in north central Wisconsin, featuring lakes and other waterways principally in Iron, Vilas, Oneida, Lincoln, Forest and Langlade Counties.

The Northern Highland stretches out as an ancient peneplain, carpeted with Precambrian bedrock; but, in most places, glacial drift covers the bedrock.

To understand better the lay of the land today, let's recap the most significant events in the geologic history of this region. The peneplain, as previously noted, formed in late Precambrian times

Water, forest, wildlife, people . . . the north woods.

In the heyday of old-time logging, really big loads were hauled by teams of horses over carefully laid out roads.

The Northern Highland is Wisconsin's leading vacationland.

181

Isolated butte in Juneau County.

Castle Mound, a castellated butte, near Camp Douglas, in Juneau County.

Big Smokey Falls, Wolf River, Menominee County.

Natural bridge at Rockbridge, in Richland County.

Elephant Trunk Rock, north of Ithaca, in Richland County.

Cold Water Canyon at Wisconsin Dells, in Sauk County.

182

Amnicon Falls, east of Superior, in Douglas County.

Granddad's Bluff at La Crosse.

The Dells of the Wolf River, in Menominee County.

Devils Gate at Copper Falls State Park, in Ashland County.

Sugarbush Hill, east of Crandon, in Forest County.

The ancient peneplain slightly undulating from stream erosion and glaciation. Southwest of Merrill in Lincoln County.

A composite aerial photo of a portion of the Northern Highland, around Minocqua, in Onieda and Vilas Counties. Note the profusion of lakes of glacial origin and the predominately forested areas. Photo taken in April, 1964, at an elevation of 8,750 feet above ground.

Very old volcanic rocks crop up at Little Bull Falls north of Pittsville in Wood County, typical of those underlying many areas in the Northern Highland.

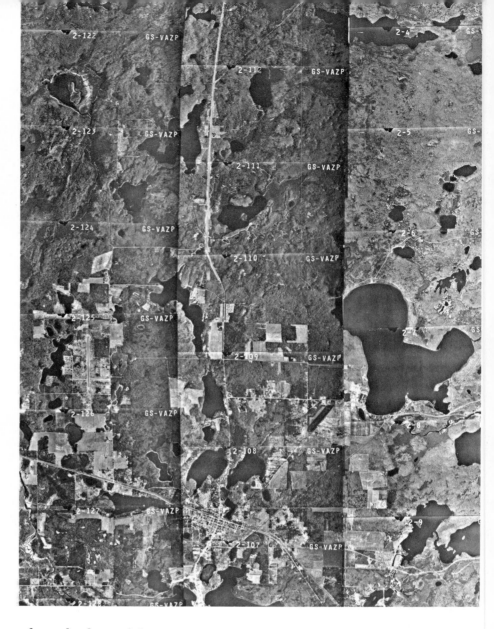

when the last of the state's mountains were leveled by erosion. It was then that Wisconsin had the appearance of a generally low undulating plain, similar to a vast tabletop covered with a slightly wrinkled tablecloth. Topographically, it was almost featureless, except for occasional hills of very resistant rock that had been too unyielding for weather and erosion to wear down to the level of the plain. Later, during the Paleozoic Era, when the state experienced submersion several times beneath the seas, the peneplain became buried under thick layers of sandstone, shale and limestone. About 350 million years ago, near the end of the Devonian Period, Wisconsin began a period of gentle uplift that has continued to the present and, ever since, the state has remained high and dry above sea level.

At the time when the state finally emerged above the seas, the Precambrian peneplain was entombed under a heavy mantle of sedimentary rocks. But soon the work of weather and streams recommenced and, over a period of hundreds of millions of years, the Precambrian peneplain, in most of the northern portions of the state, was gradually stripped of such overburden.

184

Thus, the peneplain became almost completely exhumed in the Northern Highland, revealing most of the topographical features that existed before the beginning of the Paleozoic. Since then, streams have cut new valleys, slightly dissecting the exposed peneplain, and more recently, glaciers made a series of invasions, littering much of the surface with unconsolidated rocks and soil. The only activities, since the glaciers finally retreated, have been further erosion of the surface and modification by humans.

Differences in rocks underlying the peneplain produce two distinctive kinds of topography in the Northern Highland — upland plains and several types of ridges. The plains appear as broad, even tracts with little relief above surface level. But the ridges present landscapes usually with a series of hills and vales. In some instances, the ridges are very prominent. The state's highest landforms reach toward the skies in this province. The massive rolling hills around Merrill, in Lincoln County, stretch out as much as 2 to 3 miles from crest to crest. Many of the state's ski hills are found in the northern Highland.

Where homogeneous rocks like granite underlie the surface, relatively smooth plains cover great expanses. As a consequence, roads and railroad tracks follow straight lines for long distances. In these areas, wherever the plains are incised by streams, the hills lying between the stream valleys have an insequent pattern. This aimless arrangement results from a lack of any marked difference in the resistance of the underlying rocks. The hills rise, usually, to a common level and trend irregularly with the branching of streams, following a treelike (dendritic) drainage pattern.

As tilted bedrock wears down — one massive layer after another, the ridges that develop sometimes resemble a series of terraces.

In other areas, however, the underlying rocks are not homogeneous, except along narrow belts. Wherever these rocks of varying degrees of resistance have become worn down, ridges replace the plains. The harder rocks erode more slowly than the softer ones, producing an unevenness on the face of the land. For example, in northwestern Wisconsin, the Keweenawan lava flows no longer lie in horizontal layers as originally laid down. These volcanic rocks have become tipped as a result of sagging or other deformation of the crust, leaving the layers in a tilted or diagonal position. Etched still later by weathering and erosion, they now form parallel ridges, wearing down unevenly across the exposed tops of the tilted layers. These ridges typically have a steep slope on one side and a longer gentle slope on the other.

Powers Bluff, near Arpin in Wood County.

Rising prominently above the level of the peneplain, other ridges, scattered throughout the Northern Highland, are remnants of ancient Precambrian mountains, such as the iron-rich Penokee Range, the Flambeau Ridge, the Blue Hills (formerly called the Barron Hills), McCaslin Mountain, Thunder Mountain, Rib Mountain, Mosinee Hill, Hardwood Hill and Powers Bluff.

During the Ice Age, most of the Northern Highland was overridden by the glaciers, with the topography modified noticeably by glacial deposits, including ground moraine, terminal

185

Autumn colors in Marathon County.

Kickapoo Valley, in Crawford County.

Big Manitou Falls at Pattison State Park, in Douglas County.

Appleblossom time, near Gays Mills, in Crawford County.

Mushroom family portrait.

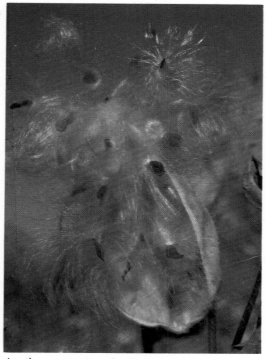

Marsh marigolds (cowslips.)

Another generation of milkweed is airborne.

The great variety of plants indigenous to Wisconsin helps make the scenery spectacular. The distribution of plant species is determined largely by climate, topography and soil.

Blackeyed Susans

Butterfly-weeds

Blazing Stars

Trilliums

A campsite on one of Wisconsin's jewel-like lakes

This composite aerial photo shows a portion of the Northern Highland, around Wausau. Note the Wisconsin River extending from top to bottom. The tributary entering from the left is the Rib River. Immediately below it, the dark area, is Rib Mountain. Photo taken May, 1962, from an elevation of 9,000 feet above ground.

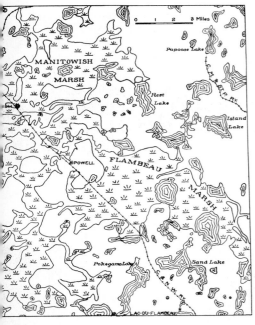

Typical area of swampland in the Northern Highland.

moraine, recessional moraine and outwash plains. Thus, the Precambrian peneplain experienced burial beneath a layer of glacial debris of varying thickness. In places, the ground moraine today is as much as 100 feet thick. Generally, it appears as a rolling surface, sometimes with broad swells and shallow sags. Extensive swamps occupy many of the larger sags and provide secluded habitat for numerous species of wildlife.

Northern Wisconsin is the setting for most of the state's inland lakes. With a rich assortment of more than 6,000 lakes, the pine-scented northwoods have developed into one of the nation's major resort areas. Brimful of sparkling fresh water, the lakes are masterpieces of the glaciers. Each is a natural wonder — a limpid blue jewel in a green forestland mounting.

The lake basins, with a great range in size and shape, have diverse glacial origins. Some occupy shallow depressions in the ground moraine, some lie behind dikes of recessional moraine and others fill hollows in outwash gravel plains. Many of the smaller hollows containing lakes are kettles produced when buried blocks of ice remained in the wake of the retreating glaciers and subsequently melted, leaving kettle-shaped indentations in the terrain.

Muskeg bogs, along with tamarack and cedar swamps, occupy a large part of the northern lake region. Some are marshes developing in the basins of former lakes, which earlier became clogged and filled in with sediments and decomposed vegetation (eutrophication); but most are areas of poor drainage result-

188

ing from an accumulation of glacial debris.

Marshes perform an important function for surface waters; they serve as natural sponges, absorbing excessive nutrients, slowing down runoff and generally improving water quality.

Unfortunately, most lakes are transitory and exist as a land-form by the reckoning of geologic time, for only a very short period before suffering destruction through eutrophication and eventually passing from the scene. Nutrients in runoff added to lake water speed the process of eutrophication through the excessive growth of algae and other aquatic plants and thus advance the ultimate demise of a lake. Stages in the destruction of a lake can be seen at the left.

State parks in this province include the following, with a brief comment on the location and dominant features:

● Council Grounds, 1 miles northwest of Merrill on State Highway 107, river scenery.

● Ojibwa, 1 mile east of Ojibwa on State Highway 70, river scenery.

● Rib Mountain, 4 miles southwest of Wausau on County Trunks N and NN, one the highest points in the state.

● Tuscobia Trail, State Highway 40, 48 and 70, 76-mile-long old railroad grade.

Among the most impressive landforms and places of interest in this province are the Penokee-Gogebic Iron Range, the Penokee Water Gaps, the dells of the St. Croix River, the Ice Age topography near Bloomer, the roller-coaster hills south of Merrill and Rib Mountain State Park. This province was host, until recent years, to most of the state's iron mining.

The scenic and historical places in the Northern Highland are numerous. The following are typical:

● The top of Rib Mountain (elevation 1,960 feet above sea level) can be reached by an excellent blacktop road ascending for 1½ miles off County Trunk N, south of Wausau in Marathon County. Composed of a mass of Precambrian quartzite, Rib Mountain is the remant of an ancient mountain. The summit, supporting a forest cover of mixed hardwoods, is occupied by a 608-acre state park, equipped with picnicking and camping facilities. The Wisconsin River flows near the base of the mountain. Long ago, the Chippewa Indians, who perennially made their camp in this area along the bank of the river, called the site "Wausau", meaning "faraway place".

● Eau Claire Dells County Park, near Hogarty in Marathon County, provides a good example of river erosion of Precambrian crystalline rock in a short stretch of contorted outcrops that have been severely incised by the Eau Claire River.

● The steeply arching Billy Goat Hills, in northeastern Marathon County, are etched with deeply furrowed valleys through which little trout streams flow. Here the state's official state rock — red granite — randomly pokes through at the surface.

● An award-winning roadway, State Highway 107 in Lincoln County, is bordered with numerous selective clearings that open

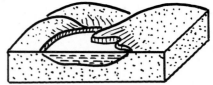

A. Initial stage at close of Ice Age

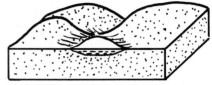

B. Partial filling of lake basins by sediments and peat

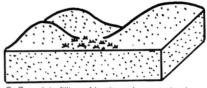

C. Complete filling of basin and conversion to peat bog.

Stages in the demise of a lake as a temporary landform.

Rib Mountain in the distance. The vertical trending light areas are ski slopes.

The Eau Claire Dells.

Stream in the Buena Vista Marsh, in Portage County.

Along a backroad, southwest of Stevens Point, in Portage County.

Copper Falls, near Mellen, in Ashland County.

Wisconsin's scenery experiences an annual cycle of change. Each of the four seasons clothes the land in an aura of beauty. Like the canvases of a master painter, each has its own distinquishing theme. Spring is the time of rebirth when the land suddenly puts on a cloak of green. Summer is the season of accelerated growth, sunshine and radiant hues. Autumn is at the end of the growing season when the woods become ablaze with color. Winter is when the land dons a white overcoat and waits out the long cold.

Outcrop of dolomite at High Cliff State Park, in Calumet County.

Red granite quarrying near Wausau.

views for a passerby of the beautiful forested banks of the Wisconsin River.

● A striking Ice-Age area — somewhat similar, on a smaller scale, to the Kettle Moraine Forests of southeastern Wisconsin — is situated in southeastern Lincoln County. Here along Highway 17, you can see a variety of rugged glacial moraines, the heavily forested Harrison Hills, several jewel-like lakes and the Prairie River Dells.

● Tons of fragmented local rock, mostly of Precambrian origin, adorn a shrine and landscaped garden located at Rudolph, just off Highway 34, 8 miles north of Wisconsin Rapids in Wood County. Called the Rudolph Grotto, this place of worship attracts many visitors each year during the summer season. The largest rock in the grotto is a Precambrian boulder weighing nearly 80 tons.

● Granite outcrops are abundant in Menominee County. But one partially buried conglomerate boulder found north of Keshena, called Spirit Rock, has special significance to the Menominee Indians. The legend of this isolated stone is told in a roadside marker just off Highway 55:

Old photo of Spirit Rock

"One night long ago, a Menominee Indian dreamed that Manabush, grandson of Ko-Ko-Mas-Say-Sa-Now (the Earth) and part founder of the Mitawin or Medicine Society, invited him to visit the god. With seven of his friends, the Indian called on Manabush who granted their request to make them successful hunters. One of the band, however, angered the god by asking for eternal life. Manabush, seizing the warrior by the shoulders, thrust him into the ground and said, 'You shall be a stone, thus you will be everlasting.' The Menominees say that, at night, kindly spirits come to lay offerings of tobacco at the rock and that, if one looks closely, he can see their white veils among the trees. The legend is that when the rock finally crumbles away the race will be extinct."

● The Penokee-Gogebic Iron Range of northern Wisconsin and Upper Michigan forms the Great Divide where raindrops go their separate ways. About 80 miles long and ½ to 1 mile wide,

Penokee Range near Hurley in Iron County

Copper Falls

Brownstone Falls, a companion waterfall to Copper Falls

the range winds an irregular course through Melon and Hurley, in Iron County, and into Michigan's upper peninsula. Rising abruptly 200 to 500 feet above the surrounding country, it reaches a high point at Mt. Whittlesey (elevation 1,866 feet above sea level), which resembles a real mountain from both sides. Streams cross the Penokees at nine water gaps, commonly coursing downslope through narrow gorges and over rapids and waterfalls. The best known and most dramatic of the waterfalls located in the Lake Superior Lowland is a feature attraction at Copper Falls State Park where the Bad River, in seething copper and white foam, plunges over a Keweenawan trap ledge. Spectacular waterfalls and rapids also mark the descent of the rampaging Potato and Montreal Rivers. These swiftly flowing rivers provide lairs for trout and other game fish.

• The Great Divide is explained in a roadside marker on State Highway 13, 2½ miles north of its junction with State Highway 77, in Ashland County. Another marker identifying a point on the Great Divide is situated in the Chequamegon National Forest, south of Grandview on County Trunk D in Bayfield County, and reads as follows:

Precipitation falling here flows into the Chippewa and Namekagon Rivers then westerly to the Mississippi River and south to the Gulf of Mexico.

Precipitation falling here flows into Lake Superior then east thru the Great Lakes into the St. Lawrence River and ultimately the Atlantic Ocean.

• Tim's Hill, the state's highest point towering to 1,953 feet, rises east of Ogema in Price County. Nearby Bass Lake offers an excellent view of the hill.

• Dave's Falls, located near Amberg in Marinette County, resembles a big spillway as sparkling water pours headlong through a rock trough.

• Beaver Dam Rapids derives its name from a rock ledge resembling a beaver dam that extends across the Flambeau River in northeastern Rusk County. The rocks of the ledge protrude intermittently above the current forming a natural stone barrier. The swiftly flowing river drops four feet in its headlong charge through the rapids, a favorite stretch of wild water for canoeists.

• Gundy's Canyon is a scenic 125-foot-deep ravine located on private land near the community of Horsman in Barron County. The ravine was carved out of the ancient rock of the Blue Hills by the erosive action of Rock Creek. A spring-fed streamlet drops over one of the ravine's walls to join the creek below, creating Signe Falls. The water splashes over a three-step precipice in producing this unusual cascade.

• The main artery of commerce for the people who settled the Lake Superior country was the Brule-St. Croix Portage, extending from Lake St. Croix to the Brule River and then down to Lake

192

Tim's Hill on a frosty morning

Upper Falls

Lower falls

Longslide Falls near Pembine in Marinette County.

Superior. Traveled by Indians, voyageurs, explorers, missionaries, traders and pioneers in the days of the frontier, it provided an important passage-way for men and supplies.

• At Montreal in Iron County, the mammoth Montreal Mine penetrates the crust to a depth of more than 4,000 feet, holding the record as the deepest iron mine in the world. Since opening in 1886 and before closing in recent years, it produced more than 35 million tons of ore.

• At Iron Belt in Iron County, giant stockpiles and abandoned shafts mark the location of iron mines that were once the principle industry of that community.

• In Iron County, Hurley, too, has piles of tailings and vacant underground workings suggesting that iron mining was associated with its heyday.

• Looking for a beautiful place to hike? The North County Trail, part of a proposed interstate pathway (extending eventually from New York to North Dakota), follows the Penokee mountain ridge across Iron County, with a number of vistas where hikers may rest and gaze. The trail winds through rugged wilderness with tall trees and fast-flowing creeks and rivers.

The Lake Superior Lowland

Underlain by Keweenawan sandstones and conglomerates, this province in the northernmost portion of the state is a lowland located on the south side of the basin of Lake Superior. Although relatively small in size, this lowland area offers a big helping of scenery. Rocky, rugged and forest-covered, the land sweeps northward down to Lake Superior. All water flowing from this northern slope empties into the lake.

Lake Superior — because of its size, tides and unruly temperament — has been referred to as "an inland sea". The statistics of

State's last standing tipple tower near Hurley, a relic of the iron mining era

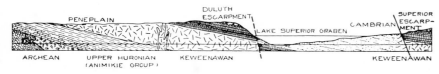
Graben at the western end of Lake Superior

Block diagram of the Lake Superior lowland in Wisconsin.

193

Lake Superior is an inland sea

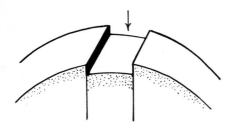

A graben forms when a section of the earth's crust slips downward between two paralell faults.

One of the Apostle Islands rising as a mass of rock.

this great body of water are impressive: it has a total surface area of 31,820 square miles and a maximum depth of 1,302 feet. Lake Michigan, in contrast, has a total surface area of 22,400 square miles and a maximum depth of 923 feet. Steeply rising walls are a unique feature of Lake Superior, the world's largest body of fresh water. All the other Great Lakes of North America have gently sloping walls.

Some geologists believe that the basin of Lake Superior is part of a graben. All recognize it as some form of huge down-warp or natural trough. For our purpose, we shall consider it to be a graben. A graben forms when a block of the earth's crust slips down between two parallel faults. The word graben is derived from the German word meaning "ditch". Near the end of the Precambrian Era, the graben became buried beneath sediments, which lithified into Lake Superior sandstone. The sandstone, over a long period of time, presumably during the late Keweenawan Period, built up to an incredible thickness, estimated at 17,500 feet. Later, the graben became partly exhumed by stream erosion and, still later during the Ice Age, by glacial scouring, forming the deep basin of Lake Superior as we know it today.

The Lake Superior Lowland occupies about 1,250 square miles, not counting 2,400 square miles more of the state which is submerged below the waters of Lake Superior. Its elevation ranges from less than 1,000 feet above sea level to about 300 feet below sea level in the depths of the lake. The surface water level of Lake Superior is normally at 602 feet above sea level. Steep escarpments mark the borders of the graben. The highland ridge south of Superior, known as the Douglas Copper Range, has a local relief of about 350 feet. It slopes northward at a rate of as much as 300 feet per mile. Short streams, flowing northward and emptying into Lake Superior, cross the ridge. Descending steeply, they plunge over many waterfalls and rapids. The waterfalls are among the highest and most handsome of any found in the state.

During the Pleistocene, the glaciers scoured the basin of Lake Superior cleaning out great amounts of sandstone. Eroding deeply, they dredged to incredible depth and cut channels between resistant segments of the basin that now rise as islands. The Apostle Islands are hilltops formed by the glaciers. The visible portions of the islands, reaching above the water level of the lake, have been carved to artistic perfection by the elements of weather and by waves pounding their shorelines.

State parks in this province include the following, with a brief comment on the location and dominant features:

• Amnicon Falls, 10 miles SE of Superior on U.S. 2, scenic waterfalls and covered bridge.

• Big Bay, on Madeline Island on Lake Superior, sand beach and natural history.

• Copper Falls*, 4 miles north of Mellen on State Highways 13 and 169, river gorge and waterfalls.

• Lucius Woods*, at Solon Springs on U.S. Highway 53, stand of virgin pine timber.

194

Big Manitou at Pattison State Park is the state's highest waterfall with a drop of 165 feet, exceeding that of Niagara Falls.

Amnicon Falls east of Superior

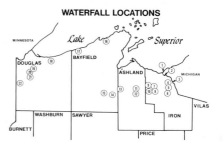

WATERFALL LOCATIONS

Iron County
1. Superior Falls
2. Power Dam Falls
3. Peterson Falls
4. Rock Cut Falls
5. Gile Falls
6. Spring Camp Falls
7. Foster Falls
   (gap in rock chute)
8. Upson Falls
9. Potato River Falls
   (Gurney Falls)
   a. Upper (grey rock)
   b. Middle
   c. Lower (red rock)
10. Wren Falls
    (water gap)

Ashland County
11. Brownstone Falls
12. Copper Falls
13. Morgan Falls

Bayfield County
14. Unnamed Falls
15. Unnamed Falls
16. Siskiwit Falls
17. Orienta Falls

Douglas County
18. Amnicon Falls
19. Unnamed Falls
20. Big Manitou Falls
21. Little Manitou Falls
22. Unnamed Falls

● Pattison*, 10 miles S of Superior on State Highway 35, highest waterfall in the state.

*Technically, these state parks are located wholly or partially in the northern Highland Province; but, because they are visited frequently by persons sightseeing in the Lake Superior Lowlands, they are included here for convenience.

Among the notable landforms and points of interest in this province are the rough-hewn coastline of Lake Superior, the Apostle Islands, the Bayfield Peninsula, Amnicon Falls, Pattison Falls and Copper Falls.

Typical of the many beautiful scenic and historical places in this province are the following:

● Legend has it that many years ago the Indians paid tribute for the use of the natural port at Superior. Fearing gods whom

Another view of Amnicon Falls

Little Manitou Falls in Pattison State Park

195

Ore docks at Ashland.

Old photo of the early French cemetery on Madeline Island.

they believed were lurking at the bottom of the lake, they sought to appease them by dropping food and other valuables into the bay. In return, they expected the gods to grant them a safe voyage across the lake.

• The 100-mile stretch of Highway 13 between Ashland and Superior has been rated by travel editors as among the top five scenic drives in the nation. Following the curving shoreline of Lake Superior from Ashland around the Bayfield Peninsula, this route offers mile after mile of scenic delight, with a view lakeward of the Apostle Islands. The densely forested islands resemble emeralds set on the lustrous sill of the lake. At Siskiwit Beach, you can watch giant ore carriers plying their way across the vast lake, while small boats, sail boats, tugs and fishing boats crisscross the sapphire-blue expanse.

• Cornucopia, in Bayfield County, is Wisconsin's northermost community. Here the wave-carved caves and towering cliffs of neighboring Squaw Bay are spectacular. This stretch of shoreline is accessible along Highway 13 (the South Shore Scenic Drive), with a panoramic view of the majestic waters of Lake Superior.

• The Burlington Ore Docks are marked by a roadside sign at Superior. Countless shiploads of iron ore have passed through these docks.

• When the smelt run is on during late April, the shores of Lake Superior come alive with fishermen. Equipped with dip nets and seines, an enthusiastic army of sportsmen launches an all-out-attack on the little silver fish that venture in big schools into shallow water during the annual spawning run. There are favorite places for smelting all the way from Ashland to Superior.

• The surf-beaten shore of Saxon Harbor is a favorite hunting ground for agate hounds. Not far away, in the Northern Highlands, fish lurk in lakes with names like Dead Horse, Mystery, Bearskull and Thirty Dollar. Nearby, there's the Northern Highland State Forest, with more lakes than a porcupine has quills. Elsewhere, there are big flowages with muskies of proportionate size. And the loudest voices of all in this green wilderness region are those of the waterfalls as rivers plunge downslope toward the cool blueness of Lake Superior. To name a few, there's Upson Falls, Potato Falls, Foster Falls, Giles Falls and the smaller cascades at Lake of the Falls Park.

• The Wisconsin Department of Natural Resources describes the natural setting at Copper Falls State Park, near Mellen, in Ashland County : "You will find a combination of waterfalls, cascades and river gorges such as are scarcely duplicated anywhere in this part of the country." The tumultuous Bad River (named for its difficult navigation) rushes headlong through the rugged terrain of the park. At one place, it plunges over a 29-foot drop and then charges through a narrow trap-walled gorge. This is Copper Falls, so named because of the color of the bedrock. About a quarter mile downstream, another river — Tylers Fork — joins the Bad River by hurtling over a 30-foot drop, producing a second steep waterfall. This is Tylers Falls. From there, the water courses wildly through a slot-like canyon with sheer rock walls

100 feet high. There is much excitement in the thunder of the waterfalls and rampaging water.

Ever-Changing Landscapes

A wide variation in physical geography makes Wisconsin a land of beautiful and constantly changing landscapes. As the seasons pass through their endless cycle, landscapes take on alluring new faces. Few places in the world offer so great a variety of scenery and natural beauty. Wisconsin is, indeed, a beautiful land.

Old photo of commercial fishing boats at Bayfield.

VII
The Nourishing Earth

Wisconsin's rocks are the parents of its soil. Soil is essential, directly or indirectly, to all forms of life inhabiting the state. Favorable ecological balances require the wise management of soil.

Description Of Soil

Soil is Wisconsin's most basic natural resource, responsible in large measure for its designation as America's Dairyland. Products of the same geologic forces that shaped its landforms, about 450 different soil types are found in the state. The variations in landscape and land use that we see in traveling around the state are partially the result of the characteristics of the soil.

What is soil? How is it formed? And what does it contribute to ecology? The answers to these questions promote a broad understanding of the natural plan whereby the members of the animal and plant kingdoms are sustained by a dependence upon the members of the mineral kingdom.

Soil is described in pedology (the science of soil classification) as a distinctive portion of the topmost mineral layer of the earth, containing air, water, plants and small animals, mixed in variable amounts. Soil constitutes the covering over most of the earth's land surface and is made up principally of mineral and rock particles. Geologists refer to soil as the shallow mantle of unconsolidated material that lies on the surface immediately above the solid crustal rocks. Most of us regard soil as the thin layer of dirt that supports the growth of plants. The State Highway Department of Wisconsin, looking at soils as important to road building, defines them as "an assortment of relatively shallow bodies that consist of unconsolidated mineral or organic matter lying within the root zone of native perennial plants and include any underlying layers developed since the parent materials were deposited."

Soil is formed over a long period of time from the weathering and erosion of rocks. The destructive forces of nature are constantly at work on all outcroppings of rock, ultimately reducing them from large masses to small particles. Thus rocks and minerals are called the parents of soil. Other soil-forming factors, varying locally and operating within a framework of time, are climate, vegetation and topography.

Soil forms in layers.

Soil provides the root zone for plants.

198

Soil is essentially a mixture in varying proportions of inorganic (mineral) particles derived from the weathering of rock and of organic matter derived largely from decomposed vegetation. Less than 10% of the dry substance of the average soil is of organic origin; more than 90% forms from inorganic mineral matter. The inorganic portion of a soil may develop from parent materials on the spot or result from the transport of sediments from elsewhere.

Residual soil is formed when weathering causes a rock to decay or decompose as it becomes soft, breaking down into granules. When soil is transported and deposited by rivers or streams, it is called alluvium. Soil moved by glaciers is called till. Fine flour-size soil blown about and laid down by wind is named loess. Decayed organic matter in soil is called humus.

Soil usually forms in layers.

Most road cuts expose soil to a depth of several feet. These exposures generally show a profile (vertical cross-section) of soil made up of horizons (layers) of topsoil, subsoil and underlying materials.

The Vanishing Topsoil

Topsoil is the essential part of the soil used for agriculture, seldom lying deeper than the blade of a spade. Topsoil is deepest in valleys, thinnest near the crests of ridges, hills and mountains. Beneath the topsoil, the subsoil reaches down generally to a depth of about 2 to 3 feet.

Soil, like all geologic features exposed at the surface, is in a state of flux, constantly being worked upon by the agents of erosion and transportation. In the erosion cycle, many of the mineral particles comprising soil remain only temporarily by the reckoning of geologic time as part of the carpet of a continent before being moved and deposited as sediments in ocean basins. Most soil eventually journeys to the sea.

Early soil scientists at work with "the most modern equipment."

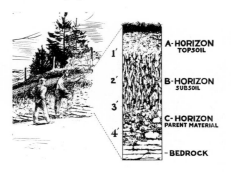

A soil profile

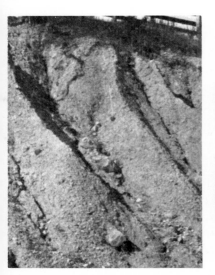

Transported soil. Glacial till in Baraboo region, boulders and clay brought from distant sections and dropped in a heterogeneous mass.

Residual soil. Weathered limestone in the Driftless Area grading downward into solid rock. This mantle rock represents the remains of a limestone layer above that shown.

199

An example of extreme erosion of farmland.

Contour plowing

The scars of erosion

Plowed fields are more susceptible to erosion than untilled land with a protective cover of vegetation. When the United States was still largely a wilderness and before plows bit into most of its fertile expanses, the average topsoil was about nine inches deep. But today after two centuries of intensified cultivation, many fields are covered with only about six inches of topsoil. Erosion has taken a dreadful toll. In some regions, more than one third of the original rich soil has been lost through careless and unwise farming.

On very uneven or hilly croplands, contour plowing (contours are lines connecting points of equal elevation) has greatly reduced erosion; in this method of plowing, plow furrows intersect slopes and follow the contours of fields, which slows down runoff, rather than going up and down slopes and crossing contours, which speeds up runoff. In addition, Wisconsin's farmers have adopted a number of other effective erosion-control practices.

Each year, up to 3,000 pounds per acre of topsoil can wash off unprotected plowed cropland. In an extreme case, all of the topsoil on a farm can be destroyed by erosion in less than twenty years, leaving substantially sterile wasteland. The National Wildlife Federation reported in 1975, "The nation is losing 3.5 billion tons of soil each year to erosion." The Soil Conservation Society recently estimated that the topsoil which Wisconsin, alone, loses annually to erosion from plowed croplands would fill enough dump trucks, lined up bumper to bumper, to encircle the earth seven and a half times. Fortunately, most plant nutrients lost from soil may be restored through fertilization. Unfortunately, however, nutrients running off fields enter surface water and cause serious environmental problems.

200

As a conservation measure at the present time, an increasing number of crops are planted without first plowing fields. The practice is called conservation tillage. This method of plowless planting keeps intact the natural structure of soil and balks erosion. A University of Wisconsin-Madison soil scientist, emphasizing the importance of this new approach to planting, said, "The real nuts and bolts of conservation tillage is saving soil." It may be of interest to note that a form of conservation tillage was one of the methods of planting practiced by Wisconsin's Prehistoric Indians.

Soil Conservation

The Wisconsin Geological and Natural History Survey comments on the use and conservation of soils in the state:

"The land is made up of the soils together with all other resources at the surface of the earth, including vegetation, animals, water, geologic deposits, air, climate, people, and structures. Some people regard the land as a commodity held in ownership; others see land as a community to which people belong, holding its ecological diversity in trust. These two viewpoints have contributed to the development of the pattern of land use in Wisconsin.

"A balance is sought between man-made landscape patterns and natural environmental corridors composed of streams and lakes, wetlands, sandy areas, wooded ridges and slopes, and rock outcrops. These corridors provide the major recreational and aesthetic resources of the state.

"Conservation of soil and water, and their efficient utilization, is fundamental to wise use of the land. For best results in soil erosion control, combinations of practices are custom-made for each kind of soil landscape within the ten soil regions . . . The experience of the Wisconsin Agricultural Experiment Station and the U.S. Soil Conservation Service personnel has been invaluable in determining how strip-cropping, grassed waterways, diversion terraces, stream bank stabilization and many other practices may best be applied to specific areas. The purposes of these practices are to promote infiltration of water into soil and to remove excess water from fields, without notable incidence of erosion and sedimentation. Increased soil productivity over many years has been the result."

Soil Use In Wisconsin

Dairy farming is the number one user of Wisconsin's soils. The state has an area of 36,148,120 acres, of which 1,136,920 acres are occupied by water and 35,011,200 acres by land. Present land uses are apportioned as follows: farms — 6%, forest — 36%, rural roads — 2.2%, urban lands — 1.1% and rural community lands — 0.7%. Land used in farming operations consists of: cropland — 59%, pasture — 15%, woodland — 8% and other uses — 18%. The state's 12,250,000 acres of cropland are utilized as follows: hay — 33%, corn — 22%, small grain — 19%, canning specialty crops — 3%, other crops — 11%, and idle land — 12%.

A typical Wisconsin dairy farm.

Oats in shocks as seldom seen in modern farming.

Hay in the field at harvesttime

The Wisconsin Geological and Natural History Survey comments upon the importance of soils in the state:

"A major use of soils is in farmland. Wisconsin's prime agricultural and silvicultural soils have four characteristics: (1) They have a balanced supply of essential plant nutrients, for health of trees, pastures, crops, livestock, wildlife and people. (2) They have a deep rooting zone in which water and air, as well as nutrients, are stored in proper proportions for plant use. (3) They are stable and do not easily slide, wash or blow away. (4) They are dry enough during the growing season to permit crops to mature.

"Soils are also important, in the engineering sense, for supporting roads and buildings, serving as sources of dam construction material, and absorbing liquid wastes and burying solid wastes safely. Soils and vegetation perform valuable functions in helping clear air of dust and pollutants and in absorbing noise."

General Classification Of Soils

A soil's texture provides a distinguishing characteristic for classifying it. Texture depends upon the size of the grains or particles composing the soil. The largest particles (cobbles and pebbles) are classified as gravel and the smallest specks as clay. Individual clay grains are too small to be seen separately with the unaided eye. The particles whose size fits between gravel and

Corn at the end of the growing season in old-fashioned shocks.

202

clay make up sand and silt. Sand feels gritty when rubbed between the fingers. Silt feels smooth and the largest grains can barely be seen by the naked eye; but for the smaller grains to be seen, magnification is required.

Few soils are comprised of pure clay, silt or sand. Most result from mixtures of various size particles. These mixtures are classified as loam. To qualify as a sandy soil, a soil must contain at least 50% sand. Likewise, a clay soil must have at least 50% clay.

Soil Profiles And Maps

A soil profile may be determined by digging a hole into the soil under study. The information shown in a soil profile is invaluable to a soil surveyor, who compiles soil maps for agricultural lands.

Soil has lateral dimensions as well as depth. It lies upon the landscape like a thick rug. Soil maps show the boundaries of each soil type. A given soil may extend over only a single acre or over several square miles of land. Soil commonly changes in characteristics from one part of a field to another, depending largely upon the topography and drainage of the area. More noticeable differences in soil types are observed when one travels some distance between fields.

Witnesses To Geologic History

A soil is influenced, of course, by all the geologic events of the past that have contributed to its present posture. If any one of Wisconsin's soil bodies had a voice, it could tell a story of its existence that in most cases would reach back into Precambrian times. It probably could bear witness to the building of some of the ancient mountains, the development of the peneplain, the transgression of the lands by the seas, the emergence of life, the invasion by the glaciers and many otherwise untold events, perhaps equally as exciting, from the state's geologic past.

Classification Into Series

Wisconsin's soil bodies differ in physical characteristics. These characteristics serve as the means for classifying soils into series, which in most cases are named after places. As an example, Withee loam is named after the Village of Withee, in Clark

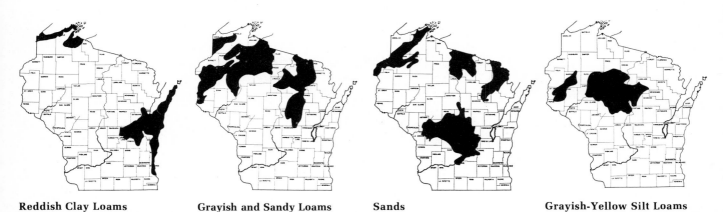

Reddish Clay Loams **Grayish and Sandy Loams** **Sands** **Grayish-Yellow Silt Loams**
TYPICAL SOIL REGIONS

The shaded areas on each of these small maps indicate the approximate location and extent of the soil region appearing in the caption. A substantial number of individual soil types, of course, are found within each region.

203

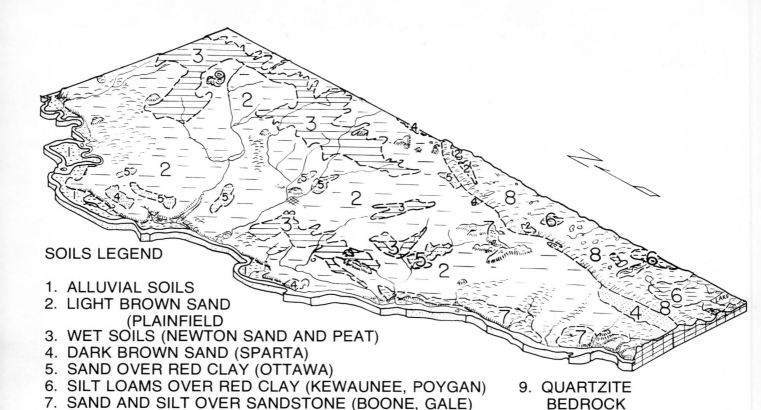

SOILS LEGEND

1. ALLUVIAL SOILS
2. LIGHT BROWN SAND
     (PLAINFIELD
3. WET SOILS (NEWTON SAND AND PEAT)
4. DARK BROWN SAND (SPARTA)
5. SAND OVER RED CLAY (OTTAWA)
6. SILT LOAMS OVER RED CLAY (KEWAUNEE, POYGAN)
7. SAND AND SILT OVER SANDSTONE (BOONE, GALE)
8. HILLY LIGHT BROWN SAND (COLOMA)
9. QUARTZITE
     BEDROCK

This is an example of a generalized soil map drawn to give an airplane view of a county. The numbers in the soil areas refer to numbers in the soils legend. Soil names are given in parentheses in the legend. This county is approximately 40 miles long and 20 miles wide.

County, where it was first studied. But some soils bear the name of geographical features such as streams.

Differing in origin, degree of fertility and other physical characteristics, the state's 450 soil types are grouped into ten general regions, with four additional subregions of predominately prairie soils. Each region is represented by a broad spectrum of soil series. Typical soils found in Wisconsin are the Fayette silt and Dodgeville black silt loam of the Western Upland, the golden Plainfield sand and Houghton peat and muck of the Central Plain, the reddish brown Vilas sand and Iron River stony sandy loam of the Northern Highland, and the fine Shawano sand and Kewaunee clay of the Eastern Lowlands and Ridges.

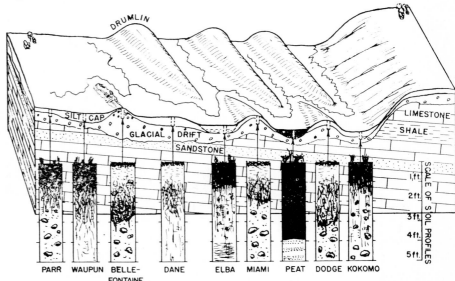

This diagram shows the relative positions of some typical soils on the hills, valley slopes, flats and bottoms of Dodge County, Wisconsin.

204

Loess

In about two thirds of Wisconsin, the soils are developed at least in part from a blanket of loess that was laid down by winds near the end of the Ice Age. As the glaciers waned, enormous volumes of meltwater forced streams and rivers to swell and flood their valleys. Later when the flooding subsided, large deposits of silt were left upon floodplains. Almost no vegetation remained then to anchor these deposits because plant communities had virtually perished under the frigid climate of the Pleistocene and the stifling effect of the ice sheet that had mantled much of the land. As the glaciers receded, large expanses covered with ground moraine and outwash deposits were left barren, serving also as sources of silt. Dried, flour-size sediments, carpeting valley floors, swirled around like powder. Dust storms formed as the silt was swept up by passing winds, broadcast and redeposited on adjacent uplands. In time, a thick layer of loess lay upon much of the land.

The Driftless Area of southwestern Wisconsin was covered in places with loess to a depth of 8 to 16 inches. Much of this fine soil was air-lifted from the floodplain of the Mississippi River by winds prevailing from the southwest.

The silty cover came to rest, from place to place, on a great variety of materials — glacial till, bedrock, red clay, blue clay, limestone gravel and acid sand. Traces of loess are found today in many distantly scattered places such as Rib Mountain, near Wausau in Marathon County, the Baraboo Range in Sauk County, and the Blue Hills near Rice Lake in Barron County.

These aeolian deposits contain an abundance of minerals contributing to the fertility of the soils of which they are now a part. As a matter of fact, most of the state's silt loams have developed since the close of the Pleistocene on this wind-laid silt.

Extensive deposits of sand also were left in the wake of the retreating glaciers. Numerous dried up glacial lake beds are noticeable because of their sandy soils. In some places, the glaciers had barely departed before fine sands were whipped about by winds forming sand dunes. Typical of this occurrence were broad areas along the Lower Wisconsin River Valley, as well as in the Central Plain and in the far northwest corner of the

Active sand dune in Adams County

Sandy Loams   **Grayish-Brown Unglaciated Silt Loams**   **Grayish-Brown Glaciated Silt Loams**   **Pink Loams**

TYPICAL SOIL REGIONS

The shaded areas on each of these small maps indicate the approximate location and extent of the soil region appearing in the caption. A substantial number of individual soil types, of course, are found within each region.

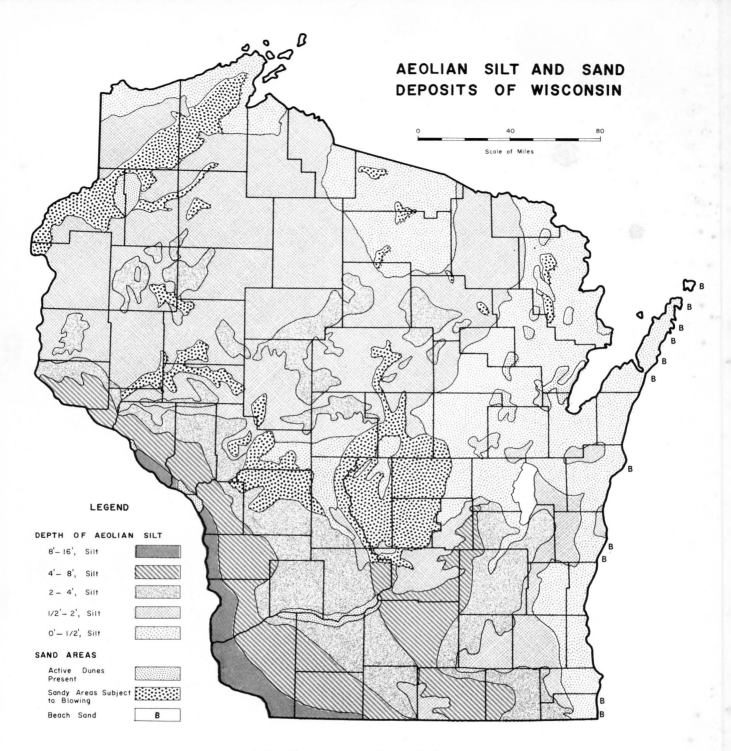

AEOLIAN SILT AND SAND
DEPOSITS OF WISCONSIN

Scale of Miles

LEGEND

DEPTH OF AEOLIAN SILT

8' – 16', Silt
4' – 8', Silt
2 – 4', Silt
1/2' – 2', Silt
0' – 1/2', Silt

SAND AREAS

Active Dunes Present
Sandy Areas Subject to Blowing
Beach Sand — B

state. Remnants of sand dunes, with some still active, may be seen today in these localities.

Denizens Of The Soil

Wisconsin's soils, like those everywhere, teem with plant life, from the diminutive lycopodium to the towering Norway pine. They, likewise, harbor animal life from the quaint little trapdoor spider to the much larger burrowing badger. The denizens of the soil both take from and add to the fertility of soil. Organic remains make soil more fertile. Small plants called bacteria aid the process of decay. Other bacteria help fix atmospheric nitrogen in soil, which is a key element in the growth of plants. Although larger plants hold soil together with their network of roots, they also help create it. With their roots prying rocks apart, they contribute to the process of decomposing rocks to soil. Burrowing animals like gophers and skunks help mix the ingredients of soil. Perhaps the busiest and most valuable of all animals influencing soil is the lowly earthworm which ingests soil into its body to obtain food and then passes it out again in a finely pulverized form.

Soil, in turn, is essential in a number of ways to the vitality and survival of living things. In order to discuss the dependence of organisms on soil, let's consider some general principles of ecology — such as habitat, natural selection, natural balances, food chains and predation.

Habitat

Why are May flowers seldom found in open spaces? Why do we see more pheasants in southern Wisconsin than in the north woods? Why do thistles grow in some fields but not in others? Why do deer tend to move out of an area as urban sprawl moves in? And why does tobacco prosper in the state only in limited areas around Madison and LaCrosse?

The kinds and numbers of plants and animals inhabiting any particular part of Wisconsin are determined largely by local topography, climate and soil conditions. These make up a habitat that is favorable or unfavorable for a given species. A favorable habitat provides an environment conducive to a species' survival and prosperity. Although climate and topography vitally influence habitat, soil, too, is a strong determining factor in the distribution, from place to place, of species.

The unique ecological conditions and location to which an organism has adapted are referred to as its ecological niche. An organism's ecological niche may be thought of as the environment in which it prospers and to which it is better suited than any other organism and which suits it better than any other environment. Ecological niche is equivalent to optimum habitat.

Natural Selection

The natural selection of species works like a giant computer wherein the progeny (offspring) of the species are the input and the surviving adults the output. The number of reproductive cells and progeny produced by plants and animals always far exceeds the number of individuals who survive all the way to maturity. As an example, in late summer, a milkweed plant, along a roadside in central Wisconsin may release fifty seeds from a splitting pod. Having downy featherlike structures, the seeds become instantly airborne as they are snatched up by passing winds and carried for varying distances, alighting in time upon fifty separate parcels of land. Some of the seeds, eventually, will take root but most will fail to germinate. All are in competition for a space to grow with other seeds, spores and growing plants occupying the same parcels. Of those developing into plants, only a few will live on long enough to reach maturity.

Burrowing Animals

Badger

Skunk

Groundhog

Mole

207

White-tailed Deer

All the comforts of home are present in a beaver's ecological niche.

The otter is ideally equipped to survive on land or water.

The big predators, including the timber wolf, no longer rule Wisconsin's wilds.

Along the way, the rest will perish. Thus, through the process of natural selection, a barely sufficient number of milkweed plants will endure to produce another generation of progeny, thereby insuring the survival of the species. The result of all this is that the milkweed species is kept in a state of balance with all other plants and animals. From generation to generation, the total number of adult individuals in a given species remains remarkably constant. Rarely does one species suddenly take over and dominate an environment that previously supported a balance of many species. Natural selection is the mysterious process that averages out the allotment of all species. Like all other organisms, milkweed plants are always found most plentiful in their very own ecological niche.

The fittest of a species prosper in environments that are the most suitable for their prevailing over territorial competitors and escaping elimination from other natural checks and balances that thin their numbers — such as hostile terrain, soil deficiencies, foragers, predators, disease, parasites, unfavorable climate, adverse weather, fires, floods and human intrusions. There is, of course, always a high mortality rate among the members of a species.

Mother Nature doesn't endow each member of a species with exactly the same physical characteristics. As a matter of fact, no

SOME VANISHED WISCONSIN BIRDS AND MAMMALS

CARIBOU (1842)

MOOSE (1921)

COUGAR (1884)

FISHER (1900-1920)

MARTEN (1925)

WOLVERINE (1870)

ELK (1866)

BISON (1832)

PASSENGER PIGEON (1899)

TRUMPETER SWAN (1893)

WHOOPING CRANE (1884)

CAROLINA PAROQUET (1844)

WILD TURKEY (1872)

208

two individuals are ever completely the same; rather, each has variations in a number of different traits. The same is true among all plants and animals: variants within a species are the rule. Because of these variants (longer legs, larger lungs, keener eyes, or more sensitive ears, as examples, in the case of white-tailed deer), some individuals are better equipped and more successful than others in competing for survival. The superior physical traits among those who ultimately survive (the fittest of the species) are transmitted through heredity to offspring. Thus, through a succession of generations, a species gradually evolves the physical characteristics which give it a competitive advantage and best allow for its survival.

In contrast with the success of individuals to survive during the lifetime of their generation, the success of a species to avoid extinction over the long haul is largely a matter of its members' adapting biologically as a class — over its span of existence, from parents to offspring, from generation to generation — to meet the demands of changing environments. Once it can't cope with its environment, it ceases to remain extant.

The more specialized an organism becomes to a particular environment, the less likely it will be displaced by others but the more likely it will be extinguished by evolutionary or environmental change. Species that live in a broad range of environments with a mixed and varied habitat are likely to avoid extinction for a long time. This pattern in the natural order reminds one of the old Arabian proverb: "The mouse that has but one hole is soon caught".

Natural Balances

Near the end of the Ice Age when the glaciers finally retreated from Wisconsin and climates gradually warmed leveling off to the moderate extremes that prevail today, the stage was set for the introduction of new plant and animal communities. Many of the creatures of the Pleistocene and the immediate post-glacial period found the new conditions increasingly unfavorable. In time, some of the earlier species became phased out and replaced by others. This change in fauna and flora affected the interrelationships of all life forms, directly or indirectly, from the largest to the smallest — including trees, flowers, grasses, sedges, bacteria, mammals, birds, reptiles, fish and insects. The elephant-like mastodon and woolly mammoth, accustomed to a chilly setting, were among the first to go. The transition, generally, was slow but orderly. (Some biologists believe that early humans' indiscriminative use of fire as a means of hunting wild animals may have pushed some species toward the brink of early extinction.)

By the time of Jean Nicolet's "discovery" of Wisconsin in 1634, the state had become a verdant wilderness with great forests of stunning magnificence covering much of the land. An estimated thirty million of the state's nearly thirty-five million acres of land bore stands of timber. Predominant among the trees in the northern regions was the majestic white pine,

Native vegetation in Wisconsin

Seeds of different plant species compete for a place to grow.

MacArthur White Pine — Forest County, one of the largest standing white pines in the nation today.

209

Among species extinct in Wisconsin.

Woodland Caribou

Bison

Puma

Lynx

Wolverine

Moose

Elk

Nicolet landing at Red Banks.

sometimes measuring at the stump as much as 8½ feet and reaching skyward as much as 250 feet. Among species of trees more limited in number and distributed variously around the state, were red pine (commonly called Norway pine), hemlock, white spruce, yellow birch, sugar maple, red oak, basswood, slippery elm and white ash. Other areas without dense forest cover stretched out as grasslands and wetlands. Some large tracts of lowlands in the north woods were occupied by tamarack and black spruce bogs. Other areas in the central and northwestern regions contained pine barrens as a result of poor soil and periodic pruning by fire.

According to the Wisconsin Geological and Natural History Survey, "Most of the southern part of the state was covered with prairie or oak savanna — an orchard-like community with a few large bur or white oaks growing in fields of grass."

Many animal species thrived in the state — American bison, western woodland caribou, American elk, northwestern moose, wolverine, Wisconsin puma, lynx, bobcat, black bear, snowshoe hare, jackrabbit, coyote, pine marten, gray fox, timber wolf, muskrat, fisher, weasel, beaver, bald eagle, golden eagle, pileated woodpecker, wild turkey, prairie chicken, great horned owl, whooping crane, passenger pigeon and a host of others.

All the creatures lived in a state of natural balance with the Prehistoric Indian hunters, who greeted Nicolet upon his arrival at Red Banks near present-day Green Bay. But soon other people immigrated from Europe in ever-increasing numbers and made inroads into the wilderness. First came traders and trappers in quest of the pelts of wild animals, especially beaver whose fur was in vogue overseas among the fashionable. Then came miners in search of lead, together with settlers bent on clearing land and developing farms. In time, villages and cities sprang up like mushrooms after a warm summer rain. Then came loggers and lumberjacks with saws and axes, determined to meet the challenge of the forests. Eventually, people came for almost as many reasons as there were immigrants. In the process, the virgin wilderness gradually vanished.

Influenced variously by these invasions of modern humans, the plant and animal communities originally inhabiting the wilderness slowly changed. We need to compare only what we have

The settler built his house of native materials.

today with what there was at the time of Nicolet to chart the changes brought about by civilization in less than 3½ centuries.

Blackhawk, the famous chief of the beleaguered Sauk and Fox Indians, recalls how it was during the time of his people:

"We always had plenty; our children never cried from hunger, neither were our people in want . . . The rapids of Rock River furnished us with an abundance of excellent fish, and the land being very fertile, never failed to produce good crops of corn, beans, pumpkins, and squashes . . . Here our village stood for more than a hundred years, during all of which time we were the undisputed possessors of the Mississippi Valley . . . Our village was healthy and there was no place in the country possessing such advantages, nor hunting grounds better than those we had in possession. If a prophet had come to our village in those days and told us that the things were to take place which have since come to pass, none of our people would have believed him."

The character of the state's lands and waterways has been drastically altered since the time of the frontier. Ecology involves delicate adjustments in the natural order that usually develop over many years between species and habitat, plant and animal, parasite and host, and predator and prey. Humans, alone among all animals, are capable of interfering with these adjustments and upsetting ecological balances.

The fate of the state's big predators since the time of Nicolet illustrates how we can unwittingly change conditions affecting other species. Predators, of course, depend upon prey. With the wilderness constantly shrinking because of human intrusions, species of prey have become diminished in direct proportion to their reduced habitat. With a dwindling supply of food provided by prey species, the big predators have gradually disappeared. As an example, the Wisconsin puma no longer stalks the wilds of the state for which it is named. Similarly, the lynx and timber

Black Hawk

Log jam of 50,000,000 board feet of white pine five miles long at head of Dalles on St. Croix River, 1886. Note arched wooden bridge across stream.

Among Wisconsin's variety of crops...

String beans

Potatoes

Cabbages

Ginseng

wolf are either endangered or extinct species in Wisconsin. At the same time, we have further hastened the decline of the biggest carnivores with our sophisticated methods of hunting.

By killing off most of the large predators, an important ecological balancing force has been upset in our remaining patches of wilderness. One or two wolves or pumas in a limited area can keep stable their favorite species of prey such as deer by devouring large numbers each year. A lack of such thinning out of prey species leads inevitably to their overpopulation, consequential depletion of available food and starvation.

We influence natural balances in many ways. But, most significantly, the way we occupy or use land determines the fate of other creatures who share space with us. By converting land to urban use, we reduce habitat for wild species. The National Wildlife Federation recently reported, "The chief threat to wildlife continues to be loss of habitat. Each day, more than 2,000 acres are converted (in the U.S.) from rural to urban use." As a consequence, in 1975 the list of endangered species in the nation grew to 126.

At the same time, we also lose farmland to urban sprawl, highway construction and lake development. Land taken away from the plow equates out to food taken away from a half-hungry world. The National Wildlife Federation commented in 1975 upon the plight of farmland, "The U.S. today is truly an oasis on a hungry planet, but a somewhat uneasy oasis . . . About 2.2 million acres of land were urbanized, paved or flooded last year."

The Federation predicted that, in the next ten years, a total area larger than the State of New Jersey will become lost to development. Also, in the process, the aesthetic values of the landscape tend to diminish. "The environmental implications of all that dredging, draining, filling, bulldozing, paving and building raise the question: How long America, the Beautiful?"

The Food Pyramid

Air, water and soil form the inorganic base of the food pyramid. Without any one of these essentials, no creature could survive. All three combine to sustain life — from the tiniest microorganism to the largest tree and mammal.

All creatures, directly or indirectly, depend upon the atmosphere. The dependence of air-breathing animals is obvious. Plants, through photosynthesis, absorb carbon dioxide and release oxygen helping to maintain an adequate supply of oxygen for the air breathers. Atmospheric nitrogen aids in keeping soil fertile.

Rainwater is distributed around the world through the hydrologic cycle. The cells of all living things require water. As an example, when deprived of water, a plant will wilt and die but, when water is plentiful, a plant's cells fill to capacity achieving a fluid-rich state called turgor.

Soil acts as an enormous reservoir for the storage of water. Water, as runoff and stream flow, carries dissolved and suspended minerals gleaned from the soil and deposits them

212

elsewhere on land, in streambeds and, ultimately, in the oceans.

Mineral and organic matter in soil and water provides nourishment, directly or indirectly, for all plants and animals. Most land plants take up nutrients from soil, air and ground water; but some marine plants assimilate them from seawater. All the nutrients have common origins. They derive variously from organic remains, air and rocks (as the parent materials of soil).

Most plants rely on such nutriment as their source of food. But some plants and most animals resort to predation to satisfy their continuing need for food. Through predation, some plants and animals consume others and they, in turn, are consumed by still others, in an endless succession that reaches to all the earth's fauna and flora. Predation is the relationship among organisms in which one captures and feeds upon another. Survival because of predation is the difference between eating or being eaten. The life-and-death contest for food involves all creatures, beginning with the lowliest plants. Lacking the ability to build tissue from the elemental substances of the soil, most animals must necessarily feast upon plants or other animals. At the end of the so-called food chains, some of the predators always emerge victorious. As an example, let's assume that a wild honeysuckle grows in a Wisconsin wood lot deriving nutrients from the soil; nectar is sipped from the honeysuckle by a swallowtail butterfly; the butterfly becomes the victim of a prowling dragonfly; the dragonfly is devoured by a leopard frog; the frog falls prey to a brown water snake; and the snake is consumed, at the end of the chain, by a red-shouldered hawk. Each food chain serves as a part of the food pyramid representing the ceaseless struggle for survival of all members of the plant and animal kingdoms. With the most varied diet — the human being — the greatest predator of all, occupies the tip of the food pyramid as the final consumer.

Rocks: The Staff of Life?

Did you ever think of rocks as a source of food or sustenance for all living things? Indirectly, it is true.

Rocks, as we discussed earlier, are the parents of soil. Soil contains inorganic mineral matter derived from decomposed rocks. Some of the mineral matter provides nourishment for plants. The plants, in turn, feed predators. Thence through the food pyramid, all organisms are sustained. Thus rocks are, indeed, a source of food or sustenance for all living things.

Ecological Balance

The dependence of living organisms upon soil, water and air and the impact of living organisms, in return, upon soil, water and air demonstrate great cyclic interactions in the natural order. Terrestrial plants, especially, point up the life-sustaining interplay constantly occurring between the lithosphere, hydrosphere, atmosphere and biosphere.

The lithosphere is the rocky part of the earth comprising the crust and upper mantle.

These determined old trees send out long roots seeking water and soil at Parfrey's Glen in Sauk County.

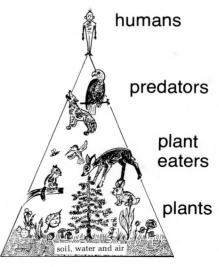

The Food Pyramid

213

SOIL REGIONS OF WISCONSIN

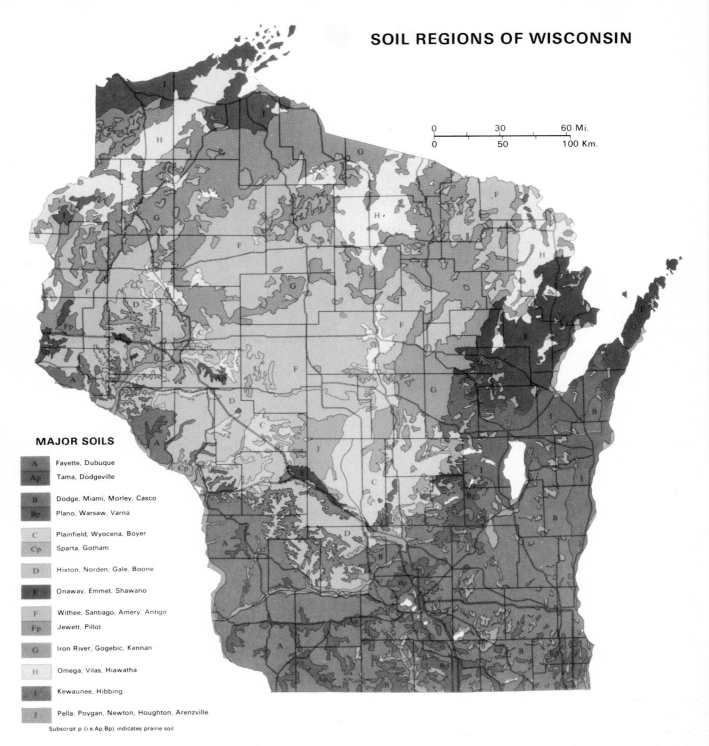

MAJOR SOILS

A	Fayette, Dubuque
Ap	Tama, Dodgeville
B	Dodge, Miami, Morley, Casco
Bp	Plano, Warsaw, Varna
C	Plainfield, Wyocena, Boyer
Cp	Sparta, Gotham
D	Hixton, Norden, Gale, Boone
E	Onaway, Emmet, Shawano
F	Withee, Santiago, Amery, Antigo
Fp	Jewett, Pillot
G	Iron River, Gogebic, Kennan
H	Omega, Vilas, Hiawatha
I	Kewaunee, Hibbing
J	Pella, Poygan, Newton, Houghton, Arenzville

Subscript p (i.e. Ap, Bp) indicates prairie soil

The hydrosphere is the surface area of the earth covered with water and consisting chiefly of the oceans.

The atmosphere, as we already know, is the gaseous mass that envelops the earth.

And the biosphere is the mass aggregate of all organisms living on earth at any given time.

The great cyclic interactions to which we refer are chemical in nature and concern an exchange of bewildering numbers of elements between the lithosphere, hydrosphere, atmosphere and biosphere. The largest fraction of the elements moving through the cycle makes up water, carbon dioxide and free oxygen. The

214

elements, through complicated chemical and biochemical processes, are continually changing in form — traveling in time from earth to sky, from continent to ocean, from gas to solid, from weathered rock to living organism and from dust to dust. In a sense, all things are related through a chemical affinity. The realities in the chemistry of the physical world are so complex and far-reaching as to challenge comprehension. As an illustration in point with our discussion, green plants take minerals and water from the soil and water and carbon dioxide from the air and give back humus to the soil and oxygen and water to the air, while simultaneously fulfilling a vital role in the food pyramid. In addition, plants utilize solar energy through photosynthesis. At the same time, bacteria help extract nitrogen from the air and fix it in soil in a form useable to plants as a nutrient.

A University of Wisconsin-Madison researcher, working on the problem of world food production, recently said, "When it comes right down to it, what we depend on in this world is photosynthesis and biological nitrogen fixation — the processes by which the plant uses the radiant energy of the sun to produce food."

The wondrous interrelationship among the members of the plant, animal and mineral kingdoms is the substance of ecology. The science of ecology may be thought of as the Declaration of Interdependence. The framework, at a given place, in which various things interact is called an ecosystem. When we consider the important role of soil in the full range of ecosystems, we recognize that the conservation of soil is essential for an all-encompassing ecological balance beneficial to all species, particularly our own. It isn't unrealistic to believe that, with our human population increasing almost everywhere at an alarming rate, we must prevent further waste of our soil through erosion and urban sprawl if we plan to avoid our own extinction as a species on the planet Earth.

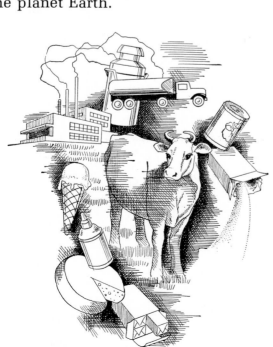

VIII Stone Age People

The rocks of Wisconsin were of prime importance to the Indians living in the state during prehistoric times. Their Stone Age cultures were based on the use of rocks for making tools, weapons and ornaments. The Indians were the first to develop the state's rocks and minerals as economic commodities.

The Prehistoric Inhabitants

The prehistoric people of Wisconsin descended from North America's original settlers. The first settlers migrated from Asia to the New World about 30,000 years ago, crossing between the two continents on a natural land bridge at the Bering Strait. The migration, no doubt, was accidental and followed the quest for game of these nomadic hunters. The oceans at that time were drawn down exposing lands usually submerged. The northern hemisphere shivered in the throes of the Ice Age and a great amount of the earth's water supply was locked in the enormous ice sheet that blanketed the northern climes.

As early as 14,000 to 13,000 years ago during an interval of reduced glaciation, the Paleo Indians found their way into Wisconsin. During the concluding prehistoric period, Indian settlers arrived in the state in a series of migrations, some spaced as much as several thousand years apart. Except, possibly, for the very earliest immigrants, the various Indian groups moved into the state generally from the south and east, with the Mississippi River Valley serving as one of the main migratory routes. Each of the Prehistoric Indian groups differed in culture, evolving distinctive ways of fashioning tools, weapons and ornaments and burying their dead. They differed, too, in the manner in which they pursued a living. Some advanced from a way of life patterned upon the hunting of wild animals to a more sedentary society based upon permanent settlement and the raising of crops as a source of food.

Cultural Stages of Aboriginal Americans

The original prehistoric immigrants to North America traveled in small family-oriented groups, dependent for their meager needs upon the success of the hunt. The large land animals of the Pleistocene, particularly the elephant-like mastodons and

woolly mammoths, were among their favorite prey. These prehistoric people supplemented their meat diet by gathering native plants, roots, seeds, berries and nuts. They dressed in furs and made use of fire as a means of keeping warm, cooking food and protecting themselves from predators. Only a rudimentary cultural inheritance had been passed down to them from their Asian ancestors, tailored to their role as unsophisticated hunters and food gatherers. This included the basic skill of shaping rock into primitive implements, with the spear as their chief weapon. They hadn't yet conceived of the bow and arrow. Bringing dogs with them, they survived on the fringes of the glaciers. Both preying upon and being preyed upon by wild beasts, these early people were a hardy lot — the pioneer force of all the prehistoric inhabitants of North America.

Eventually, during the centuries following and through a succession of generations, the prehistoric people settled in almost all parts of North, Central and South America. They populated even the Caribbean Islands, where they first had contact with the Spanish. By then, they existed in such great numbers that they had evolved about 160 linguistic stocks or languages, with more than 1,200 dialectic variations. Estimates of their peak population reach as high as 75,000,000.

The Indians advanced culturally during the many years of their inhabiting the New World, progressing from simple hunters and food gatherers to substantially more enlightened farmers and city dwellers. By the time of Columbus, the descendants of the earliest prehistoric people had left their mark on the Americas to an extent matched only rarely in the world's other great Stone Age civilizations. The monumental accomplishments of the Andeans and Incas in South America, the Olmecs, Mayas, Toltecs and Aztecs in Central America, and the Pueblos, Hopewells and Middle Mississippi People in North America mark great strides in progress in a rich variety of cultures. These include the development of numerous urban centers that provide evidence of city planning, and the development of agriculture with the domestication of many exclusively American plants, irrigation and utilization of fertilizers. These also include invention and perfection of arts and crafts — such as pottery making, weaving, lapidary art, metallurgy, dyeing, sculpturing, poetry, painting and architecture. In science, the Indians were probably the first to devise a system of numbers with zero as a numerical position. They also designed an amazingly accurate calendar, better in some respects than the one we use today. In medicine, they discovered and employed a number of effective drugs and even practiced trepanning — the surgical removal of a portion of a patient's skull bone to relieve pressure on the brain. In the U.S. alone, they built more than 100,000 earthen mounds, many of which have survived the ravages of time and now exist as reminders of their early builders' dynamic presence during the prehistoric period.

In their rise to civilization, these ancient people passed through a sequence of cultural stages with archeologists recog-

Wigwams or winter lodges

Birdstone

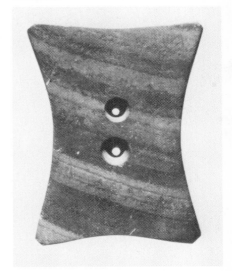
Two-hole gorget

Gorget or pendant

217

Pendant cut from sheet copper

Central American idol carved of serpentine

Disk pipe carved of catlinite

nizing five separate stages of cultural change. Arbitrary names have been assigned to each of these stages which, in the order of the earliest to latest, are the Lithic, Archaic, Formative, Classic and Postclassic.

A gradual social evolution of these early people advancing from small nomadic hunting groups to large sedentary societies based upon permanent settlement and the raising of crops as a primary source of food can be read clearly from the things that they left behind, mostly from relics of stone. The artifacts of each cultural stage reflect the manner in which the members of a group pursued a living.

Lithic Stage relics consist of primitive hunting implements such as spearpoints, scrapers, cleavers and hand axes.

Archaic Stage artifacts include a variety of tools and utensils used in the preparation of wild vegetable foods and show an increase in food gathering and fishing with less stress on hunting; typical are digging sticks, grooved hammers, arrowheads, fish hooks, drills, needles, simple storage vessels and some items of jewelry.

Formative Stage artifacts reveal a fundamental shift from hunting and food gathering to agricultural food production. Permanent settlements first appear in this stage in the form of agrarian-based villages, with tools and personal possessions consisting of adzes, hoes, mattocks, axes, spades, elaborate pottery vessels, pipes, ceremonial objects and many items of jewelry.

The Classic Stage marks a breakthrough to civilization. The remains of this stage provide evidence of great urban centers forming the nuclei of politically-oriented governments, with large buildings, temples, roadways, public works, organized religions and intellectual achievements. Advanced craftsmanship blossomed into distinctive art styles in many mediums including ceramics, stonework, woodenware, weaving and metal.

Artifacts of the Postclassic Stage point to a secularization of society with a shifting of populations, troubled times, wars and a breakdown of the regional art styles of the Classic Stage.

During the prehistoric period, the most culturally-advanced of Wisconsin's Indian groups progressed to the Formative Stage but none attained full civilization — a prerequisite of the Classic Stage. Before the coming of white settlers, the state's inhabitants were people of the forest and the confinement imposed upon them by severe winter climatic conditions retarded their rise to

Central American pendant carved of black jade

218

civilization. In due time, doubtlessly, they would have achieved civilization in their own right, even without the European cultural influences to which they were subsequently exposed. Certainly, as we shall see, they had moved far up the trail in that direction. However in historic times, the Indians' Stone Age cultures rapidly lost identity, diffused and merged with the European immigrants' civilization. Thus less than 3½ centuries ago, the state's aboriginal inhabitants were inducted abruptly into the Iron, Industrial and Scientific Ages.

Stonecrafting

All of Wisconsin's Prehistoric Indians relied upon rocks and minerals as basic materials for making tools and implements. Theirs was a rudimentary existence, a way of life rooted in the Stone Age. Few things were as integral to their everyday needs as stone and none was as imperishable. Most of what we know today about their struggle to survive in a wilderness world is recorded in artifacts made of stone. Almost everything else that measures their accomplishments has long since vanished.

One is impressed with the capacity of these primitive people to single out rocks, minerals and other materials ideally suited for the purposes for which they were used. A study of their artifacts shows that they developed a Stone Age technology in the use of indigenous materials. As an example, arrowheads, spearpoints, drills and knives were chipped commonly from chert and quartzite; axes, hoes and celts were shaped from igneous rocks that stood up under hard use and kept an edge; and cooking vessels were made of fired clay. They utilized such diverse native materials as stone, bone, shell, wood, bark, seeds, nuts, roots, reeds, clay, lead, copper and silver, along with numerous animal parts including hides, hair, quills, teeth, bone, claws, feathers and sinew.

The Prehistoric Indians were skillful craftsmen in working with stone. They employed both percussion and pressure flaking in producing projectile points for arrows and spears. In the same manner, they made awls, knives, hatchets and many other tools and ceremonial objects. A deer antler was used as a tool for working stone in the pressure flaking technique. Larger objects — such as axes, hammers, celts, banner stones, grinding stones, gorgets, bird stones, plummets and tanning stones — were shaped through a technique known as pecking and polishing. The pecking (producing a gradual pulverization on the surface of the stone worked) was done with a very hard stone and the polishing by rubbing with a flat harder, abrasive stone until the

Drills

Projectile points

Grooved axe of the three-quarter groove type

Hammer-stone showing one end abraded from use

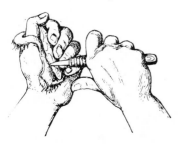
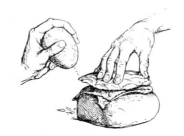
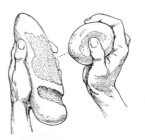

219

Pot showing conoidal base and cord-imprinted body

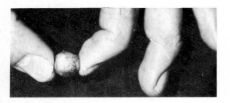

Silver bead. A wood core covered with a thin sheet of silver.

Pipestone quarry east of Rice Lake

finished product had a regular and smooth surface. These early people became proficient at making cooking and storage vessels from fired clay, mixing in crushed rock or shell fragments as a temper to hold together the finished pottery. They learned to hammer copper into many of their weapons and implements. The Hopewellians even worked a little with silver. The only Prehistoric Indians in Wisconsin known to have used a precious metal, they made beads by covering tiny wooden cores with thin sheets pounded from Lake Superior silver. Most of the early Indians carved pipes and items of jewelry from catlenite (Minnesota pipestone) and steotite (native soapstone). Kaolinite (a slightly different pipestone) was quarried near Rice Lake, in Barron County, and near Raddison, in Sawyer County. The soapstone was dug in several places in Wood County.

Sometimes cubes of galena or nuggets of imported turquoise were deposited by the Prehistoric Indians in burial mounds. This practice demonstrates the ceremonial (probably sacred) value attributed to such objects by these early people.

Early Quarrying

For thousands of years, Prehistoric Indians quarried quartzite at Silver Mound, a steeply rising butte located in the Driftless Area in the beautiful hill country, between Hixton and Alma Center, in Jackson County. The early Paleo Indians, about 11,500 years ago, first worked this site and found the rock ideal for making tools and weapons. This unusual form of quartzite — varying in color from white to red, with shades of brown, butterscotch and, most abundantly, mutton fat — breaks with a conchoidal or spoon-shaped fracture, a property essential for knapping stone by either percussion or pressure flaking. Predictably, it became a favorite material of early craftsmen for making a variety of implements. A succession of later Indian groups continued the practice of quarrying and working the stone. The refuse left by these several groups of stone workers tells much about their cultures.

Projectile points made from Silver Mound quartzite have been found the full length of the Mississippi River Valley and throughout the Great Lakes Region.

University of Wisconsin-Oshkosh archeologists excavating the ancient quarry at Silver Mounds.

Silver Mound has an interesting geologic history. As a landform, it is a steeply-rising outlier-type hill (elevation: 1,260 feet above sea level) representing a detached, resistant segment of the original layers of sedimentary rocks of which it formed. The rest of such layers departed the scene long ago through erosion. The mound is composed of sandstones lithified from sediments deposited on the floor of Cambrian-age seas. The base is Eau Claire Sandstone and this is capped by the Wonewoc Formation. The uppermost 100 feet or so, however, have become thoroughly cemented by silica, resulting in a very brittle quartzite. Unlike most quartzites which result from the metamorphism of sandstone through heat and pressure produced by over-burdening materials, the Silver Mound quartzite formed from silica precipitating out of groundwater solutions. Fossil-rich beds in the original Upper Cambrian strata are believed to have been the source of the silica. Similar quartzite occurs in lesser amounts on a ridge several miles to the northwest. Otherwise, the geologic setting at Silver Mound is unique and the quartzite, so highly prized by the Prehistoric Indians, represents an almost isolated occurrence of this material in Wisconsin. Most other quartzites found in the state are of Precambrian origin.

Cultural Remains

Wisconsin is rich in the cultural remains of its prehistoric inhabitants. Over past centuries, untold quantities of their artifacts have become buried beneath soils washed off hillsides. Occasionally, these relics become uncovered in time by further erosion and then await discovery at the surface. Relic collectors usually hunt for artifacts along the flanks of ridges where the greatest amount of erosion occurs.

The state serves as a repository for more than 15,000 Indian mounds, heaps of earth in various shapes used primarily for the burial of the dead. Many of the mounds are of a unique type, found almost exclusively in Wisconsin, known as effigy mounds. They were built to resemble the shapes of various birds, mammals and reptiles.

A large mound on the shore of Lower Clam Lake in Burnett County was excavated in 1935. It measured 16 feet in height and 270 feet in circumference. A curious fact revealed by a study of the soil of which the mound was constructed is that it is not of local origin but had been carried to the site, apparently, from the Grantsburg area about 21 miles away.

Petroglyphs (picture writing) have been found on rock ledges

Indian mounds in city park at Rice Lake, Barron County.

Making plaster casts of bird petroglyphs at Twin Bluffs, Juneau County

221

Hillock type garden beds on Carroll College Campus, Waukesha

Parallel-rowed garden beds near Oshkosh.

and in cave shelters. The scattered deposits of villages and campsites have been discovered along many of the state's waterways. The remains of garden beds show the early practice of agriculture.

A vestige of organized hunting by the Prehistoric Indians, an unusual rock wall of fieldstones is found on a hillside three miles north of Dickeyville, in Grant County. About 300 yards long and once waist high, it is believed to have been built as a gaming wall for steering wild animals to a place of ambush. It's age and origin are unknown.

Among the best-preserved petroglyphs of the Prehistoric Indians in the Midwest are those at Gulleckson's Glen Park, west of Black River Falls, in Jackson County. These primitive expressions of art were incised about 800 years ago on a vertical exposure of soft ochre sandstone by an unknown group of Indians. The impressive petroglyphs include a buffalo nursing a calf, wild turkeys in flight and human beings with their arms uplifted, perhaps, in the act of supplicating some higher power.

Sacred Stones

No doubt, some of Wisconsin's prehistoric cultural groups believed in sacred stones because this was a practice of many tribes in early historic times. Illustrations of this are the Spirit Rock and the Red Rock.

The latter, situated near present-day St. Paul, Minnesota, was known by the Dakota Sioux as "Eyay Shah" and was last visited by them shortly before their uprising in 1862. It was considered an object of worship where a supplicant might go to pray and offer a sacrifice and talk of it was "sacred talk".

Another example of a sacred stone is Medicine Rock, a large erratic boulder along the shoreline of Lake Lac du Flambeau, in Vilas County, that was held in veneration by the Chippewa Indians.

The practice was widespread because numerous large boulders, scattered throughout the Dakota Prairie were similarly regarded as sacred stones. These objects of veneration were adorned commonly with red or green paint.

Magic Stones

Wisconsin's Prehistoric Indians followed the practice, too, of collecting small natural objects to which they attributed magical powers. These included agates, unusual pebbles and other random mineral curios. Fossils were among their favorite good luck pieces, with ammonites (curly-cue sea shells from the Mesozoic Era) especially prized and traded from tribe to tribe. These magic possessions were thought to be efficacious in treating human ills and, therefore, were kept commonly in medicine bundles. Sometimes, they were covered with red paint or encased in rawhide.

The magic stones and similar possessions were products of the earth and the Indians regarded the earth as a source of supernatural power. Many of their myths and religious beliefs embodied the concept of the Mother Earth. Not only did they live

Medicine bundles sometimes contained mineral curios.

222

close to the earth but they loved and respected it. Moreover, they harbored a feeling of kinship with all creatures of the earth. An old Winnebago wise saying condenses their view: "Holy Mother Earth, the trees and all nature are witnesses of your thoughts and deeds."

Cultural Groups

In archeology, prehistoric refers to the period before records were kept. All that happened before the arrival in 1634 of Jean Nicolet, the first European to step foot in Wisconsin, is regarded as prehistoric.

Wisconsin's Prehistoric Indians are divided into groups based upon cultural criteria rather than the geographic areas they inhabited. Arbitrary names have been assigned to each group, as follows:

Culture	Circa
Paleo Indians (including Glacial Kame and Aqua-Plano)	12,000 to 4,000 B.C.
Old Copper	3,000 to 500 B.C.
Red Ochre	1,200 to 100 B.C.
Woodland (early, middle and late)	1,000 B.C. to A.D. 1634
Hopewell	100 B.C. to A.D. 700
Upper Mississippi (Oneota)	A.D. 800 to 1600
Middle Mississippi	A.D. 1200 to 1600
Historic	A.D. 1634 to present

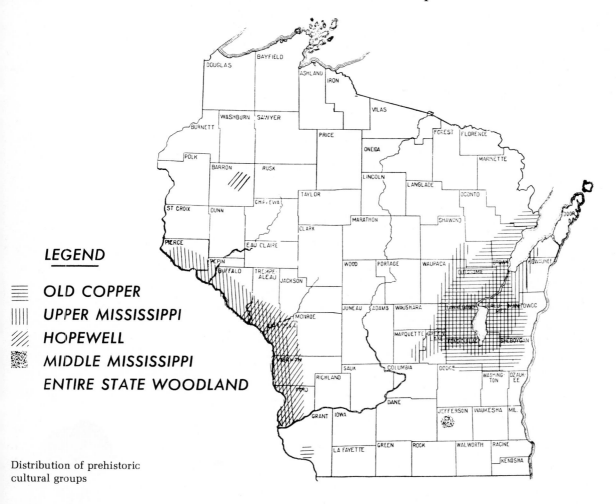

LEGEND

≡ OLD COPPER
||| UPPER MISSISSIPPI
/// HOPEWELL
▨ MIDDLE MISSISSIPPI
ENTIRE STATE WOODLAND

Distribution of prehistoric cultural groups

223

TYPICAL PALEO ARTIFACTS

Folsom type point. Note characteristic flute along length of blade. Rare in Wisconsin.

Plainview point. Fairly common in Wisconsin.

Scottsbluff Eared

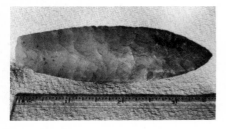

Agate Basin

TYPICAL OLD COPPER ARTIFACTS

Osceola variant spearpoint of Silver Mound quartzite.

Only two of the cultures of the prehistoric period have survived into modern times and can be linked with present day tribes. These are the Upper Mississippi people, the ancestors of the Winnebago tribe, and the Woodland people, the ancestors of the Menominees.

Paleo Indians

Little is known about the Paleo Indians of Wisconsin except that they were the first inhabitants and Ice Age hunters who stalked mastodon, giant beaver and large deer even before the glaciers finally retreated and later such animals as giant bison, elk and caribou that roamed in great herds on post-glacial plains.

Based on surface finds, Paleo sites have been defined in Dane County; but the Paleo Indians were nomadic people who covered a lot of ground in pursuit of game. There is much evidence of their originally occupying the Driftless Area as well as the fringelands of the waning glaciers.

Their stone artifacts show great skill in both percussion and pressure flaking, an art inherited from their Asian forefathers. They made large, delicately flaked stone projectile points out of quartzite, flint and chert — for use as spearheads — commonly with a long flute or groove extending upward from the base on one of both sides. They, also, made a variety of other Lithic Stage stone tools like hand axes, knives and hide scrapers. Their artifacts reveal clearly that they were specialists in big game hunting.

The earlier Paleo Indians were succeeded by later Paleo Indians and the two subgroups are distinguished by cultural differences which, no doubt, reflect ecological changes in prehistoric Wisconsin that set the stage for the kinds of wild animals hunted. A gradual shift to new species occurred with the extinction of most of the big Ice Age animals during the immediate post-glacial period. The earlier cultural subgroup is called Glacial Kame (appropriate, because they probably were there when kames formed) and the later subgroup is called Aqua Plano (from the Latin words for water and plain). The transition in cultures occurred about 10,000 years ago.

It is likely that more information about these early people will come from the archeological studies now in progress at Silver Mound. The excavation of that site is under the direction of the University of Wisconsin-Oshkosh.

Old Copper People

The Old Copper People, on the other hand, left much evidence of their way of life. They derive their name from their extensive use of copper for making various small objects. They are regarded as the state's first metalsmiths. They mined native copper on Isle Royale, an island on Lake Superior, and on the mainland of Upper Michigan. From there, they transported it for many miles to campsites located mostly in southwestern and eastern Wisconsin. Skilled craftsmen pounded and shaped the red metal into a variety of tools, weapons and ornaments, including awls,

224

needles, chisels, axes, harpoon points, fish hooks, fish gorges, knives, pikes, wedges, gouges, projectile points, beads, bracelets and pendants. Heating and hammering or cold hammering were the techniques used in working the copper. Sometimes pieces of float copper, ferreted from glacial till, were worked instead of quarried metal. Contrary to popular belief, the copper was not annealed and tempered to the hardness of steel nor is there any foundation for the frequently expressed claim that this is a lost art that disappeared with the passing of the Old Copper People.

Their chipped stone projectile points typically are of the Osceola type.

The copper mines of the Old Copper People in the Lake Superior region have been studied for many years by archeologists. A party sponsored by the Milwaukee Public Museum reported in 1929 on ancient mining operations:

"While the mineral belt was more or less pitted from one end to the other by the prehistoric miners, it was found that the most profitable deposits were located in three different groups; one on the waters of Eagle River, another at Portage Lake and the third near the forks of the Ontanagon River. In the bed of this river a chunk of mass copper, weighing nearly six thousand pounds, was found. The Indians had chipped away or cut off considerable of its bulk, and from this source and the metal obtained from nearby cliffs spread the fame of mines of copper among the ancient traders and missionaries. This mass of the red metal finally found its resting place in the National Museum at Washington.

"Rattail" copper spearpoint

"In the bottom of the pits, which sometimes were from twenty to thirty feet in depth, it was not uncommon to encounter blocks or masses of copper weighing hundreds and a few of them thousands of pounds.

Socketed-tang spearpoint with hole for peg to secure to shaft.

"As early as 1875, when the writer conducted investigations along this copper belt, practically every pit had disappeared or become unrecognizable as the result of exploration by white men. Thousands of mauls were in evidence of the same form and character as those found on Isle Royale. An occasional one, however, was reported to have a groove around the middle. In one instance a maul was secured weighing 35 pounds, and having two grooves for the attachment of handles. It was probably used by two men at the same time."

A cemetery of the Old Copper People, estimated to contain about 200 burials, was excavated in the 1950s just west of Oconto in Oconto County. No mounds were observed at the site. Burial

Knife

"Old Mine" workings in the interior, three miles from Hay Bay, Michigan.

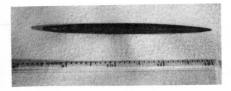

Copper needle with eye

Awl with eye

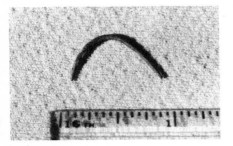

Fishhook

Bracelet

TYPICAL RED OCHRE ARTIFACTS

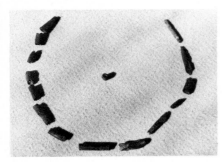

Copper beads of the Red Ochre people

Turkey-tail blade of hornstone

pits were found in gravel, covered with fine sand and topsoil. One pit contained the skeleton of a child, with a bone whistle lying at the back of the head. The whistle, presumably a favorite toy of the youngster, was made from the leg bone of a swan. Numerous copper artifacts were found, together with some chipped-stone implements, two antler tips, two lumps of iron ore and some pond snail beads. One of the most interesting finds was part of a lightning shell, a type of whelk which comes from the Atlantic Coast between North Carolina and Florida. This suggests that the Old Copper People engaged in rather far-reaching trade. No pottery was unearthed. Radiocarbon dating produced a date for the burials of 7,526 years before the present, making these the oldest known cultural remains found east of the Mississippi River, the earliest confirmed date at that time for prehistoric inhabitation in Wisconsin, and the earliest date for human remains in all northeastern North America.

The Old Copper People advanced culturally to the Archaic Stage.

Red Ochre People

The Red Ochre People, a relatively small Archaic Stage cultural group, settled in the southeastern portion of Wisconsin and derived their name from the practice of capping their burials with powdered red ochre. They were probably the earliest mound builders in the state but their efforts were feeble when compared to the accomplishments of the later effigy mound builders. The Red Ochre People fashioned turkey-tail blades of hornstone (a bluish-gray flint) the nearest known source of which is southern Indiana and Illinois. They also made tubular copper beads and many highly polished stone objects such as birdstones, boatstones, amulets and gorgets.

Woodland People

The Woodland People developed the most extensive culture in Wisconsin. Over a period of more than 26 centuries, they left considerable evidence of their presence. Remains of their culture are found throughout the state. They lived in small, nomadic bands devoted principally to hunting and food gathering. Although they tended a few garden crops, they were not full-fledged farmers who depended mostly upon agriculture for a living. Their artifacts show the use of many indigenous materials such as milk quartz, jasper, quartzite, flint, slate and chert. They manufactured large quantitites of fired pottery, usually of rather plain design. Their homes were a type of wigwam made of a framework of poles covered with mats and bark.

The Woodland Indians were a people of four seasons — spring was the time for collecting maple sap, summer the season for fishing and gardening, fall the time for wild rice harvesting and winter the season for ice fishing, hunting and games. Theirs was an Archaic Stage culture, advancing over the years toward the Formative Stage.

Most importantly, the Woodland People were the architects

226

and builders of the effigy mounds. The mounds average about three feet in height and are shaped in the form of various animals. Some of the more common shapes resemble panthers, bears, lizards, birds, turtles and buffaloes. The effigy shapes have been compared to large animal crackers. Many mounds built as companions to the effigy mounds are linear or conical in construction. The effigy mounds were first recognized as man-made antiquities in the early 1800s when some were measured by John Locke, M.D., an early amateur archeologist. The effigy mounds are found in profuse groups throughout the southern and western portions of the state. Some are located in central Wisconsin.

The longest of the effigies on record is a huge bird, on the Mendota Hospital grounds, near Madison, with a wingspread of 624 feet. Another spectacular mound is a panther, 575 feet in length, at Buffalo Lake in Marquette County.

Man Mound Park is located a short distance northeast of Baraboo, in Sauk County. Here you come upon a giant effigy mound resembling a human figure, 214 feet long and 48 feet across at the shoulders. Impressive in size, it may depict an ancient god, a lengendary person or some great leader of the Prehistoric Indians who constructed this huge earthenwork. The mound's shape is unmistakably that of a narrow waisted, walking man with a winged headdress. It represents the only known occurrence anywhere of this particular form of effigy mound. A visit to the park to see this sleeping giant of earth is a worthwhile experience.

Perhaps the most unique of the effigy mounds are the intaglio mounds in which the earth was scooped out to leave a shallow depression of an animal form. The only surviving example of this type is that of a panther at Fort Atkinson in Jefferson County.

TYPICAL WOODLAND ARTIFACTS

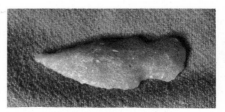

Durst stemmed. Very common in Wisconsin.

Contracting-stem

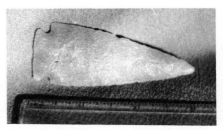

Side-notched

Contracting-stem variant

Shards of Woodland pottery. Note designs.

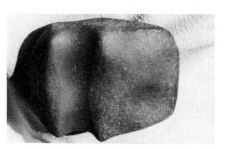

Pecked and polished ground axe

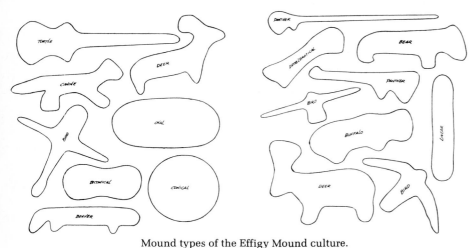

Mound types of the Effigy Mound culture.

Map of Effigy Mound distribution.

227

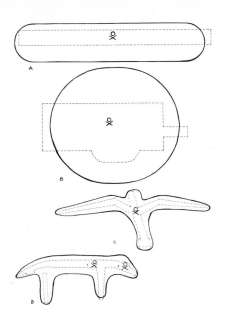

Raisbeck Mound group in Grant County

An excellent example of an effigy mound group can be seen at Lizard Mound State Park, north of West Bend. Here a number of well-preserved mounds, including the effigies of lizards, birds and panthers as well as conical and linear forms, are readily accessible along a self-guiding footpath that winds through a hardwood forest.

About 20 mounds are found at Kingsley Bend Wayside on Highway 16, just east of Wisconsin Dells. This site adjoins the Wisconsin River. Among the mounds there are several effigies of bears about 100 feet long, a panther with a tail the length of a football field and, across the highway, an eagle with a 200-foot wingspread.

Effigy mounds at Lizard Mound State Park

Typical cists, Effigy Mound culture

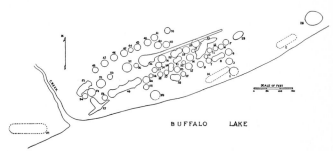

Plan of the Ross Mound Group 1

Plan of the McClaughry Mound Group, site 1

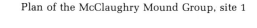
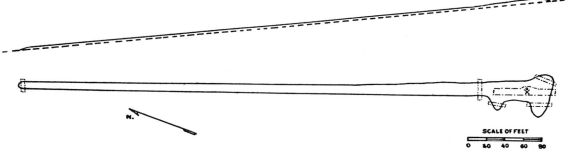

Plan of panther effigy mound, Neale Group

228

Flexed burial

The Ross Mound Group, located on County Highway Z, three miles south of Nekoosa in Wood County, is a registered Wisconsin landmark. The mounds have a unique setting. They lie on the broad top of an Ice Age terrace of the Wisconsin River, overlooking an oxbow lake formed from a former bend in the river that became cut off from the river when it migrated westward. Thirty-one mounds comprise one of the two groups of mounds found at this site. Among these are a bear effigy — 95 feet from nose to tail — and a pointed linear 491 feet in length.

Indian Mound Park, in Sheboygan, contains 18 burial mounds of the Woodland Indians (circa 500-750 A.D.). An open grave is on exhibit showing the details of an internment.

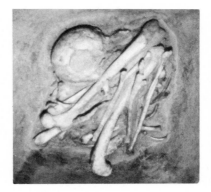

Bundle burial

The Milwaukee Public Museum has supported much archeological research on the subject of the effigy mounds. A report published in 1956 has the following explanation of the mounds' propose:

"Some of the problems surrounding the Effigy Mound culture involve the purpose of the mounds. Why were they built and why do they assume such varied shapes? If they are burial mounds, why is it that we find a wide variety of burial types? Although it is highly speculative, the writer would like to advance the following hypothesis: It is possible that the mounds of the Effigy Mound culture represent symbols, in many cases unidentifiable, having to do with certain ceremonial practices, perhaps some religious rite involving animals. This does not necessarily imply totemism, since the whole range of totems is not involved. But for whatever reason, the mounds were probably built at specific times, say once a year, undoubtedly during the spring or summer when the ground is thawed and soft. At the time of mound construction, all persons who had died during the preceding

Effigy mound building. A diorama showing Indians in process of constructing a mound.

229

Part of turtle mound outlined in lime

period were buried in the mounds. This would account for the fact that we find both single and multiple burials. Those who died nearest to the time of mound building would be buried in the flesh, whereas the bundle reburials would represent the persons who died during the winter and had been set up on scaffolds because the ground was frozen, making digging impractical. The large multiple bundle reburials of 35 or more individuals might be the remains of those who were killed in a battle or who died as the result of an epidemic or of starvation. An alternate possibility is that the large multiple bundle reburials might represent a periodic burial ceremony in which individuals previously disposed of were gathered for multiple internment. The single family units of each small group may have been responsible for burying their own dead, respectively, and more than one mound may have been built at one time.

"The mounds seldom occur more than 50 to a given group and often include fewer than that. This might be explained by the fact that the Effigy Mound people were hunters and gatherers. There is abundant evidence to show that the hunting and gathering peoples of the present day must live in small groups and move periodically in search of food in the form of game which has been scattered as a result of the proximity of human habitation, and of wild roots and plants which have become scarce in a picked-over area. The same thing may have been true of the Effigy Mound builders. Such small, wandering groups might have returned from year to year to the same spot to build their ceremonial tumuli until the time when the food quest had taken them so far from the mound group that the trip through a temporarily food-less area would be inadvisable. They would then begin another group in a new location and return to it until again forced to move to another place for lack of food. Hostile Indians or scarcity of food may have caused them to abandon a site before many mounds had been constructed, which would account for the Utley Group with only seven mounds, and the Green Lake Site with only one. There is also the possibility that other groups of Effigy Mound People, in their wanderings, came upon mound groups that had been left by a previous band and, sufficient time having elapsed for the repopulation of game animals and food plants, they then added their particular types of mounds to those already built. This could account for the diversity of mound forms in a given group."

A Milwaukee Public Museum bulletin summarizes some cultural traits of the effigy mound builders:

"Those responsible for the erection of the tumuli left a fragmentary but important record of at least parts of their culture . . .

"The authors of these mounds would seem to have had a social organization involving a high respect for social or other rank, since very large, laboriously constructed mounds were frequently built to contain the grave of but a single individual. Moreover, it is difficult to imagine any people repeatedly performing the labor required to construct the larger effigy mounds without the guiding authority of rather powerful leaders, perhaps assisted by strong, well-defined traditions.

"The association of altar-like structures with burials in laboriously constructed mounds shaped in what appear to be symbolic patterns, suggests the important influence of well-formulated religious concepts and practices."

Effigy mounds at Kingsley Bend Wayside.

231

Woodland people from a diorama at the State Historical Society of Wisconsin Museum in Madison.

TYPICAL HOPEWELL ARTIFACTS

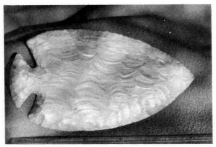

Snyders Point. Note detailed secondary flint knapping.

Side-notched quartzite blade

Platform pipe

Pot showing design areas outlined by incised lines

Hopewellian People

The Hopewellian People are distinguished as the master craftsmen of the Prehistoric Indians. They came from a center in Ohio, settled in Wisconsin mostly along the Mississippi River and lived by hunting, fishing and gardening. Their chipped-stone work was very skillfully done. Often beautiful and exotic materials were imported, in tribe-to-tribe trading, and used in fashioning a variety of implements. Examples of this practice are chalcedony from North Dakota, flint and jasper from Ohio and obsidian from the Rocky Mountains. Specimens of the stone work of the Hopewellians are sought by collectors and museums, with their daggers and knives prized as especially beautiful pieces. They elevated their Archaic Stage culture to a high level.

Hopewell Burial Mounds at Rice Lake in Barron County.

232

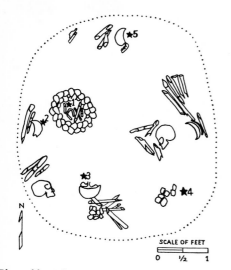 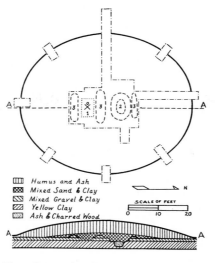 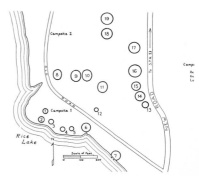

The Cyrus Thomas Mound group in Barron County. A Hopewellian burial ground.

Plan of burial in Mound 10, showing relative positions of features: (1) cremated bones on stone platform; (2) potsherds; (3) Mask 2 and cremated bones; (4) Mask 1 and cremated bones; (5) perforated canine jaw.

Plan of Mound 8, showing (1) burial (2) fire pit, and (3) embankments from pit excavations.

Humus and Ash
Mixed Sand & Clay
Mixed Gravel & Clay
Yellow Clay
Ash & Charred Wood

The Hopewellians buried their dead in conical mounds, which, usually, were built higher than similar mounds of other cultural groups. Frequently, their mounds were quite large. The Nicolls Mound, in Trempealeau County, for example, measures 12 feet in height and 90 feet in diameter at the base.

The Hopewellians followed the custom of interring in the mounds, together with the remains of their dead, select personal articles, exemplifying their fine workmanship in stone, pottery and metal. These artifacts are the principal source of most of what we know about them.

Upper Mississippi People

The Upper Mississippi People were the first farmers of Wisconsin. They settled mainly in the Lake Winnebago area and along the Mississippi River. As a consequence of the need for remaining in one place while caring for growing crops, they developed fairly large permanent villages. They made extensive use of pecked and polished stone artifacts. The most common of these was the ungrooved axe or celt usually made of gabbro or

TYPICAL UPPER MISSISSIPPI ARTIFACTS

Triangular arrowhead

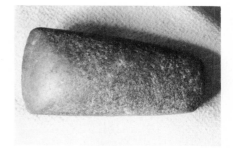

Ungroved axe

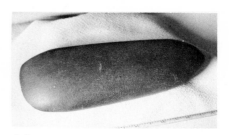

Celt

Aztalan State Park. Note mound in background

233

basalt. They also made disk pipes from catlinite and fishing lures from shell.

The Upper Mississippi People were probably the first in Wisconsin to advance culturally to the Formative Stage.

Middle Mississippi People

The Middle Mississippi People were the builders of Aztalan, on the Crawfish River, near Lake Mills in Jefferson County. This archeological showcase is the remains of a fortified village. Twenty one acres in area, it was surrounded by a 12-foot high log stockade, chinked with straw and plastered clay. Block houses were set at 80-foot intervals around the entire perimeter of the stockade. Wattle-walled houses and cornfields occupied most of the enclosure. The most impressive structures in the village were two large temple mounds built in the form of truncated pyramids, with a temple (chief's house) at the top of each. The original village had a population of about 500. Its occupants enjoyed an elaborate style of living. Radiocarbon dating places the occupation of the village sometime between 1100-1300 A.D. The refuse heap found at this site shows that the Aztalanians made much use of shell and bone.

These Formative Stage People almost achieved civilization and stopped just short of advancing to the Classic Stage before mysteriously vanishing from Wisconsin.

Aztalan is believed to have been an outpost linked with Cahokia, the great metropolitan center of the Middle Mississippi trade empire located just east of present-day St. Louis. Covering some six and a half square miles, Cahokia was an extraordinary city, flourishing between 900 and 1300 A.D., with at least 30,000

TYPICAL MIDDLE MISSISSIPPI ARTIFACTS

Notched arrow-head from Aztalan

Chipped-stone hoe

Closeup of partially restored building.

234

Artist's conception of ancient Aztalan.

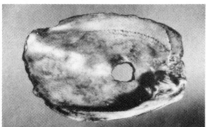

Clam-shell hoe with a hole for attachment of a handle.

Clam shell hoe

Beads cuts from clam shells

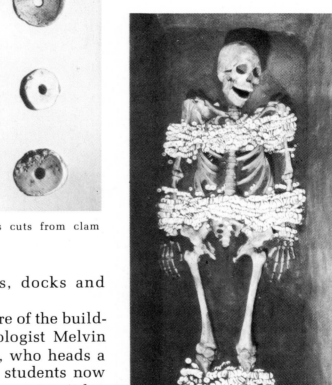

From Aztalan, the so-called "Princess Burial" found with three belts of shell beads.

inhabitants, 10-story-high structures, streets, docks and warehouses.

New information about the sophisticated culture of the builders of Cahokia is being uncovered by anthropologist Melvin Fowler of the University of Wisconsin-Madison, who heads a team of about 80 professional investigators and students now excavating the site of this early city. As a trading center, it lay upon a branching system of waterways, opening avenues for traffic in all directions. Thus, goods were imported from far away places, such as copper from around Lake Superior, lead ore from southwestern Wisconsin, mica from out east, conch shells from the Mississippi Delta and pottery, salt and flint from other remote areas.

The terraced earthern pyramids at Cahokia bear an unmistakable similarity to those at Aztalan. The remains of these ancient municipalities demolish the myth of the Prehistoric Indians as aboriginal savages.

The Milwaukee Public Museum reports on the discovery of the "Princess": "One of the exciting finds of Aztalan was an extended burial of a young woman with three belts of shell beads

235

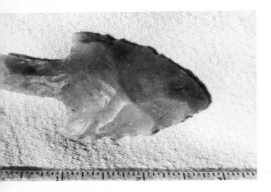

originally wrapped around her, one each at the shoulder, waist, and lower part of the legs. The belts were about four feet long and six inches wide, and were made up of a total of nearly 2,000 beads. The young lady was dubbed the 'Princess' and is now on exhibit at the Milwaukee Museum.''

The Prehistoric Period

We may use a string of beads as an analogy to compare the historic with the prehistoric period of human habitation of Wisconsin. The period of time passing since the arrival of Jean Nicolet in 1634 is approximately 350 years. The prehistoric period is 33 times longer extending back from 1634 to about 10,000 B.C. If we assume that the historic period is represented by one bead with a diameter of ½ inch, then 33 beads would have to be added to the string to represent the prehistoric period. The string then would have a length of 17 inches. If we were to complete the string by adding similar beads to represent the whole span of geologic time since the formation of the earth, an additional 14,285,688 beads would be required. The string then would be more than 112 miles long, stretching farther than the distance between Milwaukee and Madison!

Reliance On Materials Of The Earth

The Stone Age Indians of Wisconsin are people of the past. Like the ancient mountains, oceans and glaciers, they have come and gone on the state's changing scene. But unlike geologic events that end with some degree of finality, what the early Indians started in the use of rocks and minerals as raw materials to answer their material needs continues on a much greater scale in our present-day civilization. We are dependent in many ways upon mineral commodities and have ties with the earth reminiscent of the Stone Age. Our implements, weapons and ornaments may not be made of stone but most of the materials of which they are made are derived from members of the mineral kingdom.

A link with the past through artistry in stone.

236

IX
Ancient Creatures of Stone

Wisconsin's rocks contain numerous fossils which record the story of life-forms inhabiting the state during past geologic periods. Fossils tell us much about the emergence and evolution of life.

Description Of Fossils

Fossils are found in sedimentary rock beds in many places in Wisconsin. They provide us with a glimpse of life forms inhabiting the state during past geologic periods. From the tiniest microscopic radiolarian to the largest brontosaurus, fossils are a source of long-preserved information.

The word fossil is derived from the Latin *fossilis* meaning "dug from the earth". In paleontology (the study of ancient life) fossils are defined as the remains or other evidence of life of previous geologic periods. Fossils may be petrified animals or plants, molds, casts, imprints, bones, shells, tracks, trails, burrows, eggs, teeth marks, dung, castings or other organic remains. They may be only parts of the original organisms or entire mummies. These clues to bygone life are preserved in numerous materials such as sediments, volcanic ash, soil, tar, coal, amber, ice and stone. Through fossils, we can reconstruct the menageries of the past.

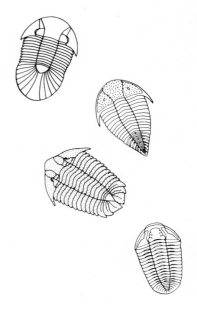

Fossils are to paleontology what rocks are to geology. Fossils and rocks, however, are generally interrelated; each is a source of information about the other. Together they constitute a storehouse of facts about prehistoric species and the geologic settings in which they lived.

Terrestrial And Marine Creatures

The Romans called the solid earth *terra firma* and these words referred to areas covered by dry land in contrast to areas covered by the sea, which they called *mare*. Derivatives of these words are part of our present-day vocabulary. *Terra* is the root of *terrain*, *territorial* and *terrestrial* while *mare* is the root of *maritime*, *marina* and *marine*. Hence, we describe land dwelling plants and animals as *terrestrial* species and those living in the oceans as *marine* species.

Tracks of ancient creatures (trilobites) that roamed the floor of a Cambrian sea, preserved in sandstone cropping out in west central Wisconsin. This specimen discovered by John Jefferson of Wisconsin Rapids, in 1976, is a major find.

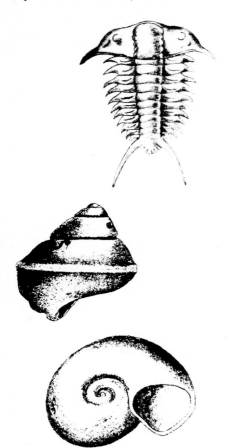

Marine fossils found in Wisconsin show that the state was submerged periodically below the waters of ancient seas. As a matter of fact, many changes in the state's geography over the ages are apparent from a study of its fossils.

By comparing present-day descendants with early life-forms preserved as fossils, paleontologists can reconstruct the climate that the state experienced. Some creatures thrive in warm environments like tropical seas, some in cold settings, and others in more moderate surroundings. Fossils of these different kinds of organisms are represented in the state's fossil record. Thus we know that Wisconsin's climate changed over the ages. The presence or absence of certain marine or terrestrial species at any given time in the fossil record tells much about the type of climate that then prevailed.

Fossils provide much other information about the earth's history not available from any other source. An example of this is an amazing discovery made recently by a former University of Wisconsin-Madison geologist. By studying the growth patterns of prehistoric organisms preserved as fossils, he determined that the earth is experiencing a gradual slowdown in its speed of rotation. A day represents the length of time required for the earth to complete one rotation around its axis. His computations assume that a year (regardless of how many hours in a day or days in a year) is a constant and represents the length of time required for the earth to orbit the sun. He probed numerous fossils with an electron beam to measure their daily rate of growth. The technique, although much more sophisticated, is similar in principle to counting the growth rings in trees to tell their ages. By comparing data obtained from fossils of different geologic horizons, he worked out a biological clock of the past showing the daily growth rate of many organisms over a long span of time. From this, he calculated that days are becoming progressively longer — by two thousandths of a second per century — and this condition, he concluded, is a direct result of the earth's spinning in space at a regular decreasing rate. For instance, stromatolites, a form of fossilized algae from extremely old South African dolomite (2.2 billion years of age) show that, at that point in time days were only about 10 hours long and 800 days made up a year; but fossilized clams and coral from 500-million-year-old rock reveal days almost 22 hours long and a year consisting of 400 days.

The correlation of daily growth rates in fossils may prove to be an accurate method for dating fossil-bearing sedimentary rocks around the world, including those making up much of Wisconsin's bedrock.

Looking ahead, we can safely assume that fossils forming from today's creatures will record, through their growth patterns, days that were 24 hours long and a year comprised of 365¼ days.

Wisconsin's Fossils

The fossils most commonly found in Wisconsin are stoney fossils of prehistoric marine animals dating back to the Paleozoic

Era. Fossils occur abundantly in certain sedimentary rocks deposited during the Cambrian, Ordovician, Silurian and Devonian Periods. Although no rocks younger than the Devonian crop up in the state, fossils of more recent origin do occasionally occur. The fossil forest of Two Creeks, in Manitowoc County, buried by the glaciers contains the remains of prehistoric animals and plants. Parts of extinct mastodons and giant beavers have been unearthed in the peat bogs of central Wisconsin where they have been preserved since the Ice Age. Thus Wisconsin's fossils span a period of more than half a billion years.

Typical stoney fossils of marine animals of the Paleozoic Era.

The Emergence Of Life

The oldest fossils found abundantly in Wisconsin are between 600 and 500 million years old. Life, however, existed on earth at a much earlier time. The oldest-known rocks, those of the continental shields, have been radiometrically dated at ages of 3.6 to 4 billion years. These show no trace of any life-forms. But rocks from Canada dated at about 2 billion years contain fossils of primitive organisms, resembling present-day fungi and blue-green algae. Similar fossils have been found in rocks in South Africa with a radiometric age of 3 billion years.

In the beginning and for a long time after forming, the young earth was an inhospitable sphere enveloped by an oxygen-free atmosphere, that offered a sterile environment for creatures requiring atmospheric oxygen. For about 2 billion years, it probably was completely devoid of life. Almost certainly, no life-forms — plant nor animal — inhabited any of the original seas or continents. The world then was totally inorganic. But more than 3 billion years ago, life, somehow, mysteriously came into existence and, ever since, the earth has been the home of living things.

Original Life-Forms

The original life-forms are believed to have been simple organisms of microscopic size originating, most likely, in the shallow, warm waters of some primeval sea. These early ancestors of all life prospered, reproduced, diversified and adapted to the changing conditions of their underwater environment. Once established, life-forms flourished and spread around the globe. From this meager origin, organisms continued to develop and multiply, through succeeding ages, to the many and diverse forms populating the world today.

Evolution Of Life-Forms

The first forms of life were represented by a limited number of species. In the process of evolution, however, organisms became more complicated in structure and more diversified in numbers as they adjusted physically to the demands of their changing environments. To survive and avoid extinction, all creatures must adapt biologically to the inconstant world in which they live. Although a few species have managed to prosper for ages with little noticeable change in anatomy and life-style and still

Time	Era	Period	Characteristic Life
0–20–40	CENO-ZOIC	Quaternary	Age of Mammals
60		Tertiary	
100	MESOZOIC	Cretaceous	Age of Reptiles
		Jurassic	
		Triassic	
200	PALEOZOIC	Permian / Pennsylvanian / Mississippian	Age of Amphibians
300		Devonian	Age of Fishes
		Silurian	Age of Corals
400		Ordovician	Age of Straight Cephalopods
500		Cambrian	Age of Trilobites
600			
	PRECAMBRIAN / Precambrian Era began 5 billion years ago.		First record of life

Geologic time chart

239

A species of reptile that once lived on earth but eventually became extinct. The drawing is a reconstruction based on fossil remains.

Ordovician algae

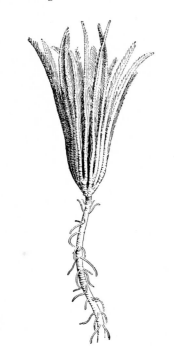

Sea lily

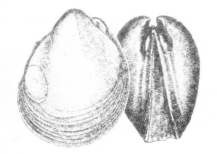

Early form of clam — a common invertebrate

thrive today, many along the way have become extinct, phased out and replaced by others. Through a succession of untold generations, the earth's plant and animal inhabitants have gradually increased in total number of species to the remarkable diversity of the present.

More than one million different kinds of plants and animals are living today. An estimate for the total number of species existing in the past during the long span of evolution, based upon a study of fossils, puts the figure at more than 500 million. By comparison, our largest dictionaries contain only 500,000 words. One thousand dictionaries would be needed for the total number of words to equal the all-time total number of species!

The Fossil Record

The science of paleontology has developed in modern times from the study of fossils, gradually unlocking the secrets of the evolution of life. Interest in paleontology was spurred when Charles Darwin announced the Theory of Evolution in 1859 by publishing *The Origin of Species*. Since then, this theory with revisions has become the guiding light of paleontology as it carefully reconstructs the history of life on our planet.

Among the earliest creatures leaving a trace were tiny one-cell microorganisms. Much later came invertebrate sea creatures such as sponges, jellyfish and sea lilies. These were followed by more complex invertebrates; then by vertebrate fish; then by land-dwelling insects like dragonflies; then by air-breathing vertebrates including the dinosaurs; and finally by warm-blooded, large-brained mammals such as mammoths, mice and humans. Plant fossils likewise record the emergence and evolution of the earth's flora.

Life-forms are preserved as fossils in successive layers of sediments, extending from one geologic age to another in a generally unbroken sequence that leads to the present. Today, sedimentary rocks sheath about 75% of all the earth's land areas.

The marine fossils of Wisconsin are peppered throughout the rocks of the Paleozoic, appearing in the full range of sedimentary deposits, including sandstone, shale, siltstone, limestone and dolomite. Coral fossils from ancient reefs are found mostly in limestone and dolomite. But shellfish and crustaceans are best preserved in shale, siltstone, fine grained sandstone and loosely compacted limestone.

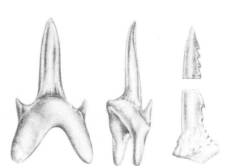

Ancient fish teeth

Drawing of mammoth made by prehistoric artist on section of mammoth tusk.

240

Classification Of Fossils

Fossils are described according to their plant and animal classification which is based upon their natural relationships. Organisms, in the broadest classification, belong either to the plant or animal kingdom, with intermediate forms of life classed as the protista. The protista provide the link between plants and animals. In the world today, according to the Milwaukee Public Museum, there are about 375,000 plant species, 1,000,000 animal species and 5,000 protistan species. The successively smaller categories of classification grading down from the most general to the most particular groupings are: kingdom, phylum, class, order, family, genus, species, race, breed or variety. The basic working unit under this system of classification is the species, which is defined as a group of like individuals who interbreed among themselves but who cannot interbreed with members of any other group.

Each organism is identified with a double Latin name (binominal nomenclature) — consisting of the name of the genus (capitalized) followed by the name of the species (uncapitalized), with both printed in italics. As an example, the scientific name for modern human is *Homo sapiens*.

There is no universal agreement among the world's scientists for biological classifications. The most widely accepted system is set forth in the following outline:

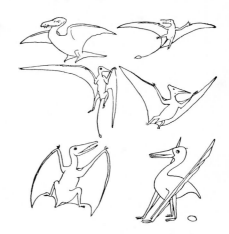

Restoration drawing of bird-like reptiles.

Leaf fossil

PLANT KINGDOM

Subkingdom. Thallophyta. Plants not forming embryos.

Phylum 1. Cyanophyta. Blue-green algae.
Phylum 2. Euglenophyta. Flagellates.
Phylum 3. Chlorophyta. Green algae.
Phylum 4. Chrysophyta. Yellow-green algae, golden brown algae, diatoms.
Phylum 5. Pyrrophyta. Cryptomonads, dinoflagellates.
Phylum 6. Phaeophyta. Brown algae.
Phylum 7. Rhodophyta. Red algae.
Phylum 8. Schizomycophyta. Bacteria.
Phylum 9. Myxomycophyta. Slime molds.
Phylum 10. Eumycophyta. True fungi.

Subkingdom. Embryophyta. Plants forming embryos.

Phylum 11. Bryophyta or Atracheata. Plants lacking vascular tissues.
    Class 1. Musci. Mosses.
    Class 2. Hepaticae. Liverworts.
    Class 3. Anthocerotae. Hornworts.
Phylum 12. Tracheophyta or Tracheata. Plants with vascular tissues.
    Subphylum 1. Psilopsida. Psilopsids.
    Subphylum 2. Lycopsida. Club mosses.
    Subphylum 3. Sphenopsida. Horsetails and relatives.
    Subphylum 4. Pteropsida. Ferns and seed plants.
      Class 1. Filicineae. Ferns.

241

Class 2. Gymnospermae. Cone-bearing plants and relatives.
    Subclass 1. Cycadophytae
    Subclass 2. Coniferophytae
Class 3. Angiospermae. True flowering plants.
    Subclass 1. Dicotyledoneae.
    Subclass 2. Monocotyledoneae.

ANIMAL KINGDOM
Phylum 1. Protozoa. Unicellular animals.
    Class 1. Mastigophora. Flagellate protozoa (e.g., *Euglena*).
    Class 2. Sarcodina. Amoeboid protozoa (e.g., *Amoeba*).
    Class 3. Sporozoa. Spore-producing protozoa (e.g., *Plasmodium*).
    Class 4. Infusoria. Ciliate protozoa (e.g., *Paramecium*).
Phylum 2. Porifera. Sponges.
Phylum 3. Coelenterata.
    Class 1. Hydrozoa. Hydroids (e.g., *Hydra, Obelia*).
    Class 2. Scyphozoa. Jellyfishes.
    Class 3. Anthozoa. Corals and sea anemones.
Phylum 4. Ctenophora. Comb jellies or sea walnuts.
Phylum 5. Platyhelminthes. Flatworms.

Classification of Fossils
    Class 1. Turbellaria. *Planaria* and related animals.
    Class 2. Trematoda. Flukes.
    Class 3. Cestoda. Tapeworms.
Phylum 6. Nemertea. Nemertine worms.
Phylum 7. Nematoda. Roundworms.
Phylum 8. Rotatoria. Rotifers.
Phylum 9. Nematomorpha. Horsehair worms.
Phylum 10. Bryozoa. Moss animals.
Phylum 11. Brachiopoda. Lamp shells.
Phylum 12. Echinodermata.
    Class 1. Asteroidea. Starfishes.
    Class 2. Ophiuroidea. Brittle stars, serpent stars.
    Class 3. Echinoidea. Sea urchins, sand dollars.
    Class 4. Holothuroidea. Sea cucumbers, sea slugs.
    Class 5. Crinoidea. Crinoids (sea lilies).
Phylum 13. Mollusca. Mollusks.
    Class 1. Pelecypoda. Clams, mussels, oysters.
    Class 2. Amphineura. Chitons
    Class 3. Gastropoda. Snails, slugs.
    Class 4. Scaphopoda. Tooth shells.
    Class 5. Cephalopoda. Squids, octopus, nautilus.
Phylum 14. Annelida. Segmented worms.
    Class 1. Chaetopoda. Earthworms, clamworms.
    Class 2. Hirudinea. Leeches.
Phylum 15. Onychophora. *Peripatus*.
Phylum 16. Arthropoda.
    Class 1. Crustacea. Crayfish, crabs, barnacles, water fleas.

Class 2. Diplopoda. Millipedes.
Class 3. Chilopoda. Centipedes.
Class 4. Insecta. Insects: bees, grasshoppers, bettles, flies, etc.
Class 5. Arachnida. Ticks, spiders, scorpions, horseshoe crab.

Phylum 17. Chordata.
Subphylum 1. Hemichorda. *Dolichoglossus.*
Subphylum 2. Urochorda. Tunicates: sea squirts, sea pork.
Subphylum 3. Cephalochorda. *Amphioxus.*
Subphylum 4. Vertebrata. Vertebrates.
Class 1. Agnatha. Lampreys, hagfishes.
Class 2. Chondrichthyes. Sharks, rays.
Class 3. Osteichthyes. Bony fishes: perch, trout, catfish, eel.
Class 4. Amphibia. Salamanders, frogs, toads.
Class 5. Reptilia. Turtles, snakes, lizards, alligators.
Class 6. Aves. Birds: ostrich, chicken, sparrow, robin.
Class 7. Mammalia. Mammals: opossum, squirrel, rat, bat, whale, horse, man.

How Fossils Are Formed

How are fossils formed? Fossils are formed accidently and under a rare combination of circumstances. Relatively few of the countless plants and animals that have inhabited the earth since life first appeared have been preserved as fossils. To qualify as a candidate for fossilization, an organism usually must have hard parts, become buried quickly to prevent decay and remain undisturbed during the generally long process of preservation. Decay, deterioration and destruction, through a variety of natural processes, dispose constantly of the remains of life-forms which might otherwise endure in the fossil record. It is highly unlikely that even one of the myriad of living things which we encounter in our lifetime will end up in future years as a fossil.

In rare instances, however, rapid burial in substances like volcanic ash or landslide deposits preserves organisms. Many dinosaur remains were preserved in this manner in some of the western states. An example of this occurrence in more recent times was the eruption of the great volcano, Vesuvius, in 79 A.D., when the cities of Pompeii and Herculaneum, on the coast of the Mediterranean Sea, were suddenly overwhelmed; countless people, animals and plants were literally fossilized overnight.

Sometimes a great number of fossils are found at a place where conditions are ideal for the preservation of organisms. As an example, an estimated 16,000 fossilized bones of small pair-horned rhinoceroses of Miocene age have been extracted from the quicksand at Agate Springs in western Nebraska.

Most of the fossils found in Wisconsin are invertebrate fossils originally deposited in shallow-water sediments when the state was submerged below ancient seas. Marine fossils occur as the most abundant fossils in most parts of the world. Waves

These hard-shelled marine animals were buried about 500 million years ago in mud on a sea bottom and, through the fossilization process, were gradually changed to stone.

243

everywhere pursue the ageless practice of sweeping fine sediments along sea floors and entombing numerous hard-shelled marine animals. As the sediments build up in layers and sedimentary rocks develop, buried organisms become transformed into fossils.

Fossils are made hard and durable in most cases through a chemical alteration of their anatomical structures brought about by the action of circulating water. All unconsolidated materials, such as soil and gravel, and most rocks lying near the surface are porous allowing water to pass through. Water penetrates deeply into the earth's outer shell. It dissolves, transports and redeposits a variety of minerals as it percolates through subterranean strata. Underground water is seldom pure. It is laden to varying degrees with water-soluble chemicals.

Water dissolves the original chemicals contained in buried organisms and replaces them with other chemicals. This alteration in structure eventually turns organic remains into stone. Common replacement compounds are silica, lime and iron. More than 20 known mineral substances preserve buried organisms. The presence of impurities (commonly oxide of iron) may add color to a fossil and intensify the detail of its anatomy. This is frequently the case with petrified wood.

What remains at the end of the fossilization process is a replica in stone of even the minutest detail of the original organism.

Where pyrite has been the petrifying agent, very striking fossils are produced. Occasionally, pyrite fossils are found in the rocks of the lead and zinc region of southwestern Wisconsin and in shale along the walls of Lake Michigan, as at Bay Settlement, in Brown County.

Sometimes fossils result from the natural enclosure of organisms in a substance, such as quicksand, peat, tar or ice, and the entombed remains experience very little, if any, petrification. Fossils thus formed are less mineralized than the stoney fossils most commonly found in Wisconsin.

Telling Time Through Fossils

Geologists use fossils as a tool for dating sedimentary rocks. Through a comparison of fossils, formations of a known geologic age are related to similar formations in other parts of the world.

Because of the evolutionary modification of species, fossils provide a chronicle of changing life-forms throughout past geologic periods. The fossil record shows an endless sequence of one kind of organism evolving methodically into another. Any slice of time from the fossil record contains its own distinguishing assortment of preserved life-forms.

The fossils of species that flourished for only a relatively short period before undergoing recognizable changes in appearance, serve as an index to the age of the rocks in which they are found. Such fossils, if widely distributed, are called index or guide fossils. They offer telltale evidence, wherever found in sedimentary rocks, of the relative age of the period of their existence.

Most geologic horizons since the late Precambrian are iden-

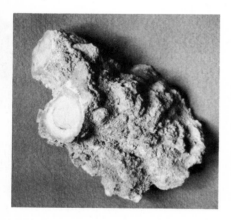

This Ordovician-age gastropod is partly filled with sparkling drusy quartz crystals — a rare find from near Wilton, in Monroe County.

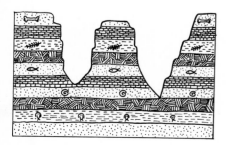

This unique coral fossil, from the same area, is replaced with chert and covered almost completely with drusy quartz.

This profile illustrates how specific fossils can serve as an index for the rock stratum in which they are found.

244

tified and dated from a study of fossil-bearing strata. Thus, the Paleozoic rocks of Wisconsin are known and correlated as a result of their fossil content.

Life-Forms In Wisconsin Long Ago

Long ago, during early, mid and late Precambrian times, Wisconsin periodically was covered by oceans. In paleontology, this long period, spanning more than 2 billion years after life first emerged, includes both part of the Archeozoic Era and all of the Proterozoic Era. Life in the seas then was primitive consisting of simple fauna and flora.

Later, with the Paleozoic Era approaching, organisms continued to evolve into increasingly more complex forms and greater numbers of species.

During the late Proterozoic Era, a limited variety of multi-celled animals inhabited the seas. Among these were sponges, corals, worms, echinoderns and mollusks. Most of these early marine creatures were endowed with soft shells and, as a consequence, seldom became preserved as fossils.

But by the dawn of the Cambrian Period (about 600 million years ago), a larger diversity of marine creatures evolved and the seas were teeming with life. Plant and animal communities enjoyed an unprecedented prosperity as large tracts of the continents became submerged. Many of the animals populating the oceans at that time were invested with hard shells, an attribute that made them ready candidates for fossilization. As a consequence, abundant fossils of the fauna then existing formed in sediments that accumulated on depositional shelves along the fluctuating coastlines of the continents, including those of prehistoric Wisconsin.

The fossil record in Wisconsin, starting with the Cambrian Period and extending for the next 250 million years, abounds in the remains of an astonishing number and variety of marine species.

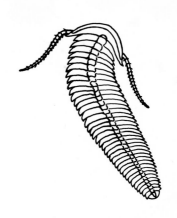

Fossil of a late Precambrian segmented marine worm, found in South Australia. This soft-bodied creature had no shell, so its fossilized remains are rare. By the early Cambrian Period, it eventually developed, through biochemical evolutionary changes, a hard, mineralized protective exterior. It is believed to be the ancestor of a more complex marine form known as the trilobite.

Cambrian fossils from southwestern Wisconsin.

245

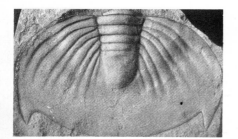

Cambrian dikelocephalus (a member of the trilobite family), from bluffs east of Prairie du Sac, in Sauk County.

Another species of Cambrian trilobite (Saukia acuta) from the Lodi Shale at Prairie du Sac, in Sauk County.

Graptolite from Spring Green, Sauk County.

Mount Washington at Eau Claire, a well-known collecting site for Cambrian trilobite fossils.

Precambrian Fossils

Only a few fossils of Precambrian age are found in Wisconsin. Oddly, two rocks usually regarded as gemstone materials by rockhounds embody some unusual forms of Precambrian fossils.

Algal jasper is a dark red rock of Precambrian origin, commonly appearing as an ingredient in glacial gravels in northwestern Wisconsin. It contains the preserved remains of algae, one of the earliest plants thriving in ancient seas.

Another Precambrian fossil of a sort is contained in jaspilite, an iron ore from the Penokee Range in northern Wisconsin. Jaspilite is composed of alternating bands of red jasper (a variety of quartz) and silver-gray hematite (an iron mineral). The hematite is believed to have been extracted from seawater and deposited on sea floors through a complicated biochemical process, in Precambrian times, by tiny marine organisms, now extinct.

Cambrian Fossils

The fossils found in Wisconsin's Cambrian-age rocks consist mostly of trilobites, graptolites, protozoans, brachiopods and petropods.

Trilobites belong to an extinct class of arthropods that emerged suddenly in great abundance during the Cambrian and survived into the Devonian. They are distant relatives of present-day crabs, shrimp and sowbugs. Their name is derived from the distinctive shape of their bodies which are divided into three longitudinal lobes (trilobed). The heads of these curious looking creatures are covered with shield-like plates.

The Cambrian Period is spoken of as the Age of Trilobites because the trilobites were then the earth's dominant species ruling the ancient seas.

Graptolites are colonial marine animals resembling branching seaweeds. Their exteriors are formed of a substance called chitin that looks like the covering on the wings of beetles. Their fossilized remains are sometimes referred to as "rock writing" because of their striking similarity to the cuneiform inscriptions on Chaldean clay tablets.

Protozoans are minute single-cell animals. The species radio-

laria prospered during the Cambrian and continued to the Recent Epoch. Although radiolaria are exceedingly small creatures, they contributed significantly to the formation of sedimentary rock. Their microscopic shells combined to form a calcium-rich ooze that covered vast sections of the ocean floors, developing in time into beds of limestone or dolomite.

Petropods are ancient marine plants whose remains in fossil form are rare.

Brachiopods emerged during the Cambrian, reaching a climax during the Devonian.

The Cambrian-age rocks of the Upper Mississippi River Valley in Wisconsin yield abundant fossils of a great variety of these ancient Cambrian age marine creatures.

Ordovician Fossils

The Ordovician age fossils of Wisconsin are more varied than those of the Cambrian and include cephalopods, brachiopods, gastropods, echinoids, crinoids, graptolites, trilobites, sponges, algae, foraminifera and an assortment of corals. The Ordovician seas literally swarmed with life. There are more than 1600 species of animals reported from the middle Ordovician Period alone. This great diversity of fauna is evidence of mild climate and quiet waters, both favorable conditions for the preservation of fossils.

The Ordovician Period is called the Age of Cephalopods. The largest and most powerful of the earth's inhabitants during that period, cephalopods belong to the phylum of mollusks which today includes nautilus, octopus and squid. Some cephalopods were more than 15 feet long; others were only a few inches long.

Brachiopods are members of a class of lamp-shelled marine animals with mismatched dorsal and ventral shells, somewhat resembling clams. Because of their plentifulness and wide distribution, they are extremely useful as index fossils in correlating rock formations.

Gastropods are ancient mollusks with coiled shells, represented in present-day species by snails and whelks.

Crinoids, although a form of marine animal, are commonly called sea lilies because they were attached to the bottom of the sea by a stem (column) composed of slightly movable disc-like

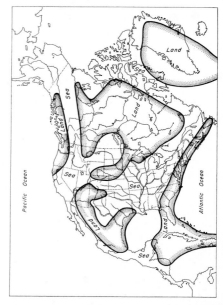

Map showing distribution of land and sea in North America during Upper Cambrian (St. Croixian) time. Land areas are dotted.

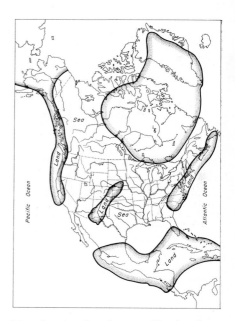

Map showing distribution of land and sea in North America during Middle Ordovician time. Land areas are dotted.

Ordovician-age fossils

Giant cephalopod

Brachiopod

Gastropod

247

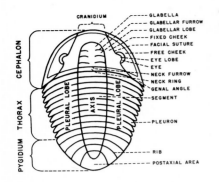

Dorsal view of a generalized trilobite showing the various structures.

Bryozoa

Other forms of gastropods

Silurian Fossils

Colony coral

Horn coral

Another unusual marine species commonly called "horsetail."

segments. The columns and column segments (discs) are the most common form of their fossilized remains. Prehistoric Indians used the fossil discs for beads and wampum.

Well-preserved fossils of the Ordovician Period are found throughout southern, eastern and western Wisconsin, wherever the sedimentary rocks of that period protrude.

Silurian Fossils

The Silurian fossils of Wisconsin differ from those of the Ordovician in the presence of new families and genera rather than in the emergence of completely new groups of marine animals. The corals, brachiopods and trilobites occurring in the Silurian age rocks of southeastern Wisconsin are among the most impressive fossils found in the state.

The Silurian Period is spoken of as the Age of Corals. Coral fossils include multiple varieties of horn coral, branch coral, chain coral and tabulate (colony) coral. Quarries in Milwaukee, Racine, Ozaukee, Waukesha, Fond du Lac and Door Counties are recommended for collecting Silurian-age fossils.

Devonian Fossils

Although the Devonian Period is referred to as the Age of Fishes, pelecypods are among the most abundant fossils of that period occurring in Wisconsin. Brachiopods and coral are also abundant.

Pelecypods belong to the family of bivalued (hatchet foot) mollusks commonly called clams.

The sedimentary rocks in the vicinity of Milwaukee provide a good source for fossils of the Devonian. It is here that one occasionally finds rare fish fragments, such as the bony spines borne by early "sharks" (which really weren't sharks). The Milwaukee Public Museum displays a variety of fossils of this period, including parts of spiny sharks, bizarre armored fish, brachiopods. crinoids, cystoids, coral, cephalopods and seaweed.

During the Silurian Period, land areas may have supported

Branch coral

Chain coral

some forms of early vegetation. But not until Devonian times do the remains of luxuriant forests of primitive trees first appear in the fossil record. Devonian plant fossils are common around the world. However, no evidence of this great forest cover is found in the rocks of Wisconsin. This lack of plant fossils is probably the result of the state's submergence below the sea during most of the Devonian Period.

Fossils After The Devonian

The formation of marine fossils in Wisconsin came to an abrupt end, near the close of the Devonian Period, when the state experienced a gentle uplift that has continued to the present. Ever since, Wisconsin has remained high and dry above sea level, escaping later transgressions of the seas that left marine fossils of more recent geologic age in neighboring states. No bed rocks younger than the Devonian are found in Wisconsin. Thus, the state's fossil record is barren of specimens from the last 345 million years — which vast span includes the Mississippian, Pennsylvanian and Permian Periods as well as the later Mesozoic and Cenozoic Eras — except for occasional organic remains found in Pleistocene-age glacial deposits. Bones, teeth and tusks of animals of the Pleistocene, especially mastodons and woolly mammoth, are found in peat or gravel beds. Recently, a four-foot section of tusk from a woolly mammoth was unearthed in a gravel pit in Washington County. This elephant-like creature probably roamed the steppes of that area in front of the advancing ice mass.

In addition, fossils of more recent origin than the Pleistocene are found in peat bogs and marl deposits — many of which are entirely post-glacial in age. These relatively recent fossils consist mostly of freshwater snails and clams with some plant remains and vertebrate parts, such as the bones of deer.

Organic remains of the Recent Epoch, although not mineralized to the extent of older fossils, are regarded nevertheless as true fossils provided that they have been preserved by natural enclosure or burial in sediments. Remains of organisms that have not become buried but are found still lying upon the surface are referred to as sub-fossils. Bleached snail shells taken from the present bottom level of a pond are sub-fossils but those collected from some depth below the bottom, such as in a bed of marl, are true fossils.

Unique sources for fossils, spring ponds in north central Wisconsin have been found to yield the bones of post-glacial-age animals through dredging operations. The ponds are restored by removing bottom sediments that have accumulated ever since the ponds formed. The deepening is undertaken because the ponds are presently too shallow to support game fish. This facelifting can turn the geologic time clock back as much as ten thousands years. But dredging doesn't "de-age" a choked pond all the way back to the original bottom level representing the Ice Age because going beyond a restored bottom level of about 12 feet in depth is not economically feasable. Nevertheless,

Plate of pelecypods, from Milwaukee

Mammoth Tooth

Mastodon Tooth

A few bones pumped out of a spring pond

249

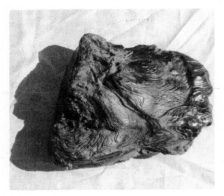
Specimen of petrified wood from St. Croix Falls

Dinosaur

Mammoth

Early horse

a variety of bones of prehistoric creatures have been pumped out in such operations. The oldest identified bones so far recovered are of woodland bison that roamed the state about 6,000 years ago.

The Milwaukee Public Museum displays a number of Pleistocene-age fossils found in Wisconsin, including the tusk, neckbone and teeth of mastodons, the lower jawbone of a giant beaver, remains of black spruce trees and parts of giant bison.

Although giant vertebrates, such as the dinosaurs, probably roamed Wisconsin during the Mesozoic Era, none appear in the state's fossil record.

Petrified Wood

Specimens of petrified wood are sometimes found in gravel deposits in northwestern Wisconsin, especially around St. Croix Falls, in Polk County, and Holcomb, in Chippewa County. Usually striking in color (commonly a rich coffee-brown) and in the preserved detail of the cellular and grain structure of the original wood, these specimens, however, are not native to the areas where found. Instead, they represent erratic materials that were moved in from outside Wisconsin — probably from Canada — and deposited as part of the drift by the glaciers during the Ice Age. Later, they probably were redeposited by meltwaters draining from the glaciers, becoming members of the gravel beds where they now await discovery. These materials became petrified, of course, long before the beginning of the Ice Age and are identified with much earlier geologic periods.

Fossils Forming For The Future

Fossils of course continue to form. Our civilization is leaving its imprint in many ways in the fossil record. In future millennia, our municipal dumps should yield abundant evidence of our way of life.

Meanwhile, we are reaping benefits from prehistoric fossils in many ways, such as when we drive a car, cook a meal or heat our home. Fossil fuels provide energy for many of the comforts of our civilization. Chemically transformed deep within the earth, oil and coal come from the remains of ancient organisms.

Fossil Collecting As A Hobby

A trip to a fossil-bearing formation in Wisconsin opens the door to an interesting and challenging hobby. Adventure awaits fossil collectors because of the widespread distribution, plentifulness and variety of fossils occurring in the state. A puzzling find makes an outing at a fossil-hunting locality a day to remember. Through their discoveries of new species, amateur paleontologists frequently contribute to our total knowledge of prehistoric life. As varied and numerous as the fossil record is, it is estimated that only about one out of a thousand of the many species of prehistoric life-forms that inhabited the earth have as yet been found. Every fossil collector will confirm that fossils are a never-ending source of amazement.

X Mineral Riches

The rocks and minerals of Wisconsin fulfill a vital role in answering our material needs. The state has a long history of mining and quarrying of mineral commodities.

The Importance Of Mineral Commodities

Our civilization depends upon the riches of the mineral kingdom. In an age when we look to the heavens for new frontiers, it is easy to forget that we have ties with the earth that, in another sense, are inseverable. Just as primitive man turned to stone as the basic material for making tools, weapons and ornaments, every major industry today relies to some degree upon mineral commodities. The earth provides the fuel to run our factories, the raw materials for finished products, iron and steel for tools and machinery, copper for electric lines and transformers, chemical elements and compounds for thousands of uses and many other things that we rely upon daily and usually take for granted. Inorganic substances play a major role in answering our material needs. Human progress is a story of a growing dependence upon rocks and minerals. From topsoil to uranium and from window glass to drinking water, we reap a bountiful harvest from the earth's mineral wealth.

Manufacturing produces the largest share of the great total income in the United States. Without abundant natural resources, this country would not have grown into one of the most prosperous industrial and commercial nations in the world. Cheap supplies of coal and iron are behind much of its success. The same is true of immense deposits of petroleum, copper, zinc, lead and other mineral raw materials.

PHOSPHATE MINE.

Not only is the earth our base of operations but it is also the source for most things that fulfill our material needs. This old engraving shows early mining.

251

The Coat of Arms

The Great Seal

Fond du Lac Stone Company quarry at Fond du Lac

Wisconsin's Mineral Producers

Wisconsin is popularly known as America's Dairyland but it supports a substantial number of mineral producers who glean mineral commodities from the state's ample reserves. The Great Seal and Coat of Arms of the state of Wisconsin illustrate the importance of mining when these insignia were adopted for official use in 1887. One of the two figures depicted in the design is that of a yeoman attired as a pioneer lead miner. The inner shield contains a pyramid of pig lead and a crossed pick and shovel — the tools of early mining.

Today, the value of minerals produced in Wisconsin annually is nearly $100 million. Nonmetallic minerals account for more than 2/3 of this production, with the rest coming from metallics. Sand and gravel are the most important of the mineral commodities, representing 43% of the total value earned from nonmetallic minerals. Stone, both crushed and dimension, runs a close second accounting for 35% of the total value. Clay, lime, peat, abrasive stone, cement and gemstones combine for 12%. Iron, zinc and lead are the principal metallic minerals presently mined.

A Look Ahead

The demand for construction materials in Wisconsin is expected to increase in the future, with a prediction that it will double by the year 2000. An increased need is forecast, also, for all other available mineral commodities. Because existing sources appear inadequate for future needs, geologists anticipate accelerated exploration and development throughout the state for new deposits of rocks and minerals.

At the present time, several large mining companies are in the process of taking a closer look at the Precambrian rocks of central and northern Wisconsin. One of the objectives of this prospecting is the potential development of open-pit mining of copper, silver and associated minerals.

In making an appraisal of the state's metallic mineral wealth, a University of Wisconsin-Madison economic geologist recently described central and northern Wisconsin as "a large pudding within which, hopefully, are some small plums, very sparsely

252

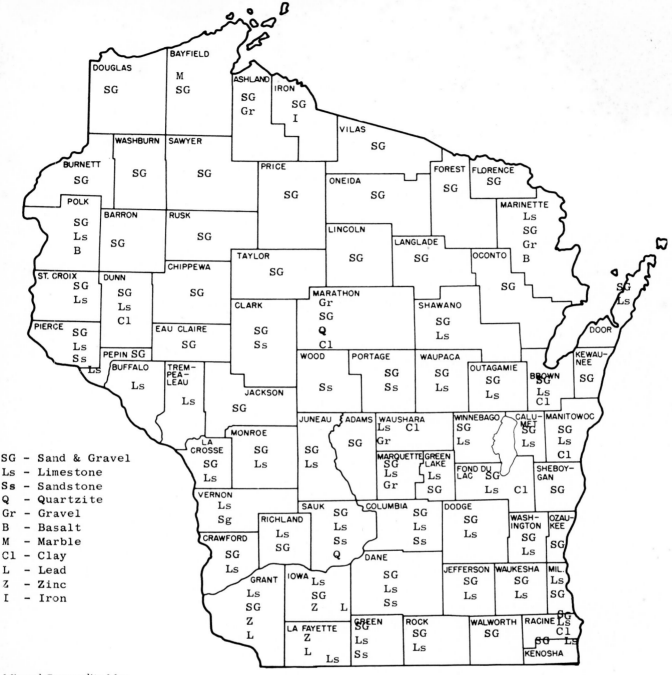

SG - Sand & Gravel
Ls - Limestone
Ss - Sandstone
Q - Quartzite
Gr - Gravel
B - Basalt
M - Marble
Cl - Clay
L - Lead
Z - Zinc
I - Iron

Mineral Commodity Map

distributed; and finding them is not easy". He stressed that locating economically exploitable mineral deposits in those areas is difficult because the best available maps are incomplete and most sulfide mineral deposits in Precambrian rock are deeply covered with materials laid down by the glaciers. Even if one knows where to look, he cannot tell in advance whether the find is worth mining. He must first resort to core drilling to sample the substrata concealed below.

Nonrenewable Assets

The mineral commodities of Wisconsin generally are non-renewable; once depleted, they cannot be replaced. Most are the products of interacting geologic processes that reach far back into time. As to quantities, none are without limit.

Mother Nature has left us a mineral bequest sufficient for our present needs. But looking to the future, we must use the state's mineral resources cautiously and wisely by practicing conservation and avoiding waste or, predictably, there won't be enough of certain mineral commodities to go around in the future.

The Wisconsin Geological and Natural History Survey comments on the state's mineral resources:

"As mineral deposits are nonreplaceable assets, it is self-evident that the future supply rests upon three fundamentals:

1. *Conservation.* Wise use of the minerals that we have, in order that the maximum present and future benefits may be assured for society.

2. *Geological studies.* The most easily found mineral deposits have already been developed; hence, finding new deposits calls for geologic studies utilizing the most up-to-date methods.

3. *Technologic research.* New uses must be sought for minerals that are abundant and substitutes developed for those that are scarce or lacking. Research in mineral processing must be diligently pursued."

Mining And Quarrying In Wisconsin

According to the last *Summary of Mineral Production in Wisconsin* prepared by the U.S. Bureau of Mines, the state's leading mineral commodities are sand, gravel, stone, zinc, iron and lime.

Starting in prehistoric times, a variety of mineral commodities have been mined and quarried in Wisconsin. The materials gleaned from the earth reflect the complex geologic history of the state.

The harvest of the state's mineral wealth depends, of course, upon the geologic horizons of exposed rocks in each region, with the rocks and minerals lying near the surface yielding the materials exploited.

The quarrying of sedimentary rocks is limited mostly to those

Old lime kilns at Lime Kiln Park in Menomonee Falls. These lime kilns were built in 1890 by G.A. Mace. The construction was part of an expansion of the original business started in 1845 by Frederick Nehs founder of Menomonee Falls. In operating the kilns limestone was quarried across the river and hauled via a trestle to the kilns. Surrounding these kilns was a wooden building known as a lime shed into which the lime was laid for cooling after firing. The kilns ceased operating in 1894 shortly after the business was sold. The Lime Kiln Park property was purchased by the village in 1954 and preservation of the structures was begun in 1965.

254

areas of the state which are still underlain with rocks of the Paleozoic. Limestone and sandstone quarries, although present in many places in southern Wisconsin, are conspicuously absent in most of the northern half of the state where sedimentary rocks have generally disappeared because of erosion. However, where ancient crystalline rocks carpet the surface in the northern regions, quarries are found in deposits of granite, quartzite, basalt, rhyolite and gabbro.

Mine dumps and quarries provide a ready opportunity for one to inspect the bedrock and subsurface rock of a locality. Much can be learned about the geology of the area by studying such exposures. Many interesting specimens of common and, sometimes, uncommon minerals are found at these locations. However, caution in the interest of safety is always in order when one visits a commercial site. Furthermore, a visit should not be made unless permission has first been obtained from the owner.

Sand And Gravel

At the present, sand and gravel are dug commercially in almost all areas of the state, except in the extreme southwestern corner. Composed of a great variety of cobbles, pebbles and sand, gravel is used extensively for road building. It is also a major ingredient in concrete for many kinds of construction. In most cases, gravel is processed before use by being washed and crushed into uniform size. But sometimes apart from screening, it is used exactly as found. It is then referred to as aggregate.

Gravel pit south of Delafield, in Waukesha County.

Generally, stream-deposited gravels are well sorted in size and rounded in appearance. Lake gravels tend to be flat and less sorted in size. Glacial gravels, although varying much in the mode of deposit, are less well formed, sometimes sharp and angular and commonly unassorted in size.

A compound of many ingredients, gravel contains a mixture of rocks and soils that have been worked upon by the agents of erosion responsible for its deposition. Thus, gravel suggests the places of origin of the different rocks of which it is composed. The path of a river or glacier may be traced to some extent from the rocks in its gravel. As an example, Lake Superior agates, although originating in bedrock near Lake Superior are found in gravel deposits as far away as the delta of the Mississippi River in Louisiana, having been transported that incredible distance by the river and its tributaries. As another example, rocks from Canada and Upper Michigan are found frequently in glacial gravel in the Kettle Moraine area of southeastern Wisconsin.

In 1964, the state geologist (then Dr. George F. Hanson) reported on Wisconsin's sand and gravel deposits: "Unconsolidated deposits of sand and gravel are widely distributed throughout the state. The most important were formed as a direct result of the last glacial period and are generally found within the boundaries of glaciation, although some river gravels may occur along stream valleys in the Driftless Area in the southwestern quarter of the state.

"When the glaciers advanced over the state, they first depos-

Typical sand and gravel deposit

255

Quarrying of red granite north of Wausau

ited a heterogeneous mixture of rock fragments, boulders, sand and clay which is known as till. However, as they began to melt, the meltwater washed the till and separated the various components according to their size. The fine clay was deposited in lakes or carried to rivers and washed away, but the coarser sand and gravel could not be transported as far and was deposited in front of the retreating ice margin in broad flats known as outwash plains. Such outwash deposits now constitute the most important source of sand and gravel used in construction.''

''The largest deposit of sand and gravel in the U.S.'' is claimed to exist at Janesville where it has been dug commercially since 1907. About a million tons of glacially-deposited materials are removed annually from an immense pit resembling a natural canyon. Mastodon bones and tusks have been found at this site, radiocarbon dated at 15,000 years before the present, indicating that these elephant-like creatures roamed the region before the glaciers finally retreated from Wisconsin.

Harvest Of Rocks And Minerals

Dimension granite is quarried in Ashland, Marathon, Marinette and Marquette Counties.

Red granite, the official state rock of Wisconsin, is quarried at several locations north of Wausau, in Marathon County. For many years, this beautiful ruby red rock has been widely distributed as a monument stone. It ranks among the most attractive granites found anywhere in the world. Other granites of various colors and textures come from the area of the red granite.

A similar red granite was quarried years ago at Cary Bluff, west

256

of Pittsville in Wood County.

Named after the stone quarried there, Redgranite, a village in Waushara County, is typical of many Wisconsin communities that trace their roots to the development of a local mineral commodity. Quarrymen who earlier had operated a granite pit at Berlin, in Green Lake County, first started working the Redgranite outcrop in 1889. With the venture proving successful, large quantities of red granite were removed in time from four quarrying operations until as late as 1932. With a peak payroll of about 600 employees, earning as much as $70,000 per month, the quarries were located a few miles apart at Redgranite, Lohrville, West Point and Shawville. In addition, two quarries developed at Glen Rock, six miles away.

The quarrying was slow, hard work. The stone was split with hand tools such as chisels, bull wedges and hammers. Air drills were used to reduce the size of larger masses, sometimes removed in excess of 15 tons. As more and more rock was taken out, the quarry at Redgranite eventually reached a depth of 230 feet.

Blocks of the quarried material were used extensively as paving, construction and monument stones, with Chicago and other large cities in the Midwest as principal markets. Monument stones were hauled to Montello for polishing. When the quarry was in full operation, about 25 loads of paving blocks were shipped out each spring and fall.

One old-time employee recalls that "water boys started working at the quarries as young as age ten, earning 22¢ an hour as wages".

Today, the five-acre abandoned quarry pit at Redgranite, owned by the village and set aside as a park, is brimful of water. Fishermen now soak bait where quarrymen once toiled.

A well-known pink granite is quarried as a monument stone at Montello, in Marquette County. This handsome rock is claimed to be the world's hardest granite, weighing 200 pounds per cubic foot. It was selected, from among 282 entries, representing four continents, as the stone for the sarcophagi of President U.S. Grant's famous tomb in New York City. It was also chosen for General Custer's monument in the Black Hills and for various Civil War memorials throughout the nation.

Gabbro is quarried near Mellen, in Ashland County, and marketed as black granite. This stone has a beautiful and distinctive pattern and was selected to mark the grave of President John F. Kennedy.

The Wisconsin Geological and Natural History Survey reports on granite in the state:

"Granite, unlike limestone which is often soft rock of many purposes, is an extremely hard rock of very limited uses. The resources of the state are immense and include stone of a wide variety of textures and colors; indeed it has been written that:

'For monumental purposes the granites of Wisconsin have been selected by competent judges in preference to granites from any other part of the United States and, in one conspicuous instance, in preference to granites of three compet-

Early stone saw with automatic feed, 1878.

Outcrop of pink granite at Montello

Gabbro quarry near Mellen today

257

ing continents. In point of color, durability and finish, they have no superior.'

"The following granite mining areas are among Wisconsin's most important:

1. *Montello area*, Marquette County. This granite is fine-grained and red to grayish red.
2. *Berlin area*, Green Lake County. The stone produced here is technically a rhyolite but is commonly referred to as granite. It is very dense, extremely durable and almost black.
3. *Waushara area*, Waushara County. This granite is quarried some 10 miles north of Berlin and is very similar to that of Montello but a little lighter in color.
4. *Waupaca area*, Waupaca County. A very coarse-grained stone is produced here which varies in color from pink to red.
5. *Utley area*, Green Lake County. Rhyolite, which is very similar to that of Berlin, is quarried in this area.
6. *Granite City area*, Green Lake County. The granite is reddish or gray with a red tinge.
7. *Granite Heights area*, Marathon County. This area lies about 10 miles north of Wausau and is the most active granite mining area in the state at the present time. A wide variety of colors is produced varying from gray to the striking ruby red.
8. *Amberg area*, Marinette County. This is the second-most active area at the present time and is noted for the wide variety of colors and textures of the granite. Some of the finest grained stone as well as some of the coarsest is found here and the colors range from red through pink to gray. An exceptionally coarse gray granite is quarried at Athelstane."

In 1964, the state geologist made an appraisal of the future of granite mining in Wisconsin: "The use of granite as a construction stone has been steadily decreasing as cheaper construction materials have been adopted. It will always be in demand as a monumental stone as long as the finest possible product is desired. Skilled craftsmen are necessary to produce dimension stone and therefore the availability and cost of such skilled labor is extremely important.

Wisconsin's official state rock — red granite — being extracted in the Granite Heights area.

258

"All first-class granites are about equally durable and sales depend greatly upon cultivating the taste of the public for a particular variety; hence, advertising and salesmanship are more important here than in many other mineral industries. The granites of Wisconsin are second to none in quality and reserves are great; expansion of the industry is limited only by the demand and production costs."

Basalt, from the Keeweenawan lava flow, is quarried, broken and crushed at a large-scale operation at Dresser Junction, in Polk County, and is widely distributed as trap rock for use as construction aggregate and railroad ballast.

Greenstone (metabasalt) is quarried and crushed for roofing granules near Pembine, in Marinette County.

Shale is quarried near Oakfield, in Fond du Lac County.

Bad River Dolomite, a Precambrian dolomitic marble, is quarried southeast of Grandview, in Ashland County, and is used to make terrazo chips.

Rhyolite for making roofing granules is quarried in Marathon County, northwest of Wausau. A finely crushed quartzite from this locality is used for manufacturing sandpaper.

Trap rock quarry at Dresser Junction

Old quartzite quarry near Devils Lake

Decomposed syenite, locally called rotten granite, is found in a broad area in central Marathon County. It is dug by power shovels at more than a half-dozen pits and used for surfacing roads, driveways, playgrounds, patios and parking lots.

Disintegrated quartzite used for highway construction is dug and crushed in Wood County, near Pittsville and Arpin.

Green and plum-colored aventurine is quarried and crushed for road surfacing at two outcroppings near Veedum, in Wood County. Few places in the world have roadways paved with this material which usually is classified as a gemstone.

Quartzite is quarried and crushed as a highway surfacing material at Necedah, in Juneau County, and at the Seven Sisters, in northeastern Adams County.

Rotten granite pits south of Marathon City

260

Crushed quartzite is produced near Baraboo, in Sauk County, for use as grinding pebbles and at Rock Springs, in Sauk County, for use as railroad ballast.

Dimension sandstone is quarried for masonry and other uses in Clark, Manitowoc, Marathon, Sauk, Wood and Portage Counties.

Marl (calcium carbonate precipitated out of groundwater) is dug commercially on a small scale in Burnett County. It was removed in large quantities from spring ponds in past years in north central Wisconsin and used to sweeten acid farmlands.

Onyx (travertine) is taken from cave deposits in sedimentary bedrock near Westby and Viroqua, in Vernon County.

Broken limestone is produced in Buffalo, Manitowoc, Monroe, St. Croix and Winnebago Counties.

Portland, masonry and white cements are produced from limestone at Manitowoc and Milwaukee.

Quicklime and hydrated lime are produced from a number of quarries located in Brown, Dodge, Douglas, Fond du Lac and Manitowoc Counties.

Dimension limestone, used extensively in building construction, is obtained in Brown, Calumet, Door, Fond du Lac, St. Croix and Waukesha Counties. Lannon stone, quarried at Lannon and Sussex, in Waukesha County, is a well-known and widely distributed limestone used in the construction of many homes and other buildings in southeastern Wisconsin.

Magnesium hydroxide for milk of magnesia is produced at Rockwood, in Manitowoc County. Selenite crystals are found in the dolomite quarry at this location.

The Wisconsin Geological and Natural History Survey comments upon the importance of limestone in the state: "The rocks which are commonly called 'limestones' in Wisconsin are actually dolomites. The difference between the two is not very precise, however. Limestone is composed essentially of calcium carbonate while dolomite also contains carbonate of magnesium. It is this magnesium content that causes Wisconsin limestones to be unsatisfactory for the manufacture of Portland cement.

"There are three separate dolomitic rock units which outcrop in the state: they are the Lower Magnesian (or Prairie du Chien), the Platteville-Galena and the Niagara. The Lower Magnesian is used for building stone and agricultural lime, but it is of particular importance as a source of crushed rock aggregate for concrete construction in the Driftless Area, where sand and gravel for construction is lacking. The Platteville-Galena group, which is the host rock for the lead-zinc deposits, is used primarily for agricultural lime. It has been used for building purposes but disintegrates rapidly when in contact with water. The Niagara dolomite is a good all-purpose stone; it is used for agricultural lime, crushed rock, aggregate, building stone, refractory, iron ore flux and a variety of other uses. The well-known Lannon stone, which is used extensively for building, is quarried from this formation near Lannon in Waukesha County. Stone of similar quality may be obtained from this formation at numerous locations throughout the eastern part of the state.

Huge quartzite quarry at Rock Springs

Quarry of the Fond du Lac Stone Company near Fond du Lac

Panetti Stone Quarry near Fond du Lac

Crushed limestone operation of the Vulcan Materials Company at Sussex

Quarry of the Sussex Lannon Stone Company at Sussex

261

Limestone quarry near Trempealeau

Old lime kiln at High Cliffs State Park on Lake Winnebago

Pipestone quarry east of Rice Lake

Prehistoric pipestone quarry, way back in the woods, east of Rice Lake.

"The reserves of limestone are so large as to be virtually unlimited. In most cases the successful operation of a limestone quarry is the result of factors other than the availability of the stone, such as strategic location of the quarry with regard to transportation and market, availability of labor, and demand for the product."

Soapstone (talc or steatite) was mined on a commercial scale in 1929 and 1930 at a number of sites north of Milladore and, also, near Rudolph, in Wood County. This was a continuation of an earlier exploitation of the soapstone by Prehistoric Indians who used the material for making pipes, utensils and ornaments. In recent years, this very soft material has become a favorite medium of rockhounds for stone carving. Some specimens of soapstone contain well-formed magnetite crystals and, rarely, almandite garnet crystals, some up to one inch in diameter. Other minerals found associated with the soapstone include actinolite, serpentine, long-fibered chrysotile asbestos, brucite and antigorite. The actinolite commonly comes in needle-like crystals arranged in radiating fans.

Another easily carved material, pipestone was quarried by Prehistoric Indians at several places east of Rice Lake, in Barron County, and near Radisson, in Sawyer County. Unlike the well-known pipestone of Minnesota, cropping up at Pipestone National Monument, which is catlinite, the Wisconsin variety is kaolinite.

Zircons were gleaned from pegmatite in a small scale commercial venture at two sites, in the 1940s, in the town of Weston, west of Wausau, in Marathon County. The zircons, containing some hafnium, are fluorescent and can be detected by exposure to ultraviolet light.

During the same period in this locality, a thorium shaft mine was operated with unknown results. Among more than 20 different minerals found at this site is an attractive massive purple fluorite in syenite. Crystals of dark green acmite are commonly associated with the fluorite.

Molybdenite-bearing quartz veins occur in the central part of Marinette County. Operations there in 1939 and 1940 netted 6,094 pounds of concentrates containing 47.82% molybdenum and 50 parts per million of rhenium. Molybdenite is the ore of the metal molybdenum used in the manufacture of special steels.

Mafic rocks in the Florence area have been explored by drilling for the presence of nickel. This metallic mineral is known to occur there but the results of the tests have not been released.

Gold Mining

Gold mining has been tried in past years on a small scale, presumably with little success, near Rudolph, in Wood County, south of Mosinee, in Marathon County, and northeast of Wausau, in Marathon County. As an illustration of the scarcity of this precious metal, all the gold mined throughout the course of human history will fit between the home plate and pitcher's mound on a baseball diamond. It can be stacked in a cube 60 feet high, 60 feet long and 60 feet wide.

Gold has never been profitably exploited in Wisconsin, although it is known to exist as a minor ingredient in some of the state's Precambrian rocks. Exploration in the Mountain-Amberg area of northeastern Wisconsin has yielded a sample containing 0.16 ounces of gold and 12.79 ounces of silver per ton. Two specimens of gold-bearing quartzite from the Barron area were assayed at one ounce of silver per ton. One sample contained 75% copper.

Radioactive Minerals

Radioactive minerals are found at 12 locations in western Marathon County. These consist of thorogummite, thorium-bearing zircon, allanite and thorium, all of undetermined commercial value. A Geiger counter registers a strong reading in this region, where radioactive minerals occur as a residuum in syenite and greenstone. Rare earths (mainly columbium and cerium) are reported in this same general area but have not yet been found of economic value.

Uranium In Wisconsin?

A good example of detective work by present-day geologists is reported in the 1972 Professional Papers published by the U.S. Geological Survey. The report concerns a study of the mineral wavellite found a few miles north of Black River Falls, in Jackson County. The wavellite occurs inconspicuously as thin botryoidal crusts and small spherical masses in a weathered outcrop of Eau Claire sandstone of late Cambrian age. The mineral is believed to be the product of materials dissolved out of the sedimentary rocks originally covering that area. Because it forms from the redeposition of other materials, wavellite is called a secondary mineral.

Phosphorus and aluminum are the main chemical constituents of wavellite. These elements were probably leached from the original sedimentary rocks by groundwater, carried in solution through the porous and permeable sandstone and then deposited as wavellite in openings along bedding planes and joints in the sandstone.

The solutions transporting the phosphorus probably moved downward or laterally from fossil-bearing beds to the site of deposition of the wavellite. Among the fossils originally contained in the sedimentary beds were brachiopods and trilobites, rich in phosphatic shell material. The aluminum was probably dissolved and carried by groundwater passing through decomposing grains of feldspar that were part of the original sedimentary materials. All of these sediments, of course, were initially deposited when the area lay below the waters of late Cambrian seas, more than 500 million years ago.

The wavellite leads to some exciting implications as a result of its known geologic relationship to a much more important mineral — uranium! Important because it is a radioactive mineral, uranium is a prime source of atomic energy and has become one of the most urgently critical of all geologic products.

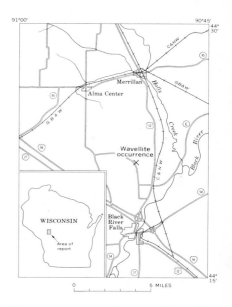

Index map showing location of wavellite occurrence in Jackson County, Wisconsin.

Botryoidal wavellite

263

Comparing the Jackson County deposits to others elsewhere with similar characteristics, geologists believe that the original sedimentary rocks in this region of Wisconsin could have produced uranium. The geologic setting is much like that in the Bone Valley Formation in Florida and the Phosphoria Formation in Idaho where uranium is present in phosphate-rich rocks.

When uranium decays through a spontaneous emission of radioactivity, it forms a daughter product known as radiogenic lead.

Although conditions were once ripe for the development of uranium and radiogenic lead in Jackson County, the presence of these minerals today is not detected in an analysis of the bedrock. This suggests to geologists that the uranium and its daughter product, radiogenic lead, may have been leached from the original host rock, taken into solution in groundwater, carried southbound down the dip of the bedrock and redeposited elsewhere.

Galena (lead ore) found in the zinc-lead deposits of southwestern Wisconsin is known to contain anomalous amounts of radiogenic lead. The ratio of radiogenic lead to common lead there appears to be greatest in the northeastern corner of the district, which is directly downslope of the Jackson County sedimentary deposits. The geologists studying the area are of the opinion that the Jackson County sedimentary rocks may have been the source of the radiogenic lead. They believe that the uranium was also deposited somewhere in Wisconsin and most likely before the radiogenic lead was deposited. Thus they conclude in their report:

"The questions arise whether this uranium may have been deposited in disseminated form throughout a large volume of the same aquifers (water-bearing substrata) through which it was

Generalized stratigraphic section of Paleozoic sedimentary rocks near Black River Falls, Jackson County, showing approximate position of the wavellite occurrence.

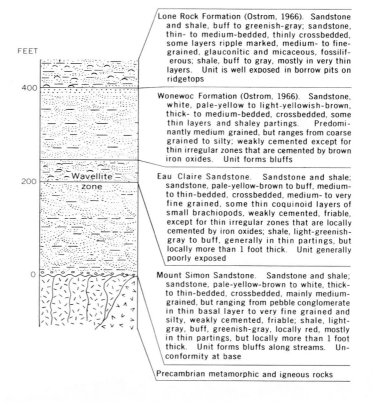

transported or whether it was deposited somewhere in concentrations that may be of economic interest."

Further exploration of this very interesting area may lead to the discovery of economically exploitable concentrations of uranium, thanks to the super sleuthing of the geologists of the U.S. Geological Survey. This is an instance of earth science detectives starting with only meager clues and working up a convincing case about the possible presence in Wisconsin of a high-priced mineral commodity.

Gemstones

Lake Superior agate and algal jasper are the principal gemstones harvested commercially in the state. Both are found as pebble-size ingredients in glacial gravel. The agate occurs throughout the watershed of the Mississippi River. The jasper is most plentiful in northwestern Wisconsin.

Man-made hill formed from waste pile of large sand mining operation at Portage, in Columbia County.

In addition, jade, recently discovered in Marathon County, is marketed as a cutting material. According to an article in *Wisconsin Trails* magazine, "If recent news reports are true, 40% of the rocks along County Trunk I may be jade." Labradorite, popularly known as Wausau moonstone, is another established cutting material from Marathon County.

Wisconsin's Diamonds

Diamonds have been found at scattered places in Wisconsin. These precious stones were distributed at random by the glaciers, apparently with no concentration at any one place.

During the 19th century, diamonds were discovered near Eagle, in Waukesha County; near Kohlsville, several miles northwest of West Bend, in Washington County; near Oregon, in Dane County; in the town of Rock Elm, on Plum Creek, in Pierce County; near Saukville, in Ozaukee County; and near Burlington, in Racine County.

The Eagle gem was found in till brought to the surface from a depth of seventy feet during the drilling of a well. It weighed about 16½ carats and was described as "a very transparent stone with a wine yellow color". In November, 1883, Mrs. Clarissa Wood sold this raw diamond for the paltry sum of one dollar to a Milwaukee jeweler, Col. S.B. Boynton. Later, Mrs. Wood became aware of the stone's true value and sued for its return. The lawsuit was appealed eventually to the Wisconsin Supreme Court where the colonel was adjudged to be its legal owner (*Wood vs. Boynton*, 1885, 64 Wis. 265).

The Kohlsville diamond resembled the Eagle gem in color but was somewhat larger weighing 21¼ carats.

The Oregon diamond, at 3.83 carats, was partially transparent, superficially gray in color, and was sold to Tiffany's of New York, which placed it uncut in its Exposition Collection.

An early journal refers to the Jesuit explorer-missionaries as finding diamonds in 1670 on some of the islands in Green Bay.

The source of Wisconsin's diamonds remains unknown but some geologists believe that these gems were transported from

265

the north for long distances by the glaciers. The diamonds probably originated in the buried pipes of an ancient volcano, now leveled by erosion and tucked away, most likely, in the Hudson Bay region of Canada.

Professor William H. Hobbs of Madison speculated in *The American Geologist,* in July, 1894, that the Menominee-Marinette region, on the northeastern boundary of Wisconsin, may someday produce a significant harvest of diamonds. He based his prediction on the similarity of the geological features of that area to those of the South African diamond fields. In both places, basic intrusive rocks cut across carbonaceous shales.

Another likely location for diamonds, according to some geologists, is the Precambrian bedrock of central Wisconsin between Junction City, in Portage County, and Rudolph, in Wood County. Some of the peridotite cropping up there approximates that associated with the South African kimberlite which contains mineable concentrations of diamonds.

For the information of any budding prospector with diamond fever, kimberlite is a variety of mica peridotite consisting essentially of olivene, phlogopite, and subordinate melilite, with minor pyroxene, apatite, perovskite and opaque oxides.

No more than a total of 20 diamonds have been found in the state, oddly all before the turn of the present century and for the most part by amateurs at a time when far less interest existed in rocks and minerals than today. Like the proverbial needle in the haystack, the chance of finding one of these precious stones in Wisconsin is exceedingly rare.

Pearls From Wisconsin

Until about the time of World War II, clamming was a thriving industry on many Wisconsin waterways, especially on the Mississippi and Wisconsin Rivers. Clams (several species of freshwater mollusks) were harvested from boats towing clam drags along river bottoms where the hard-shelled creatures lived in great profusion in beds.

A clam drag is an elaborate rig consisting typically of a long metal bar and many trailing chains to which a great number of four-prong hooks are attached. When the device is dragged over a clam lying open, the clam closes tightly around one of the barbless hooks, thus sealing its own doom.

The different kinds of clams were known by very descriptive names, such as pocketbooks, pig-toes and muckets.

Following harvesting, the soft parts of the clams were removed by cooking and usually discarded but the shells were cleaned and sent to factories where they were made into mother-of-pearl buttons. The factories purchased the shells by the ton, with prices rising in the 1930s to $65/ton. Usually the buttons were made of discs bored from the shells. Markets developed worldwide. A well-known button factory was located for many years at Fremont on the Wolf River; others were at Janesville on the Rock River.

In the old days, huge piles of shells along river banks were a

Old photo of a steam shovel digging molding sand in a pit at Beloit

266

common sight, marking the places where clammers had set up camp — a sort of landmark of the industry. However, with the advent of plastics, new materials replaced mother-of-pearl in the manufacture of buttons and big-time clamming gradually came to an end.

During the period when clamming prospered, Prairie du Chien, near the confluence of the Mississippi and Wisconsin Rivers, became one of the principal river ports serving the industry.

When commercial clamming was active in the state, freshwater pearls were commonly found in the process of opening clams. Some pearls were well-rounded, lustrous and of gem-quality. Others, called slugs or baroque pearls, were misshapen in form and of little value. The round pearls were much in demand for jewelry. Occasionally, an exceedingly large pearl of superior quality was extracted; such a pearl commanded a top price as a semiprecious stone. One flawless, jumbo Wisconsin pearl, currently valued at $20,000, found its way, eventually, into the highly prized crown jewels of England.

Today, clamming in Wisconsin is an almost extinct activity, except that some clams are still sought along the Lower Wisconsin and Mississippi Rivers for manufacture into mother-of-pearl beads. The tiny beads are exported to Japan where they are inserted as seeds or nuclei into captive saltwater oysters to produce cultured pearls. Cultured pearls perennially continue in vogue for modern-day jewelry.

Clams were gathered in Wisconsin in prehistoric times, especially along the Rock and Crawfish Rivers by the inhabitants of Aztalan, who used the soft parts as a foodstuff and the shells as a material for making implements and ornaments. The refuse heaps left by the Aztalanians contain an abundance of clamshell remains. Doubtless, while cleaning clams, they came upon freshwater pearls and recognized them as rare objects with great natural beauty. The prehistoric Indians were too alert and interested in the things of nature making up their everyday world to have overlooked such obvious detail. We know that the Hopewellian People, earlier, made jewelry from freshwater pearls. A necklace of such pearls was among the archeological treasures discovered in the Nicholls Mound, in Trempealeau County.

According to the U.S. Bureau of Fisheries, approximately 26,000 tons of mussel shells with a value of more than one million dollars were taken by fishermen in 1922. These shells furnished materials for over eight million dollars' worth of manufactured products, such as buttons and pearl novelties.

Old-time clam fisherman in a boat equipped with a clam rig

Foundry-sand mine near Maiden Rock, in Pierce County.

267

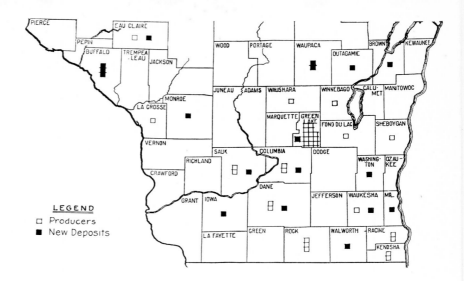

LEGEND
□ Producers
■ New Deposits

Distribution of molding sand deposits by counties

Silica Sand

Silica sand is mined at the present in Columbia, Dane, Pierce, Rock, Green Lake and Winnebago Counties. According to a 1971 report, "The sand is used chiefly for industrial purposes including foundry (molding), glass manufacture, sandblasting, traction (engine), filtration and hydrofic (oil)." The report concluded that Wisconsin has an abundance of high-quality silica sand suitable for a wide variety of industrial uses. An earlier study listed 28 localities producing this mineral commodity. For many years, the district around Berlin, in Green Lake County, has been a major producer.

A sand widely used for blast sand comes from Eau Claire and, because of its pronounced red color, is known in the trade as red flint.

The Bay City Sand Company mines red blast sand from a bluff southeast of Bay City, in Pierce County. The bluff is honeycombed with more than 12 miles of tunnels, some of which are 30 feet high. The buildings there have the appearance of a western mining operation, arousing the curiosity of many travelers who stop in to inquire.

Peat

Peat bogs are common throughout the glaciated portions of Wisconsin. Peat forms in water-soaked areas from an accumulation of partly decayed vegetable matter. It usually consists of decomposed trees, mosses, sedges, ferns and other vegetation, representing an early stage in the formation of coal.

Peat is one of the oldest fuels in service to man. The Irish, traditionally heavy users of peat, refer to it as "burning the auld sod". Though low in caloric value, peat burns cleanly. When well dried, it contains a heat value of up to 8,000 BTUs (British thermal units) per pound, approximately 2/3 that of coal. Peat is used also for fertilizer and other purposes.

In the U.S., Wisconsin has the second-largest reserve of peat, exceeded only by Minnesota. Wisconsin's 2.5 billion tons amount to about 1/5 of the country's total supply. Wisconsin's

268

peat reserve has a projected value at current market prices of more than $12.5 billion.

In the past, only small quantities of peat have been harvested in Wisconsin, with production and sales of little economic importance. At the present, peat is dug as a mineral commodity in Lincoln and Waukesha Counties and used principally as seed inoculant. However, with the world's gas, oil and coal reserves dwindling, peat has great potential as a fuel of the future.

Clay

In the late nineteenth century, quantities of kaolin were taken from deposits near Wisconsin Rapids and shipped to Milwaukee for making fire bricks. The kaolin was described, in 1876, as "a pure white clay, the only impurity of importance being quartz, from which it can readily be separated by washing". Specimens of this variety of clay have been tested and found suitable for making fine pottery.

Clay is dug for manufacturing sewer pipes near Elmwood, in Pierce County, and for bricks near Menomonie, in Dunn County. Until recently, clay drain tile was manufactured near Union Grove, in Racine County.

The State Geologist reported: "In 1960, clay production was listed from Brown, Dunn, Fond du Lac, Marathon, Manitowoc, Racine and Waupaca Counties and was valued at $156,000."

In past years, clay has been dug in many localities for the manufacture locally of brick and tile. Many of the state's older homes are built of bricks made in small factories and sold at local brickyards. An example of this is the red brick in many older buildings in central Wisconsin, manufactured more than a half century ago from clay removed from beds at Vesper, in Wood County.

The first brick house built in Wisconsin, now a registered state landmark, is located in Brown County on the river side of the road from Green Bay to De Pere, near the state reformatory.

Mineral Water

An interesting bit of Wisconsin history concerns the spring water surfacing at Waukesha. In 1869, a New York visitor drank some of "the sparkling water" and proclaimed that it had cured his previously untreatable ailments. A health fad followed and the small springs at Waukesha became famous as a watering spa where throngs of sick people came to be healed. The mineral springs and mud baths blossomed into a local industry, with 34 boardinghouses and hotels. In 1893, the spring water was dispensed even at the Chicago World's Fair. The fad peaked by the end of the century, although bottled spring water is still a mineral commodity of Waukesha.

Iron Mining

A wide variety of valuable metallic mineral deposits have been found in Precambrian rocks in many parts of the Canadian Shield, which extends southernmost into northern Wisconsin.

Wisconsin's last standing tipple tower at Pence, in Iron County.

Five-and-a-half-foot diameter solid rock core from the main shaft of the Cary Mine, near Hurley, through which all miners and supplies passed.

269

THE CITY OF MONTREAL
SITE OF THE WORLD'S DEEPEST IRON MINE

The City of Montreal, incorporated in 1924, known for a short time as the Village of Hamilton, is a combination of the communities of Montreal and Gile.

Gile, on the river, was the center of the area's timber industries. The largest, the Montreal River Lumber Company, operated from 1884 until 1904, milled 80,000 board feet of white pine a day. Lumbering continued here on a smaller scale until 1915.

Montreal, on the hill, was the site of the Montreal Mining Company facility which shipped its first ore in 1886. Mining followed the Penokee Range iron formation slope to the north, extending one mile west and three-fourth miles east of this marker. This industry, operated by Oglebay Norton Company, shipped a total of 45,747,708 tons, and at its closing in 1962 had reached a vertical depth of 4,335 feet.

Erected by
THE IRON COUNTY HISTORICAL SOCIETY
1970

Sign at Montreal explaining "the world's deepest iron mine"

But iron ore, mined mostly in the Gogebic Range, is the only metallic mineral successfully exploited in the Precambrian rocks of Wisconsin.

The story of early mining ventures in the Gogebic Range is capsulized in a historical marker located ten miles west of Hurley on U.S. Highway 2, which reads as follows:

"The Gogebic Iron Range, which may be seen to the south of here, extends for 80 miles from Lake Namekagon, Wisconsin, to Lake Gogebic (Chippewa for 'place of diving') in Michigan. Prior to the discovery of iron ore, the area was relatively uninhabited as the land was ill-suited to agriculture. Nathaniel D. Moore uncovered ore deposits in Penokee Gap near Bessemer in 1872, but it was not until 1884 that the first mine shipment was made. The news spread rapidly, attracting speculators, investors and settlers. By 1886, there were 54 mines on the range and the area was boomed as having 'inexhaustible deposits of uniformly high-grade Bessemer ores'. For a brief period, stocks rose 1200 percent. The crash in 1887 ended the extravagant prosperity."

The iron-bearing Gogebic Range, with Hurley-Ironwood as the hub, reaches northeastward into Upper Michigan. Iron ore was extensively produced in both states, until 1965, in some of the world's deepest shaft mines. The total production in the district was more than 295 million tons of iron ore, of which 71 million tons were mined in Wisconsin.

In past years, about four out of every five tons of iron ore mined in the United States came from deposits around Lake Superior — in Wisconsin, Michigan and Minnesota, including the highly productive Mesabi Range in Minnesota.

The iron ore of the Gogebic Range lies in the Ironwood Iron-Formation. Of the Lake Superior type, it was deposited originally during Precambrian time in sediments laid down upon ancient ocean floors. It is composed of interbedded iron-rich and silica-rich layers, totaling 650 feet in thickness, averaging about 30 to 35% iron. The iron-rich strata consist mostly of varying amounts of siderite, hematite and magnetite, with lesser content of chert

270

and fine-grained silicate minerals. The silica-rich layers, on the other hand, are made up of the same minerals, but with the iron content subordinate to the silicate content.

Direct-shipping ores are described as those that are sufficiently rich in iron to permit direct shipment to smelters. Not all ores are direct-shipping ores. Lesser ores must be processed before being shipped to smelters by removing impurities in order to improve quality and reduce shipping expenses. Lean ore is concentrated before shipment through a process called beneficiation.

As an example, taconite is beneficiated by being first crushed to a fine powder. Then the iron powder is separated from the mass by magnets. In the next step, the iron powder is moistened, rolled into balls about one-half inch in diameter and burned in a furnace to make pellets. Finally, the pellets, as a marketable concentrate, are shipped to iron and steel mills.

Mining in the Gogebic Range came to an end in recent years as the result of competition with direct-shipping ores from other iron-rich regions. No successful method of beneficiating the ores of the Ironwood Iron-Formation has been developed because of the high proportion of very fine hematite particles present in such ores. However, the rocks of the western part of the Gogebic Range in Wisconsin have been metamorphosed to such an extent that the grain size of the iron-bearing and silica-bearing minerals is large enough to make concentration by magnetic methods possible. Studies are currently underway to determine the commercial feasibility of concentrating the ores from this area.

In 1964, the State Geologist reported on the Gogebic Range:

"The Gogebic Range is a narrow band of iron-bearing rocks of Precambrian age which is some 80 miles long but locally not much more than half a mile wide. It extends in a southwesterly direction from Lake Gogebic in Michigan to Lake Namekagon in Wisconsin, and, although 53 miles of its total length lie in this state, the greater production has come from the east end in Michigan. Mining on the range has been continuous since 1884 and some 300,000,000 tons of ore have been shipped. At the time of writing, there is one active mine in Wisconsin, the Cary Mine."

In its heyday, Hurley was a flamboyant town, throbbing with the lustful excitement and glamour that attach to a mining community during a period of prosperity. But now, with the closing of the mines, all that is gone. The old-time miners still remember "the good old days" when a guy picked an apple from the

Plant for beneficiating iron ore at the Jackson County iron mine, east of Black River Falls.

271

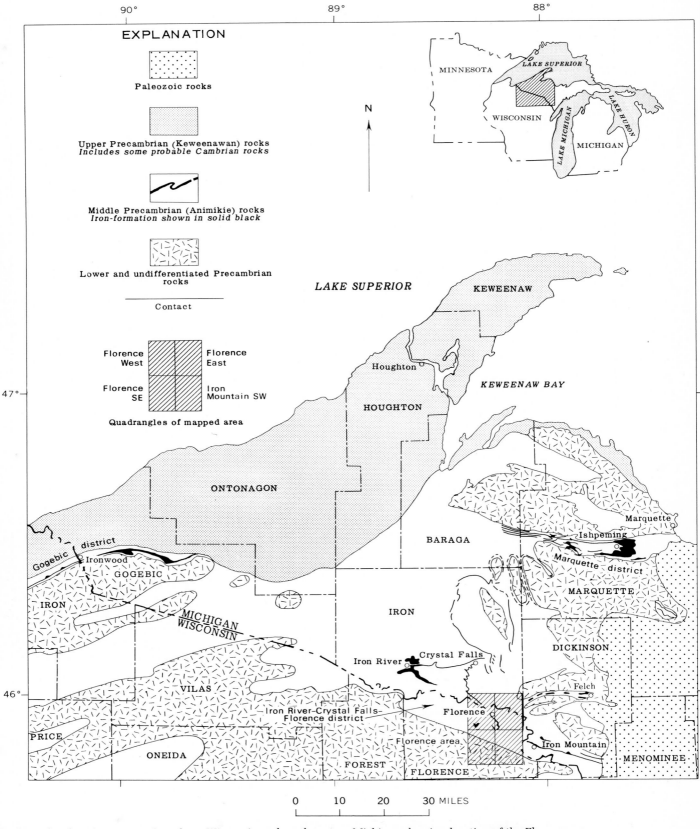

Generalized geologic map of northern Wisconsin and northwestern Michigan showing location of the Florence area

272

inevitable tree at the mouth of a mine and took it with him underground to add "a little sweet" to his toil. They also recall the good times when eating out meant a plate of steaming pasties or cabbage rolls, two favorites of Cornish hardrock miners everywhere. Times are remembered, too, when disaster struck without warning in any one of a hundred ways "at whatever level it was" in the Stygian blackness of a mine.

Mining of direct-shipping iron ores from Precambrian rocks apart from the Gogebic Range has been undertaken in past years at several places in Wisconsin. The Riverton Iron-Formation in the Menomonie Range, near the communities of Florence and Commonwealth in northeastern Wisconsin, was mined until 1932 from several open pits and underground operations. A small mining venture was active there again from 1953 to 1960.

Almost 8 million tons of direct-shipping iron ore were produced in this district from 1880 to 1960, consisting predominantly of soft hematite and limonite, with a high content of phosphorus. Among the iron mines of this area were the Florence, Badger, Buckeye, Commonwealth, Davidson and Ernst Mines. At a number of other localities in this region, exploration has been carried out, without apparent success, through test pits and shafts with limited underground workings.

The Baraboo Range has hosted iron mining in past years. The iron-bearing unit there occurs in the basal strata of the Freedom Dolomite, as a mixture of hematite, chert, iron carbonate and dolomite. The iron content of the ores averages about 53%. One mining operation was in production in this area from 1904 to 1916, another from 1919 to 1925. The two ventures, both located in Sauk County, experienced about equal production and contributed to a total of 643,000 tons of ore. The old mines were known as the Sauk Mine and Illinois Mine, both located near Seeley Creek within a mile radius of La Rue and the Cahoon Mine, in the terminal moraine about two miles southwest of Baraboo.

Even earlier, from 1850 to 1873, iron was mined about one mile south of the village of Ironton, in Sauk County, with a total quota of 25,000 tons of ore, which produced 11,000 tons of iron. The ore was taken from an old fault in which chert and iron oxide were deposited, in part at least secondary, after marcasite in openings in the fault rubble.

Iron was mined in the past also, in the Niagara dolomite outcropping in Dodge County. The mining was begun in 1849 with the opening of the Iron Ridge Mine at Neda and continued there, with one interruption, until 1914. A second mine, the Mayville Mine, at Mayville, was in production from 1892 to 1928. The ore occurred in a thin horizontal bed intermixed with clay. It was described in an old mining journal as "an oolitic iron ore, scarcely coherent and often crumbling to a considerable extent". The production from the two mines over the years totaled 2,580,000 tons. An official historical marker identifies the site of the state's first iron smelter at Mayville.

The only iron mine in operation in the state at the present time

Old mine dump near Hurley

273

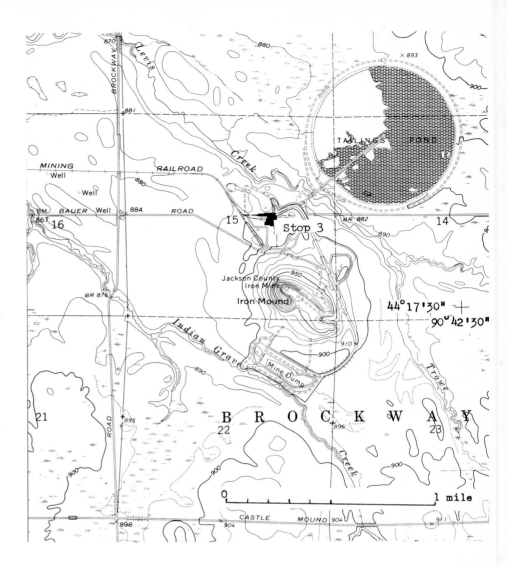

Jackson County Iron Mine area

View in the distance of the Jackson County Iron Mine

is the Jackson County Iron Mine, located about six miles east of Black River Falls. This is a multi-million dollar mining and processing plant where the iron ore is concentrated and pelletized as taconite before shipment to smelters.

The ore is derived from a quartz-hematite-magnetite iron formation, averaging about 30-35% iron. The ore is beneficiated at a ratio of three tons of lean ore to one ton of marketable concentrate of at least 65% iron. This operation has an expected annual production of 750,000 tons of pelletized concentrate for a twenty-year period. The output in 1973 amounted to 940,000 short tons of taconite pellets.

Schist associated with the iron formation at the Jackson County Iron Mine consists, in varying proportions, of quartz, biotite, chlorite and garnet. Mineral collectors have found that some specimens of the schist contain well-formed crystals of red almandite garnet. Other specimens contain embedded bundles of slender brown sillimanite crystals resembling the bristles of a paintbrush.

Before mining was undertaken by modern means in this region, the State Geologist reported, in 1964, on the Black River Falls District:

"This district is located in Jackson County and centers around

274

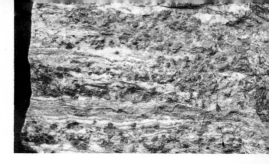

a large butte known locally as Iron Mound. Production of ore has been reported as early as 1857, but has met with no success due to the low grade. However, it has been calculated that some 300,000 tons of concentrates could be produced annually from this district over a period of about 40 years, with the aid of beneficiation."

Mine dumps yield a variety of mineral specimens in the vicinity of Hurley and Montreal, in Iron County, and Florence, in Florence County, including hematite, goethite, limonite, calcite, gypsum, psilomelane and rhodochrosite.

Hematite as highly prized needle or kidney ore is found occasionally in the tailings of the mines at Montreal and Hurley. Some of the needle ore has bladed crystals more than a foot long. Pure crystalline hematite sometimes occurs in nodules, suitable for cabbing and faceting.

Closeup photos of garnet schist at the Jackson County Iron Mine

The Jackson County Iron Mine is an open-pit mine, more than ½ mile across.

Closeup photo of actinolite at the same site

Gargantuan trucks haul the ore from the mine to the processing plant at the Jackson County operation

275

Graphite Mining

Wisconsin has never produced graphite as a mineral commodity. But an interesting account of a graphite mining venture, one mile north of Junction City, in Portage County, was reported in 1908, in *The Geology Of North Central Wisconsin*:

"Especial attention is called to the form of the carbon in these deposits in view of the fact that companies have been organized and stock sold for the purpose of mining graphite from them.

"The richer portions of the carbonaceous shale, bearing from 10 to 15 percent carbon, are put through crushers and rollers and separated by flotation in air. The product is similar to that of the so-called Baraga graphite of Michigan and the so-called graphitic anthracite of Rhode Island.

"It is an evil practice, however, to apply the name 'graphite' to the ordinary form of carbon like that occurring in the carbonaceous schists at Junction City and foist upon the public the sale of mining shares in so-called graphite mines. The carbon in these deposits has a legitimate use in certain manufactured products and the writer has no wish to criticize the legitimate exploitation of these deposits or the product manufactured. By the use of the name 'graphite paint' little deception can be worked upon the purchaser of paints. The principal evil lies in the sale to the unsuspecting public of stock in so-called graphite mines and claiming for the carbon of these deposits all the virtues of true graphite."

The same book describes the mining of an iron-bearing schist, a few miles southwest of Junction City. The schist was crushed for mineral paint. Apparently, the carbonaceous pigment from the "graphite" mine was mixed with the iron oxide from the second mine to produce various colored paints.

The Diamond Mining Swindle

A classic swindle involved "a diamond mining venture" in Wisconsin in the late 1800s. Col. Samuel B. Boynton — the same gentleman who earlier had purchased the Eagle Diamond from its finder for the paltry sum of $1.00 (see page 265) — salted an area around the village of Eagle, in Waukesha County, with a passel of uncut diamond crystals. The colonel then went to the pretense of discovering some of the gems and formed the Diamond Producing Company of Wisconsin. He and an associate in the swindle found eager buyers for the sale of stock in the enterprise which gave promise of instant wealth because of the apparent concentration of gems. Business boomed and the deliberate fraud seemed headed for success, until the salted diamond crystals were proved by a suspicious investor to be of South African origin. Thus exposed, the colonel and his confederate ran afoul of the law.

The Great Oil Well Hoax

Another rip-off involving pretended mineral riches in the state was perpetrated more than a century ago. A "gentleman" from LaCrosse purchased some land at Sparta where he secretly

buried several barrels of crude oil attached to some impressive-looking pipes and valves. To all outward appearances, the apparatus was a real oil rig. When the dark liquid began to flow, the gentleman encountered little difficulty in selling shares to local investors in his newly-formed Gem Petroleum Company: Before the "well" ran dry, he skipped town with fifty thousand dollars.

No oil has been pumped in a legitimate operation in Wisconsin because no oil-rich rocks suitable for exploitation are known to have formed in the state during the geologic periods producing petroleum deposits. For the same reason, mineable coal deposits are absent in the state.

Civil War era drilling operations

Copper Mining

Copper has been mined, in historic times, in several localities in Wisconsin but the results have never been profitable.

The Prehistoric Indians mined copper around Lake Superior for making implements and ornaments. Although many copper artifacts have been found in Wisconsin, there is no evidence suggesting that these early people undertook any copper mining in the state. However, much evidence exists of their mining activities in Upper Michigan, from where the metal was transported to scattered campsites in Wisconsin. Nevertheless, some artifacts were made from float copper distributed to many parts of Wisconsin by the glaciers.

The Keweenawan rocks of northwestern Wisconsin have long been known to be copper-bearing. These rocks continue southwestward from Michigan, where for many years they have been exploited for mineable deposits of copper.

Miners setting rock bolts to support roof of a lateral drift

Metallic copper and copper minerals are present locally in extrusive-igneous and sedimentary rocks in a broad belt located south of Superior. The belt covers about 3,000 square miles and lies in Douglas, Bayfield, Washburn, Burnett and Polk Counties.

This district was the scene of several copper mining ventures in past years. In the 1880s, "a copper rush" hit the area. Copper mining companies were organized to develop mines on the Montreal, American, Brule and Bad Rivers. Extensive prospecting was undertaken on the Potato River, Silver Creek and Braunsch-Wilers Creek. Mine shafts were sunk south of Superior at the Lower Black River Falls and at several other locations. Among these were the Copper Creek, Wisconsin and Percival Mines. However, every attempt at mining copper in this region proved unsuccessful. The best effort repaid only about one-tenth of the cost of working a mine.

Old-time method of moving ore

In 1972, the U.S. Geological Survey published a report on a recent study of the copper-bearing rocks of northwestern Wisconsin. The abstract of the report reads:

"Metallic copper or copper minerals are locally present in flows, conglomerate, siltstone and shale of Keweenawan age that underlie about 3,000 square miles of northwestern Wisconsin. Representative samples taken from 24 of the reported occurrences in lava or conglomerate contain 0.0075 to 0.69 percent copper; 10 of them have more than 0.10 percent. No study was

277

Occurrences of mineral commodities exclusive of quarries.

Name of commodity	Township North	Range	Sections	Name of commodity	Township North	Range	Sections
Asbestos	36	21E	24	Gold	28	7E	24
Cerium	29	6E	22	do	36	20E	8,17
Chromite	37	21E	21	do	36	21E	16
Columbium	29	6E	22	Graphite	25	6E	34
Copper	33	6W	16	Iron	21	3W	4,15,17, 18,19,20, 25,26
do	24	7E	8				
do	29	8E	35	do	21	4W	1,11,12
do	30	6E	33	do	22	3W	31,32
do	36	11E	20	do	24	2W	22
do	38	19E	19	do	40	17E	25,35
do	33	18W	6,16	do	40	18E	20,21,27, 31,32,33, 34
do	33	19W	11,14				
do	35	18W	2,4, 8,9,16	do	41	1W	21,28,29
do	36	17W	19	do	41	1E	2,4
do	36	18W	10,21,28, 33	do	42	1E	22,23,24, 29
do	37	16W	7,9,10, 15,18,21 23,29,35	do	44	3E	23,26,27, 28
do	37	17W	13,31	do	44	1W	6
do	37	18W	25	do	44	2W	1,2,8, 9,10,17 18
do	39	19W	9				
do	42	10W	2,4,5, 18	do	44	3W	9,13,14, 15,16,17, 18,19
do	42	11W	13,22,28, 33	do	44	4W	13,14,19, 20,21,22, 28,29,30
do	42	15W	9				
do	43	8W	2,4,14, 18,19	do	44	5W	23,24,25
do	43	9W	4,5	do	44	6W	24,25,26, 27
do	43	10W	1,12,14, 22,28,33	do	45	1W	25,26,27, 32,33,34
do	43	13W	6				
do	43	14W	2,6,9, 23	do	45	1E	1,10. 11, 12,15 16,19,20
do	44	5W	6				
do	44	6W	1,2,11	do	45	2E	6
do	44	7W	4,15,20, 29	do	46	2E	24,25,26, 27,32,33
do	44	8W	26,29	Magnesite	37	21E	21
do	44	9W	15,23	Molybdenite	33	20E	18
do	44	13W	11,14,15, 21,22,23, 27,28,31	do	38	19E	33
				Nickel	38	19E	30
do	44	15W	32,33	Pegmatite	Many local occurrences		
do	46	2E	9,17	Pyrrhotite	31	16E	11,12,13
do	46	15W	11	do	31	17E	6,18
do	47	11W	6	do	36	11E	30
do	47	12W	3,6	do	38	19E	19,30
do	47	13W	1,2,8, 10,11,16, 17	do	38	20E	7
				do	39	18E	27
do	47	14W	14,15,21, 28,31	Pyrite	29	7E	24
				do	34	8W	9
do	48	10W	21,27,29, 30	Silver	28	7E	24
				do	33	6W	16
do	48	12W	28,29,31, 32	do	36	20E	8,17
				do	36	21E	16
do	48	13W	36	do	43	7W	20
Gold	26	7E	8	do	44	6W	2,11
do	27	7E	32	Talc	25	5E	10,11,15
do	27	8E	13	do	25	6E	7,
				Zircon	29	6E	15,22,23

made to appraise the geologic settings of the sampled sites as guides to possibly more significantly mineralized rock. The siltstone and shale sequence is sparingly exposed in Wisconsin but was not sampled; exploratory drilling has shown that it is mineralized locally."

Measurable amounts of silver, gold and nickel were reported from some samples. Among other minerals found in the rocks examined were native copper, malachite, prehnite, epidote, chalcopyrite, chalcocite, quartz and calcite.

Some of the old mines in the region which had become filled with water through years of idleness were pumped out to permit sampling. At the Weyerhauser location, a sample was taken from the fourth level of the mine at a depth of 225 feet. One is impressed with the extent of the underground workings of this unsuccessful turn-of-the-century mine.

Unlike the successful copper mining ventures in the same rock formations in Michigan, those attempted in Wisconsin did not pan out. Unfortunately, copper has failed every time to become one of the state's significant mineral commodities.

However, a copper mine under development by the Flambeau Mining Company is presently going into operation at Ladysmith, in Rusk County, while other outcroppings of Precambrian copper-bearing rock in central and northern Wisconsin are currently under investigation by several mining companies.

Some matte copper was produced years ago in the lead and zinc district of southwestern Wisconsin. A small copper mining operation exists at this time at Esofea, near Viroqua, in Vernon County.

In 1976, the discovery of a large concentration of copper and zinc in northeastern Wisconsin was reported by Exxon USA. The mining company announced plans for developing the deposit. Located about six miles south of Crandon, in Forest County, the ore body was reported to be in an area of Precambrian bedrock not previously exploited. Even though more exploratory drilling was necessary for a full assessment of the lode, the company gave it a high rating: "Early indications are that it could be a major discovery, ranking among the top ten known massive copper sulfide deposits in North America." An analysis of ore samples showed gold, silver and lead as secondary minerals associated with the primary minerals — zinc and copper.

Wisconsin's early copper mines were hidden away in the backwoods.

Aerial Surveying

Aerial surveying is a modern method for determining the location of certain metallic minerals. Aerial surveying is accomplished by use of a magnetometer dragged from an airplane. This sensitive instrument shows variations in the earth's magnetic field, thus indicating the presence of near-surface magnetic minerals. In recent years, the Precambrian rocks of northern Wisconsin were surveyed through this technique. North-south flights were made at a barometric altitude of 3,000 feet and at east-west intervals of six miles. The flight pattern coincided with the range lines of the land subdivision laid out earlier in the

Aerial surveying with a magnetometer

original government land survey. Flights were more closely spaced in a few small areas of special interest. Based upon data obtained from the aerial survey, a detailed aeromagnetic map of the Precambrian rocks of northern Wisconsin was prepared by the U.S. Geological Survey. This map will be a valuable tool for further studies of these ancient rocks and is of special interest to mining companies in weighing the potential of developing iron and copper deposits in northern Wisconsin.

The Point Of Beginning

The subdivision of land is at the heart of orienting mineral deposits once found. The point of beginning of the original public land survey in Wisconsin is commemorated with a historical marker on the state line just south of Hazel Green, in the southeast corner of Grant County. The inscription on the marker reads as follows:

"Back in 1831, when Wisconsin was still in Michigan Territory at a point 45 chains (2,970 feet) east of here, Lucius Lyon, United States Commissioner, on the survey of the Wisconsin-Illinois border, built a mound six feet square at the base and six feet high to mark the intersection of the border and the fourth principal meridian.

"From this point, all Wisconsin public land surveys began, including sixteen townships in southwestern Wisconsin, which Lyon surveyed in 1832 and 1833. Lyon was completing these surveys, which opened Wisconsin to legal settlement by white men, when he was nominated Michigan Territory's delegate to Congress.

"The mound he built on this border disappeared long ago, but every surveyor's monument in the state, the borders of all townships and counties, the locations of villages and cities, the position of roads, lakes and streams, all were determined and mapped from lines and distances measured from this point of beginning."

280

Geochemical Sampling Of Spring Water

The Wisconsin Geological and Natural Survey has employed a novel method in recent years for locating zinc deposits in the southwestern portion of the state. The mineral content of spring water is sampled as an index to the mineral content of subsurface rock. Measurements were made of the amount of pH, zinc and iron contained in 7,210 samples of spring water. This geochemical technique has been used successfully during the past 15 years in both the U.S. and U.S.S.R. as a means of locating bodies of ore. A zinc abundance was found in many of the spring waters of southwestern Wisconsin. This information will be very useful for future exploration of lead and zinc in this region.

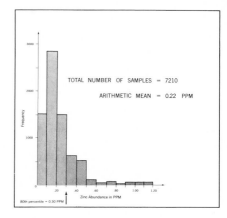

Distribution of zinc abundance in spring-water

Lead And Zinc Mining

Lead was the first mineral commodity mined in Wisconsin during historic times. Lead mining in the southwestern portion of the state dates back more than 288 years and has continued sporadically to the present. As a result, this region has become the oldest continuously producing zinc-lead district in the United States. Appropriately, galena, the lead mineral, has been designated as Wisconsin's official mineral.

Prehistoric Indians treasured galena cubes as keepsakes for decorative and ceremonial purposes. Some of these have been found in their burial mounds and at village sites. The early Indians may have picked up float galena instead of mining and smelting the lead sulfide before their contact with white men. However, deer antlers, presumably used as digging tools, have been found in diggings beyond where miners had reached in historic times, suggesting some mining activity by the Prehistoric Indians. The Indians are known to have used lead for patching wooden bowls and for inlaying carved stone objects such as ceremonial pipes.

Located in the Driftless Area, the zinc-lead mining area of southwestern Wisconsin comprises the major portion of the Upper Mississippi Valley Base Metal District. Smaller parts of the district lie in northwestern Illinois and northeastern Iowa.

Nicholas Perrot, an early French explorer, is credited with the first exploitation of the district when he mined lead for a short period in 1685. His small-scale operation was situated on the west bank of the Mississippi River near Catfish Creek, just south of Dubuque, Iowa. Indians were hired to perform this early mining.

After Perrot's departure, the Indians on their own initiative continued to mine lead throughout much of the district, operating mines intermittently for the next 140 years until well into the 19th century.

In 1700, Pierre Le Sueur ascending the Mississippi River reported stopping at an Indian lead mine, presumably near Snake Cave, at Potosi, in Grant County, where he replenished his dwindling meat supply with a quantity of rattlesnakes.

Limited to such tools as were at hand, the Indians' method of mining at first was necessarily the crudest. Typically, a small

281

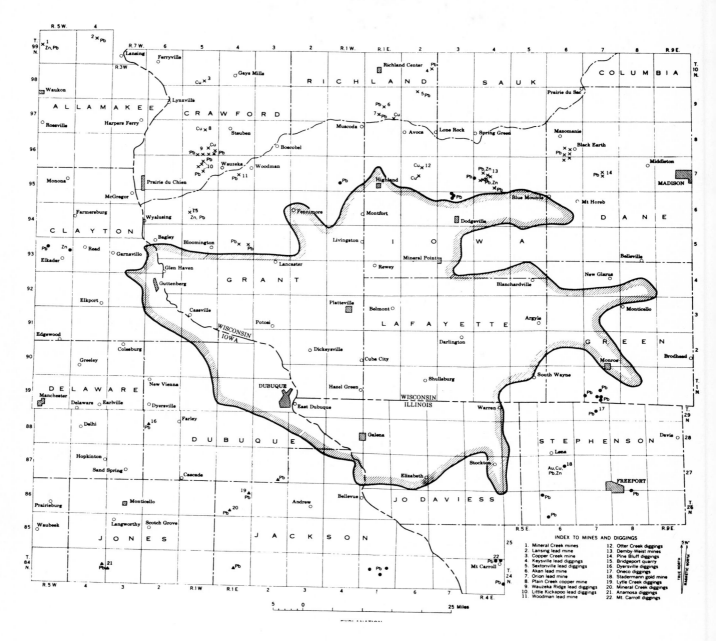

INDEX TO MINES AND DIGGINGS

1. Mineral Creek mines
2. Lansing lead mine
3. Copper Creek mine
4. Keysville lead diggings
5. Sextonville lead diggings
6. Akan lead mine
7. Orion lead mine
8. Plain Creek copper mine
9. Wauzeka Ridge lead diggings
10. Little Kickapoo lead diggings
11. Woodman lead mine
12. Otter Creek diggings
13. Demby Weist mines
14. Pine Bluff diggings
15. Bridgeport quarry
16. Dyersville diggings
17. Oneco diggings
18. Stadermann gold mine
19. Lytle Creek diggings
20. Mineral Creek diggings
21. Anamosa diggings
22. Mt. Carroll diggings

Map of the main part of the Upper Mississippi Valley district and mineral deposits in outlying parts of the district

opening was dug into a hillside, forming a tunnel, through which the ore was drawn out in a buckskin bag. Squaws carried the ore in baskets woven of birch withes to a nearby smelting place. The smelter consisted of a pile of burning logs. The ore was emptied on the fire and the mineral was melted, sinking to the bottom, where it was raked out of the ashes as lumps of fairly pure lead. The Indians bartered the production of this enterprise to white trappers and traders.

Even though these primitive methods were wasteful, 400,000 pounds of lead were thus raised and extracted in 1810. Under the circumstances, this was a remarkable output.

By 1819, the Indians improved their smelting techniques by building hoppers. A hopper consisted of a hole, about two feet deep, dug into a hillside from which a small trench led downslope to a smaller bowl-shaped hole. Brush was burned in the upper hole into which the ore was dumped. The lead melted,

282

Old-time lead miners underground in a drift illuminated by candlelight

In the early years, mining towns along the Mississippi and its larger tributaries were served by riverboats.

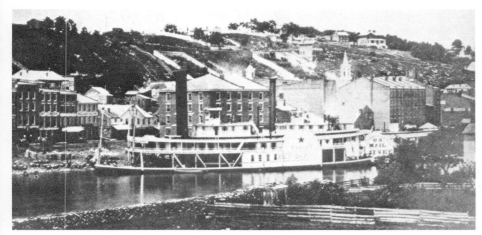

running down the trench to the smaller hole, where it cooled and solidified, forming a plat or pig weighing about seventy pounds.

In 1815, the United States acquired title to the lead region through a treaty with the Sac and Fox Indians.

In 1824, the first permanent mining camps were established by white settlers at New Diggings, in Lafayette County, and Hardscrabble (Hazel Green), in Grant County, both at sites of older Indian digs. During the next few years, thousands of immigrants came into the region and mining expanded over a large area. The area became known popularly as "the diggins". Soon a lead rush was on!

The early mining for lead began with pick and shovel. Production was mostly from float deposits along hillsides. Typically, the pioneer miners dug a pit to reach bedrock and then flared out in all directions, dragging the galena to the center. This system, called suckering, produced many pitted and pockmarked landscapes, a trademark of the area today.

Wisconsin derives its nickname, the Badger State, from these early miners. From a distance, their winter homes, hastily dug into hillsides, sometimes resembled the burrows of badgers.

Underground workings of old lead mines.

283

Hauling lead in ox-drawn wagons to Cassville in the 1830s.

Cross-section of a lead mine

Plant of the Mineral Point Zinc Company

Roasting furnace and acid plant, Cuba City, 1928.

Thus, the miners were whimsically referred to as badgers.

Soon explosives and more sophisticated mining tools were introduced into the mining activities, making it possible to penetrate into deeper crevices for ore. Suddenly the hills buzzed with activity. This was the heyday of lead mining in the Driftless Area. Smelters were built at such places as Mineral Point, Dodgeville and Platteville.

Toilsome as it was, life among the miners and farmers who settled in the region as the mining prospered was not all hardship. Taverns dotted the highways providing social centers for the male population, especially from each Saturday night until Monday morning. Stories were told among taverngoers about many a lucky strike in a honeycomb run of lead, with increasing animation as the night wore on. Tap beer from local breweries and whiskey brought up the Mississippi by riverboat were poured endlessly. Besides the bar, standard furnishings at most roadside inns included card tables, roulette wheels and faro banks. The wealth gleaned from the hills didn't remain long in the pockets of some of the miners.

During this early era, Mineral Point was a prospering center,

284

called Shake Rag, to where the principal persons of the region traveled for groceries, supplies and the fineries of the day.

There was law and order of a fashion in the territory, frequently dispensed, according to one early account, in harsh pronouncements by those "ignorant and vicious officials, themselves little better than many of the offenders brought before them."

The hospitality of the frontier surfaced almost everywhere in the mining community. Most persons held out a hand of welcome to newcomers. Doors were seldom locked. The worldly goods of one person were usually at the disposal of all others, with a wholesome respect for each person's property. Claim-jumping seldom occurred.

Many of the miners were illiterate, God-fearing, hard-working men, whose women had corresponding traits of frugality and fortitude necessary "to make do on a little".

A Scotch hearth blast furnace in use after 1866 to smelt lead ore.

Slavery rarely existed in the region. The census of 1840 showed only 11 slaves in Grant and Iowa Counties (a practice, however, that even so limited was in violation of the Ordinance of 1787 which expressly prohibited slavery in the territory).

The main artery of travel in the mining country was the Mississippi River, with the chief markets downstream at St. Louis and New Orleans. Ferryboat rates were fixed according to French and Spanish coins, which were then in common use at those two major river ports. Home styles and political sympathies trended toward those of the South.

In 1859, interest in the mining of zinc ores began. Zinc had long been recognized as an abundant associate of lead in the rocks of the region but had not been exploited earlier. The zinc ores mined initially were called "dry-bone" (smithsonite-zinc carbonate) and occurred above the water table. Not until the end of the Civil War did mining start in the underlying deposits of zinc occurring below the water table. These were called "black jack"(sphalerite-zinc sulfide).

Mining of lead and zinc in the district has continued down through the years to the present on a boom-or-bust basis. Two peak production years were 1917 (64,000 tons of metallic zinc) and 1952 (34,716 tons of metallic zinc and 3,532 tons of metallic lead). The gross value of these metallic minerals in 1952 was more than $12,663,016. Some matte copper has been produced in this region but with limited tonnage. The production in the district in 1973 for lead was 840 short tons and for zinc 9,260 short tons, representing an increase over 1972 of 11% and 20% respectively.

Steam rock drill

Sulfuric acid, a by-product of iron sulfide roasting from the lead and zinc ores, was manufactured in large quantities in an earlier operation at Mineral Point and later at Platteville, from 1940 to 1948, by the Vinegar Hill Zinc Company.

Even though deposits of lead, zinc, copper and iron sulfides occur in most of the Cambrian, Ordovician and Silurian strata exposed in this district, the major portion of the known commercial mineral deposits lies in the middle Ordovician formations. The ore deposits are believed to have been concentrated by

Compressed air drill

285

Old shaft house west of Shullsburg, from 1975 photo.

This abandoned lead and zinc mine was photographed around 1930 in the Linden area.

Diagrammatic plans and sections illustrating typical patterns of gash-vein lead deposits and underlying pitch-and-flat zinc deposits and their stratigraphic position to one another.

hydrothermal (hot water) solutions permeating the sedimentary strata long after deposition.

The ore bodies in the district are classified as pitch-and-flat deposits (veins and replacements in faults), gash-vein deposits (discontinuous veins along joints), stockwork-like deposits, bedded replacements, solution-collapse breccias, fissure veins, fissure lodes, rare ore-lined giant vugs and small sulfide-encrusted caves.

Occasionally, galena is found in vugs (cavities in the bedrock) with the original walls armored with sparkling golden pyrite. These beautiful, encrusted crystal sections are prized by mineral collectors.

Three successive crystallization habits of galena occur: the earliest deposits form in cubes, later deposits concentrate in cubo-octahedrons and the last gather in octahedrons (eight-sided crystals).

Among the minerals associated with the lead and zinc ores of the district are quartz, chert, jasperoid, illite, dolomite, pyrite, marcasite, wurtzite, celadonite, sericite, selenite, barite, chalcopyrite, millerite, enargite, calcite, digenite, djurleite, fluorite, silver and gold.

Nodules of bedded pink and buff-colored chert are common in mineralized deposits throughout this region. But, occasionally, the chert occurs in a form where its color is altered to dark gray or black. Black chert is usually found in the vicinity of large commercial ore bodies, deriving its color from the presence of microscopic iron sulfide crystals. Some prospectors search for black chert because they believe that it is a sure-fire sign pointing the way to rich deposits of lead and zinc.

The State Geologist commented on the extent of mining in the district: "The number of mines which have produced lead and zinc is not known. Some are mere holes in the ground. Over 300 zinc mines in the state have been large enough to deserve names, and the number of lead mines is even greater."

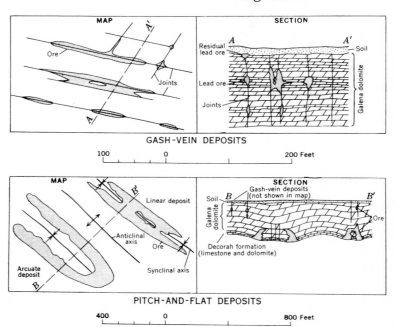

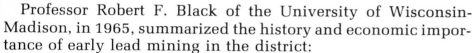

Mineral Point today (Shake Rag Street)

Professor Robert F. Black of the University of Wisconsin-Madison, in 1965, summarized the history and economic importance of early lead mining in the district:

"In 1697, Le Sueur obtained permission from the ministry to work lead mines and colored earths on the Mississippi River and copper deposits near Lake Superior. He was delayed several times by 'politics' and other reasons and did not reach the lead mines near Galena, Illinois, until 1700. In 1701-1702, not being a geologist, he laboriously sent back to France by canoe and ship more than 3,000 pounds of worthless greensand (Cambrian-age quartz sandstone of the Franconia formation with abundant green glauconite — a complex hydrous silicate of potassium, iron and other elements) which he mistook for copper ore. Although he died discredited, the deposits of the zinc-lead district he first explored have been worked with only slight interruption ever since. (Bain, 1906, p. 2, credits Nicholas Perrot with the actual discovery in 1690 of the lead deposits). Incidentally, in Wisconsin alone, those deposits have yielded conservatively at least $435,000,000 of zinc and lead using an average price of 15 cents per pound. Without question those deposits have dictated policy at all levels from the individuals directly involved to the remote Federal Government. They led to the first permanent settlement by United States citizens in Wisconsin beginning in 1819. Hazel Green and New Diggings were settled in 1824, and 10,000 people flooded into the Upper Mississippi Valley from

Pendarvis

287

Relics of the days of old, from the mining museums at Mineral Point, Shullsburg and Platteville.

In present-day mining, the mine's entrance shaft is sloped diagonally to permit ore trucks to drive in and out. More than 18 miles of roads lie underground in this zinc mine south of Shullsburg.

1825 to 1828. Lead production jumped commensurately.

"Certainly those deposits, or more specifically the wealth they represented, were involved in the abortive attempts to establish the Wisconsin-Fox River route for steamships between the Mississippi River and Lake Michigan. They were paramount in the planning of the Milwaukee-Rock River canal which never got started, in the Lake Michigan-Illinois River canal which was completed, and later, in 1858, in the railroad linking Milwaukee and Prairie du Chien. One can only reflect on the special 20-ton hand-propelled riverboats that carried lead to Louisiana or the hundreds of ox-drawn wagons that hauled lead to Milwaukee via Madison or Janesville. However, a not-so-rosy picture can be painted of the Black Hawk war which broke out in 1832 between the miners and local Indians."

The published decisions of the Wisconsin Supreme Court, from the time when Wisconsin became a state (1848) until about the time of World War I, contain a substantial number of cases involving mining disputes. However, very few mining cases arose in later years. These cases reflect the greater intensity and importance of lead and zinc mining during the state's early years. They also reflect the evolution of laws regulating the activities of mining. Most of the litigation centered around mining rights, claims, contracts and conveyances. Typical is the 1889 decision of *Raisbeck vs. Anthony, 73 Wis. 572,* in which the court held that a mining company, under license from an owner of land to mine a lead range, has a right to work a second deposit as part of the contemplated mineral range, "when it finds the crevice pinched out and barred by a solid wall of rock before it reaches the point to which it was limited and sinks a shaft beyond the barrier and, by drifting, finds a crevice of the same general character and running in the same general direction as the former crevice and works the same to the point originally limited."

The names of the mines in operation during the banner years of the district reflect some of its lusty spirit and color. Among these are: Coon Hollow, Red Dog, Kennedy Dry-bone, Snowball, Davy Pegelly, Old Harris Diggings, Great Northern, Capitola, Dugdale, Whig Branch, Tippecanoe, Lucky Four, Eclipse, Lucky Hit, Hardy, Gritty Six, Little Elm, Honest Bob, Strawberry Blond, Sallie Waters, Mermaid, Benton Star, Empress, New Deal, Black Jack, and Eberle.

The names of many of the towns and cities developing in this region ring with connotations of the mining era, such as New Diggings, Hazel Green, Shullsburg, White Oak, Strawbridge, Beetown, Platteville, Benton, Fair Play, Dutch Hollow, Mineral Point, Highland, Mifflin, Linden, Montford, Dodgeville, Jamestown, British Hollow, Diamond Grove, Cassville, Rockville, Cuba City, Bigpatch, Drybone (Centerville) and Belmont.

The Upper Mississippi Base Metal District, off and on for a total of 20 years, has been the fourth to twelfth largest producer of lead and zinc in the U.S. Geologists predict a bright future for this region because of its abundant mineral reserves, principally, lead and zinc and, secondarily, copper and barite. Large deposits of oxidized and mixed oxidized-sulfide zinc and lead ores await new smelting techniques now being devised which promise another boom for this district in the future.

At the present time, most of the zinc-lead mining in Wisconsin is concentrated in the Hazel Green-Shullsburg area. Two mines, on last report, are in production near Shullsburg. An 800-ton-per-day flotation mill was scheduled to become operational, recently, near Cuba City, in Grant County.

According to a survey made by the State Geological and Natural History Survey, where a great number of mines were opened in the district in the past, only four mines were in operation in 1967.

In 1964, the Wisconsin Geological and Natural History Survey commented on the future of lead and zinc mining in Wisconsin: "No mining industry is more at the mercy of fluctuating prices than that of lead and zinc, and the question of how to insure a healthy mining industry has been the subject of much debate, but no satisfactory solution has been found. Many smaller mines open or shut down as the price of ore dictates." The erratic production is reflected in the table below:

Sections of Chandler's map of 1829 showing majority of mines then operating

Mine Production of Lead and Zinc in Wisconsin
(In terms of recoverable metal)

Year	Lead Short tons	Lead $ Value	Zinc Short tons	Zinc $ Value	Total $ Value
1952	2,000	644,000	20,588	6,835,216	7,479,216
1953	2,094	548,628	16,830	3,870,900	4,419,528
1954	1,261	345,514	15,534	3,355,344	3,700,858
1955	2,065	615,370	18,465	4,542,390	5,157,760
1956	2,582	811,000	23,890	6,546,000	7,357,000
1957	1,900	543,000	21,575	5,006,000	5,549,000
1958	800	187,200	12,140	2,476,560	2,663,760
1959	745	171,350	11,635	2,676,050	2,847,400
1960	1,165	272,610	18,410	4,749,780	5,022,390
1961	680	140,080	13,865	3,188,950	3,329,030
1962	1,394	256,496	13,292	3,057,160	3,313,656

Source: U.S. Department of the Interior, Bureau of Mines, *The Mineral Industry of Wisconsin in 1962.*

As To The Future

Looking to the future, the Wisconsin Geological and Natural History Survey reported in 1964:

"There is a wide variety of minerals in the state that may, at some date, have some economic value but have not been developed due to inadequate known reserves or poor quality. Among them are:

Asbestos. Known to occur in Marinette County but quantity is inadequate to develop.

Beryl. Occurs near Tigerton in Shawano County but present reserves do not warrant mining.

Copper. Large copper deposits may exist in northwestern Wisconsin as the same formation is present there that is host to the Michigan copper deposits. The rocks, however, are obscured by a thick blanket of glacial deposits which renders prospecting extremely difficult.

Marl. Marl is a form of lime which is deposited in lakes. It is

New Jersey zinc company processing plant south of Platteville

289

Eagle Pitcher Company mining operations south of Shullsburg.

Old mine dump west of Shullsburg.

The technologies of the future will make new demands on mineral producers.

used locally for agricultural lime but is generally more expensive to process and is less satisfactory than ground dolomite or limestone.

Peat. There are extensive areas of peat in the state but no use is made of it other than in very minor quantities as a soil conditioner.

Diamonds. Diamonds have been found in glacial deposits in Waukesha, Pierce, Dane and Racine Counties. About 20 were found between 1875 and 1885. Their source is not known and, in spite of rather intense prospecting, none have been found since.

Kyanite. Kyanite is a silicate of aluminum used for special refractory procelains as that of spark plugs. Deposits are found near Powell in Iron County but the use of this mineral has now been largely displaced by synthetic products.

Feldspar and Nepheline. Feldspar and nepheline are alkali silicates of aluminum used in making glass and ceramics. Deposits are known near Wausau in Marathon, but the quality at the known locations is poor.

Talc. Talc deposits occur and were mined in 1929 and 1930 near Milladore in Wood County. The quality was too poor for economic competition.

Zircon. Zircon is a silicate of zirconium and is used for refractories at very high temperatures. There is evidence that sizeable deposits may exist near Wausau. Only minor deposits have as yet been located.''

The mineral resources of Wisconsin, throughout the years, have contributed much to the state's prosperity and, no doubt, will play an important role in its future.

XI
Rocks on Parade

Wisconsin's rocks and minerals were put on exhibit to help promote the state during the nation's first centennial celebration. Since then, our knowledge of these earth materials has greatly increased.

The First Centennial Celebration

In 1876, the United States was 100 years old. Its birthday was celebrated in many places around the country. That same year, the Wisconsin legislature voted to have the state participate as an exhibitor in the most prestigious celebration of all — the International Exhibition of Arts, Manufacturers and Products of the Soil and the Mine — at Philadelphia. The promoters of the Wisconsin exhibit at the Centennial Exhibition, as it came to be called, decided to display a variety of products typical of the Badger State, including an assortment of the mineral riches that had contributed so much to its early economy. Nearly 1,000 specimens of rocks, minerals, crystals and ores, representative of the state's mineral wealth, were hastily gathered and assembled in an impressive exhibit. To these were added a large assortment of fossils borrowed from private collections and almost 3,000 stone and copper Indian artifacts on loan from the State Historical Society of Wisconsin.

The exhibition, held at Philadelphia's Fairmont Park, attracted more than 30,000 exhibitors from 50 countries. Never before had the nation staged such a colossal celebration. From May 10 through November 10 of that year, more than 9 million visitors toured the grounds.

The catalog published for the Wisconsin mineral exhibit reflects the enthusiasm of those who worked on the project. Typical of the high hopes expressed by the exhibitors is this comment from the catalog's preface:

"But it is hoped the matter contained on the following pages will be found of interest to the reader and will be the means of attracting the attention of the people of other states and nations and of causing many of them to become inhabitants of our excellent state."

The Coming Of Age Of Geology

In the catalog, the mineral specimens making up the display were described individually and listed according to rock horizons. Despite the assertion that "accuracy has been kept constantly in view", the identification and stratigraphic assignment of some of the specimens would make a modern-day geologist raise an eyebrow.

One must remember, however, that geology as well as most of the other earth sciences was virtually in a state of infancy when this catalog was published 100 years ago. Allowances have to be made when reading any older publication dealing with the earth sciences. Since the first centennial, geology has grown to become a fully disciplined science. In a relatively short period, geologists have explored and mapped most features of the earth's surface, classifying and describing in remarkable detail nearly all exposed rocks and minerals.

During the same period and since the announcement of the Theory of Evolution which led to the emergence of paleontology as a full-fledged science, the study of fossils has become much more important. The preserved remains of ancient organisms have become an index for establishing the relative ages of geologic events and a source of information about the interactions of living things during prehistoric periods.

In the last half century, in particular, our understanding of the earth has greatly increased through the application of modern chemistry and physics. Analytical and quantitative research has produced a wealth of information about the amazing properties of rocks and minerals, while great technological advances have surged forward in every branch of the earth sciences. Complicated new tools and techniques have been put to use in unlocking the secrets of the earth, including microphotography, X-rays, seismographs, ultraviolet light, Geiger counters, electron probes, mass spectometers, laser rangers, infrared radiometers and high-speed computers.

Today, at the dawn of the Space Age, geology looks to new frontiers to help resolve the great mysteries surrounding the role of our planet in the universe. At the same time, geology, as an earth-oriented science, is at the spearhead of the campaign to protect and clean up our environment and to develop satisfactory ecological balances. In short, geology has come of age in our time.

Most of what we know about Wisconsin's rocks, minerals and geology has been learned since the nation's first centennial.

The Catalog Of Wisconsin's Rocks And Minerals

Among the specimens of special and historical interest listed in the catalog (set forth exactly in the language by which they were described) are the following:

Laurentian Series: pink granite, Montello, Marquette County; violet granite, Oconto River, Oconto County; talcose slate, Black River Falls, Jackson County; diorite "from a dike transversing granite", Grand Rapids (Wisconsin Rapids), Wood County; orthoclase, Beron's Mill (Biron), Wood County; yellow quartz, 5 miles north of Grand Rapids; black granite, Garrison's Mill, Grand Rapids; pink granite near Grand Rapids; jasper, Randolph

THE

STATE OF WISCONSIN,

EMBRACING

BRIEF SKETCHES

OF ITS

HISTORY, POSITION, RESOURCES AND INDUSTRIES,

AND A

CATALOGUE

OF ITS

EXHIBITS AT THE CENTENNIAL AT PHILADELPHIA.

1876.

MADISON, WIS.
ATWOOD & CULVER, PRINTERS AND STEREOTYPERS.
1876.

The title page from the catalog of Wisconsin rocks and minerals displayed at the Centennial Exhibition in 1876.

(Rudolph), Wood County; porphyritic greenstone, Grand Rapids; brown hematite, Randolph; chloritic slate, Beron's Mill; feldspathic granite, Ashland County; talcose slate, Pemee Falls, Menomonee River; kaolin, "Garrison's Land", Grand Rapids; and red pipestone, Rice Lake, Barron County.

Huronian Series: porphyrite, Penokee Range, Ashland County; quartzite, Grand Rapids; quartzite, Portland, Dodge County; quartz crystals on quartzite, Ableman, Sauk County; rose quartz crystals, Grand Rapids; quartz and specular hematite, Baraboo, Sauk County; chalcedony, 5 miles north of Grand Rapids; amythistine quartz, Grand Rapids; magnetic schist, Penokee Range, Ashland County; talcose schist, Devil's Lake, Sauk County; magnetite, Penokee Gap, Ashland County; "banded ore", Penokee Gap; magnetic slate, Penokee Range;

magnetic schist, Penokee Gap; siliceous slate (novaculite), Penokee Gap; black plumbaginous slate, Penokee Gap; yellow ochre, Black River Falls, Jackson County; graphite, Black River Falls; octohedral hematite, Lake Superior; "banded ore", magnetite and jasper, Lake Superior; specular iron ore on quartzite, Prairie du Sac, Sauk County; novaculite, Carp River, Lake Superior; blast furnace slag, Milwaukee; and pig iron, Black River Falls.

Copper Bearing Series: gabbro, Bladder Lake, Ashland County; melaphyre, Fond du Lac Mine, Douglas County; epidote containing copper, Percival Mine, Brule River, Douglas County; "rock", Percival Mine; amygdaloid, Percival Mine; melaphyre, mouth of Tylers Fork, Bad River, Ashland County; native copper in quartz and melaphyre breccia, Wisconsin Mine, Douglas County; calcareous crystalline rock, mouth of Kettle River, St. Croix River, Burnett County; amythistine quartz on amygdoloidal conglomerate, Lake Superior; trap rock containing opide of manganese, Lake Superior; calcite and native copper, Lake Superior; barite, Lake Superior; azmite, north shore of Lake Superior; native copper and pectolite, Lake Superior; prehnite, Lake Superior; copper glance, Lake Superior; malachite, azmite and calcite, north shore of Lake Superior; greenstone, Ashland County; feldspathic sandstone, "Welton's", White River, Ashland County; trap breccia, St. Croix Falls, Polk County; and lammontie, Lake Superior.

Lower Silurian – Potsdam Sandstone Series: brown sandstone, Basswood Island, Ashland County; sandstone and clay concretions, Lake Superior; quartzite conglomerate, Devils Lake, Sauk County; sandstone containing quartz pebbles, Grand Rapids; sandstone, Madison, Dane County; ferruginous sandstone, Black Earth, Dane County; hematite and ferruginous sandstone, Ironton, Sauk County; goetite, Brush Creek, Richland County; shale, Delton, Columbia County; indurated sandstone, Wisconsin River; banded sandstone and flint, Madison; yellow ochre, Ironton; brown hematite (10 specimens) Ironton; ochre, Ironton; sandy brown hematite, Ironton; malachite, Kickapoo, Vernon County; green marble, Marquette County; glaucomite, Mt. Moriah; yellow sand, Dekorrah, Columbia County; white sand "superior for glass making", Dekorrah; conglomerate, Mt. Sterling, Crawford County; and sandstone containing ripple marks, Lemonweir River, Juneau County.

Lower Magnesian Limestone Series: calcite, Black Earth Creek, Dane County; limestone, "Wood's Farm", Sauk County; calcareous shale, Grant County; ferruginous concretions, Sauk County; drusy quartz, Sauk County; galena and cerussite, Doylestown, Columbia County; galena, Orion, Richland County; Mendota limestone, Madison; pyrolusite markings on limestone, Madison; glodiferous limestone, Sec. 12, T.7, R 10E; limestone, "Dividing Ridge", Sec. 29, T.7, R 2W; chert, Sec. 1, T.16, R 2W; vein stone, Mt. Sterling; concretion, Mt. Moriah; marble (calcite), Marble Ridge, Richland County and pleurotomarie (?) Fikey's Quarry, Sauk County.

St. Peter's Sandstone Series: ferruginous sandstone, Blue

Centennial Emblem, 1876

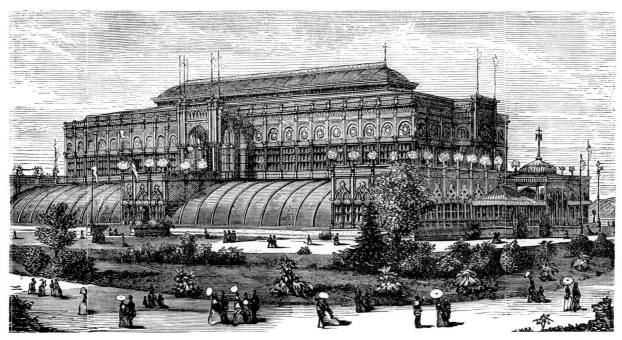

Horticultural Hall was filled with collections of rare plants and offerings from the states including over 200 varieties of apples, pears, crabs, grapes, etc. from Wisconsin. Landscape gardening and the business of the florist was also variously illustrated.

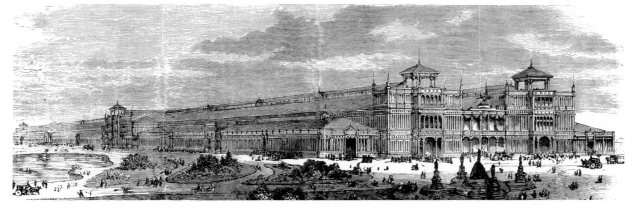

Machinery or Mechanical Hall had a floor space of 12 acres. Plantation and freight wagons, fanning mills, wind engines and mills, sawing, sewing and milling machines and a 10-horsepower threshing machine were among the marvels of Wisconsin mechanical ingenuity displayed at the Exhibition.

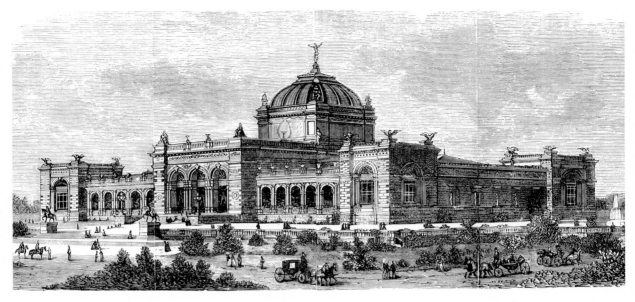

In the Exhibition Art Gallery, Wisconsin was represented by a full-sized marble statue — The West — by Miss Vinnie Ream, a native of the state; and by busts, medallions and crayon portraits by a Miss Fillians. Paintings of Lake Monona and Lake Mendota with a view of the city of Madison and the state capitol, by Thomas Moran, a celebrated landscape artist, were also on display.

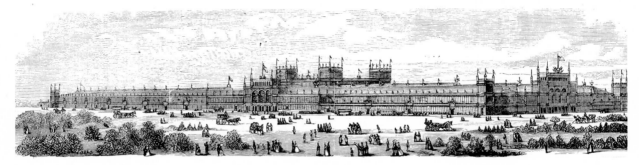

The Annex to the Exhibition Main Building contained the large exhibit of the mineral riches of the Badger state. The cabinet of productions from the Wisconsin mines belonging to Increase A. Lapham formed an important part of the exhibition. Many specimens of minerals, rocks, crystals and ores from other collections of institutions and individuals from throughout the state were also added. The main building also contained an exhibit of the educational advantages of Wisconsin.

The exhibits in Agricultural Hall at the Centennial Exhibition were reported to be the greatest display of agricultural implements as well as agricultural products appearing anyplace in the world. Wisconsin displayed 300 to 400 grains and seeds, various woods, corn in the ear, hops, tobacco, wool, draft horses, sheep, butter and the largest number of cheeses of any state.

Harrison Ludington, governor of Wisconsin (1876-1878) during the 100th anniversary of the United States, was active in securing from the legislature a $20,000 appropriation to assure that the Badger state was properly represented at the Centennial Exhibition in Philadelphia.

President U.S. Grant issued a proclamation on July 3, 1873, for a Centennial Exhibition to be held at Philadelphia from the 19th of April to the 19th of October in 1876.

The Centennial Medal was sold to help defray the cost of the Exhibition. Over 20,000 foreign exhibitors combined with U.S. exhibitors to make a total of 30,864 exhibitors. Approximately 9,789,392 people attended the Exhibition. On no day did the attendance fall short of 50,000 and the daily average was 81,960.

Postmaster General Jewell, issued a stamp to be used at the Centennial Exhibition.

On September 27th, 1876, the Exhibitor Awards were presented. About 12,000 were awarded solely as evidence of merit. The medals were of bronze, four inches in diameter, the largest ever made at that time and they were struck at the Philadelphia Mint.

THE MILWAUKEE LITHO & ENGR CO.

WISCONSIN HEADQUARTERS, PHILADELPHIA,

The Wisconsin State Board of Managers for the Centennial Exhibition deemed it important to erect a house on the Centennial grounds to be known as the Wisconsin Headquarters. A writer of the day makes mention of the Wisconsin House as follows: "The State of Wisconsin does not challenge admiration by the beauty of arrangements which she has made for the accommodation of her commissioners and citizens. There is no superfluity of ornament here, but the interior shows that the more important objects of comfort and convenience have been studied. The dimensions are 45' x 50' in height, two stories with a central round-headed window and window door in front at the second story and a double round-headed window on each side. A small cupola of pyramidal shape rises above the ornamental pediment and is surmounted by a flag staff. A piazza, supported by plain pillars, extends around the eastern, western and southern sides of the house. From the main entrance door a hall extends through the building, seven feet wide. On the western side a ladies parlor 16' x 20' is connected with a retiring room in the rear. The floor is covered with Brussels, the walls with gilt paper, the ceiling with light blue and panelings of thick Wisconsin paper in imitation of woods being arranged at the proper places. On the east side there is a reception room 20' x 16' for gentlemen, baggage room, washroom and a reading room which is furnished with papers published in Wisconsin. A stairway leads to the second floor upon which the main hall running from north to south is of the same width of the one below. The story is divided into six rooms used as sleeping apartments by employees in addition to a business office. There presides the war eagle, 'Old Abe' a bird which can boast of a biography the particulars of which some of the Badger state attendants will be glad to relate." Colonel Elisha Starr of Milwaukee, an old settler of the state and well-known to the people, was selected as superintendent of the Wisconsin Headquarters.

Mounds, Iowa County; stalactitic ferruginous sandstone, Green County; modular sandstone, Green County; variegated sandstone, Sauk County; red sand, Sec. 7, T.8, R. 12 E, Dane County; banded sandstone, "Henry's Quarry", LaFayette County; red sandstone, Messenger's Quarry, Dodge County; hematite concretions, Skinner's Creek, Green County; yellow sandstone, Medina, Dane County; palaeophycus tubularis, Janesville, Rock County.

Trenton Buff Limestone Series: Oalitic limestone, Janesville, Rock County; shale, LaFayette County; limestone, Mineral Point, Iowa County; Cytherina Fabulites (?), Beloit, Rock County; Streptelasina Corniculum, Sun Prairie, Dane County; Murchisonia _____ (?), Baraboo; Orthiceras _____ (?), Janesville, Rock County; and _____ Vertebrate, Janesville.

Trenton Blue Limestone Series: blue limestone (3 specimens) Green Bay, Brown County; sphalerite (sulphide of zinc) Mineral Point; chalcopyrite (sulphide of copper) Mineral Point; pyrite (sulphide of iron) Mineral Point; galenite (sulphide of lead) Mineral Point; chalcopyrite, azurite and malachite, Mineral Point; "glass rock", Mineral Point; limestone containing pyrite, Dane County; Buthotrephis Corniculum, Green Bay; _____ Expansa, Doty's Island, Lake Winnebago and "Buckler of a Trilobite", Mineral Point.

Galena Limestone Series: limestone, Mt. Sterling; galena coated with cerussite, Silverton Mine, Iowa County; crude shot, Helena shot tower; galena in chert (glass rock), Mineral Point; sphalerite and calamine, Mineral Point; copper glance, Mineral Point; melachite, Mineral Point; fibrous pyrites, Mineral Point; pyrite, galena and blende, Mineral Point; barite, Shullsburg, Iowa County; dogtooth spar, Mineral Point; bituminous shale, Shullsburg; Receptaculites Oweni (galena limestone, common); and Endoceras, Exeter.

Cincinnati Group Series: limestone, Scales Mound; shale, Monoseesee Falls; limestone (below shale), Mayville, Dodge County and Biforata, Rennicks Quarry, LaFayette County.

Upper Silurian Clinton Epoch Series: fossil iron ore, Green Bay; red hematite, Iron Ridge, Mayville, Dodge County; red chalk, Mayville; iron pyrites, Mayville; pig iron, "from Iron Ridge fossil ore"; steel "from Iron Ridge fossil ore"; fossil ore, Monoseesee Falls; fibrous gypsum, Fairplay; gypsum, Little Sturgeon Bay; compact limestone, Green Bay; shale, Calumet County; concretions, Fair Play; and chalcedony, Blue Mounds, Iowa County.

Niagara Limestone Series: lithographic limestone, east side of Door Bluff; porous limestone, Menomonee Falls; chalcite, Wauwatosa; and Favosites Favosa, Milwaukee.

Racine Limestone Series: Receptaculites _____ (?), Racine; crenoid stems, Racine.

Devonian – Hamilton Series: shale, Milwaukee; fluorite, Milwaukee; pyrite, Milwaukee; mineral tar, Milwaukee, calcite, Milwaukee; atrypa aspera, Milwaukee; trilobite fragments (phacops bufo), Milwaukee, and slab of limestone, containing several spirifers and also the impression of a fish bone.

Glacial Series: agates, Lake Michigan; agates and carnelians, Milwaukee; red porphyry, common boulder in southern Wisconsin; pyrite in limestone, Milwaukee; goetite, Dane County; bituminous shale, Milwaukee; muscovite, Milwaukee; native copper boulder; pebbles, Lapham's Park; celestite, Milwaukee; gypsum, Oconomowoc; glacial striae, Sheboygan; unknown coral; slab containing crenoid, fenestalla and orthis; and aviculapecten duplicatus, from Mr. Becker, Walworth County.

The catalog contains the following comment on the part of the state that later was named the Driftless Area:

"That portion of Wisconsin lying south of Pepin, Eau Claire, Clark and Wood, and west of Waushara, Marquette, Columbia, Dane and Green Counties, is almost entirely destitute of drift phenomena. No satisfactory explanation has yet been offered to account for this peculiarity. The fact merely is known."

Recent Series: brick clay, Milwaukee; tile clay, Milwaukee; polishing powder, Berlin, Green Lake County; mackinaw limestone, Milwaukee; travertine (marble) Sec. 27, T. 10, R. 3E, Sauk County; shell marl, Milwaukee; light red clay, Little Lake Butte de Morts; bog iron ore, Lake Mills, Jefferson County; sandy bog manganese, Grand Rapids; fossil wood (silicified), Waukesha; portion of a mastodon's tooth, Fairplay; and vertebra of a mastodon, Rochester.

Miscellaneous Series: Native copper boulder containing native silver from the drift . . . weight 30 pounds, Wauwatosa; one lot of 300 cream-colored pressed bricks from George Burnham & Sons, Park Street, Milwaukee; clay from which the bricks are made; oxide of iron (burnt sienna) light red, Clintonville; oxide of iron (yellow ochre) dirty yellow, Clintonville; glass sand, Rio; pig iron, from Ironton ore; bog iron ore, Necedah, Adams County; smithsonite (dry-bone), Highland, Iowa County; flesh colored granite (when polished resembles the Scotch granite very closely) Wood County; "nine irregular blocks, cemented together and polished to illustrate the different varieties of Wisconsin granite. One of these specimens, a reddish black, containing disseminated grains of quartz and very little mica, is remarkable for the fine polish which it takes, as well as for the beauty of the piece. It is from 'Big Bull Falls', Yellow River, a few miles above the village of Dexter, Wood County. The other specimens are from Wood and Clark Counties."

Thus, with a display of its mineral riches, including such dazzling materials as blast furnace slag, pig iron, fool's gold, 300 bricks, crude shot, "limestone from Wood's farm" and "sandstone from Henry's Quarry", the great state of Wisconsin, less than 30 years into statehood, put its best foot forward at the prestigious International Centennial Exhibition at Philadelphia. From all reports, the display was a whopping success!

300

XII
Rockhounding in Wisconsin Today

Wisconsin's rocks and minerals beckon to rockhounds, who are variously interested in the treasures of the mineral kingdom. Rockhounding is a rich and rewarding hobby.

Universal Appeal Of Rocks And Minerals

In modern times, rockhounding has become a worldwide hobby. Rocks and minerals are of interest to a growing number of hobbyists for a variety of reasons, some of which reflect the advanced status of the earth sciences.

During the last century, geology has ascended to the rank of a fully disciplined science, fulfilling a vital role in our space age civilization. The moon rocks brought back by the astronauts have captured the public's imagination.

Paleontology also has grown to maturity with the general acceptance of the Theory of Evolution. As a consequence, fossil collecting has taken on a fuller meaning.

Since the time of our grandparents, mass education has resulted in the enlightenment of hundreds of millions of people, especially in subjects pertaining to the world around us. Rarely is a newspaper of general circulation published at the present without some news story or feature article focused upon the environment and the rocks and minerals so basic to it.

Leisure time, a by-product of our intense technology that provides a tool or machine to do almost everything for us, has opened the door to the pursuit of numerous hobbies.

Modern lapidary equipment has become mass produced in the last thirty years or so making it relatively easy for anyone to cut and polish gemstones.

It is little wonder then that, today, the primordial materials of the earth arouse the curiosity and hobby interest of so many persons.

Rocks and minerals are fascinating things. Crystals suggest the marvelous order in nature, fossils . . . the interrelationship among all forms of life, soils . . . the interdependence of the plant and animal worlds upon the mineral kingdom, meteorites . . . the immensity of space, rocks . . . the enormity of geologic time, ores

Agate nodules — cut in half.

301

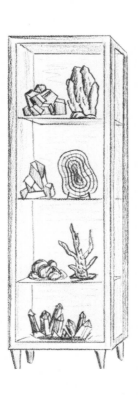

. . . the economic importance of mineral riches, and gemstones
. . . the inherent beauty in the inorganic world.

Rockhounds

You may ask, "How does a person become a rockhound?" One method suggested by a rockhound friend with a sense of humor is for you to buy a dozen marbles. Place them in your pocket. Then go to a place where rocks are found. Each time you spy a pretty stone, pick it up, put it in your pocket and throw away a marble. Keep doing this. When you've finally lost all your marbles, you'll qualify as a rockhound!

Rockhounds share an appreciation in common for rocks and minerals. But they are variously attracted to these materials of the earth. Some collect rocks, minerals or fossils. Some concentrate on collecting crystals. Some pursue lapidary art, fashioning rough gemstones into attractive jewelry stones. Others develop specialties in different phases of rockhounding. Rockhounds are amateur geologists, mineralogists, paleontologists, archeologists and lapidaries. Many have interests directed toward several aspects of the hobby.

Wisconsin beckons to rockhounds. The state represents a vast geologic storehouse with immense reserves of rocks and minerals.

Horizons For Rockhounds In Wisconsin

What are the opportunities in Wisconsin for this popular hobby? They are varied, indeed. There are rocks, crystals, minerals, fossils and ores, seemingly without limit, for almost every kind of collection. But there's much more. Gem materials await discovery by those drawn to stone as a medium for a delightful art form. Whether for use in making jewelry, inlaying or carving, gemstones may be found in bedrock as well as in cobbles and pebbles broadcast by the glaciers. Fluorescent rocks are sought by rockhounds with mineral lamps who are fascinated by the rainbow of colors revealed by ultraviolet light. There are stone relics of the Prehistoric Indians, for the collectors of artifacts, surfacing at random locations, mostly near waterways, marking ancient campgrounds and village sites. Rock oddities are found unexpectedly by those with an eye for the unusual. Different-colored soils provide materials for those who do soil painting. The places to go for collecting these treasures include beaches, riverbanks, stream beds, gravel pits, outcrops, mine dumps, quarries, rock piles and road cuts — wherever there is a concentration of rocks and minerals making exploration worthwhile. No matter what the individual interest, there's usually something in Wisconsin for every rockhound.

The Wisconsin Geological and Natural History Survey has prepared a pamphlet for distribution entitled "Mineral and Rock Collecting in Wisconsin". This publication is intended as a guide to the general areas which are known to be productive of certain rocks and minerals so that a collector being thus informed may proceed with individual initiative. It contains much useful field trip information.

Field Trip Suggestions

Very little equipment is necessary to collect specimens in the field. A geologist's pick, hard steel chisel and magnifying glass are helpful. Newspapers or paper bags to wrap specimens in are a must. Damage to fragile materials can be avoided with careful handling. Always take along paper and pencil to record pertinent information about the place where specimens are found. Notes on the apparent geology of the area may prove useful later when making a positive identification of the materials gathered in the field. And something to carry specimens in is recommended, such as a knapsack, gunny sack or ore bag.

The following basic "do's and don'ts" are suggested for collecting rocks and minerals:

(1.) Don't go on the property of another without the owner's permission.

(2.) Always respect the rights of an owner by not littering nor damaging the premises.

(3.) Practice care constantly for your own safety. Don't forget that rocks frequently are slippery and never provide a soft landing. At quarries, beware of deep ponds, falling rocks and blasting caps.

(4.) Don't collect more specimens than you reasonably require. Remember that rocks and minerals are a part of an irreplaceable natural inheritance in which other persons, as well as future generations, are entitled to share.

Rock club members on a field trip.

Rock Clubs

Many of Wisconsin's several thousand rockhounds belong to local rock clubs. These organizations have been chartered in most communities throughout the state. All are affiliated with the Midwest Federation of Mineralogical & Geological Societies, which, in turn, is a member of the American Federation of Mineralogical Societies, dedicated "to the promotion of popular interest and education in the earth sciences and lapidary". Rock club members are persons of all ages and occupations — rockhounds and pebble pups, alike. Through the club, the members — with diverse interests in the hobby — are brought together in the great fraternity of rockhounding. Commonly, entire families enjoy membership and participate in the activities of a club. Regularly scheduled meetings usually center around a program on some phase of rockhounding. During the warmer months, field trips are conducted at frequent intervals and the members explore outcrops and other places where rocks and minerals are found and collect materials for their hobbies. Many clubs publish a monthly bulletin or newsletter that unites the membership by apprising it of coming events and disseminating information about rockhounding. One of the most rewarding aspects of being a member in a club is the sharing of knowledge of common interest. Many lifelong friendships are made through this association. Most clubs have an active educational program, loaning rock and mineral displays and making speakers available to local schools. The highlight of a club's activities is the annual rock

303

A typical display at a rock show. In this case, a collection of fossilized turtles from South Dakota.

The conversation at a rock show seldom concerns the stock market, fishing or the weather.

A diamond slab saw

Grinding a cabochon on an arbor

Buffing the cabochon to a final polish

show where the members engage in competitive displays, field trips, silent auctions and swapping rock and mineral specimens. Usually, a show is open to the public and includes rock dealers who rent space to display and sell their wares. In many ways, a rock show is reminiscent of the oldtime county fair; but rocks and minerals, instead of the products of the farm, are king for the day.

Lapidary Art

In lapidary art, gemstones are ground and polished in several ways. They may be tumbled, cabbed or faceted. In each method, the stone is used as found or is first cut into slabs and trimmed by means of a diamond saw. Then, it is ground to the shape of the proposed jewelry stone. In the final step, it is polished to a mirror-like finish.

Rocks may be ground and polished in a tumbler or on an arbor or lap. A tumbler is nothing more than a motor-driven plastic or rubber-lined barrel containing the stones to be tumbled, water and a small amount of silicon carbide grit. Silicon carbide is an extremely hard and abrasive substance. The rocks are ground against each other and the grit as the barrel revolves, removing all sharp edges, corners and surface imperfections. A tumble-polished stone, fortuitous in shape, is called a baroque.

An arbor consists of a motor-driven series of silicon carbide or diamond-bonded grinding wheels, ranging in degree of abrasiveness from coarse to fine. Before being ground on an arbor, a stone is attached to a short length of dowling, called a dopping stick. Melted dopping wax holds the stone to the dopping stick, which serves as a handle on the stone as it is rotated in the hands of the lapidary and addressed to the grinding wheel. A finished jewelry stone with a regular domed shape — usually oval, round or square — is called a cabochon. Stones are polished as baroques or cabochons with the use of a polishing agent, such as tin oxide, cerium oxide or chrome oxide.

A precious or semiprecious stone is ground and polished with facets on its surface, according to an exact plan, through the use of faceting equipment. This consists of a faceting head (by which

304

A vibrating lap for polishing flat surfaces on rocks

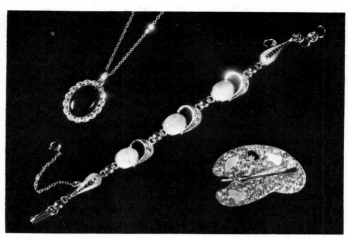

Gemstone jewelry

the stone is held) and a revolving lap (on which it is ground and polished). Diamond abrasives are employed in this process and the finished stone is known as a faceted stone.

The fun and excitement of creating beautiful jewelry stones is available to everyone. Lapidary equipment is easy to use and need not be expensive. Some is well within the reach of the pocketbook of a person even of limited means. Good diamond saws are on the market for as little as $50.00. Complete tumblers retail for less than $15.00. In every way, the door is wide open for this delightful hobby.

Assortment of finished cabochons

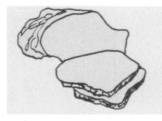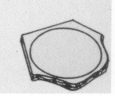

Slabs of rock cut by a diamond saw.

A cabochon outlined on a slab. A template can be used for making a standard size.

Slab trimmed on a diamond trim saw.

Rock Shops

Rock shops are scattered here and there around the state. These unique retail outlets stock materials and supplies pertaining to every phase of rockhounding. There you will find cutting materials, crystals, mineral specimens, fossils, lapidary equipment and supplies, collecting paraphernalia, geology hammers and chisels, jewelry mountings, findings, books on rockhounding and numerous other products related to the hobby. The rock and mineral specimens offered for sale include those from Wisconsin as well as others from worldwide sources. A visit to a rock shop is always an exciting experience. Frequently, there is something new or unusual in stock which intensifies one's interest in rockhounding. Because of the wide selection of materials available, rockhounds refer whimsically to browsing around at a rock shop as "silver-pick prospecting". The proprietors of most rock shops are knowledgeable about the rocks and minerals found in their locality. Usually, they are an accurate and friendly source for local field trip information.

Rock And Mineral Books And Magazines

Many good books are available on geology, paleontology, mineralogy, archeology, lapidary art and rockhounding. Publications covering some of these subjects are offered at small cost by the Wisconsin Geological and Natural History Survey and the Milwaukee Public Museum. Field trip atlases, stocked at most rock shops, cover most geographic regions of North America and tell where rocks and minerals may be found. Several nationally circulated magazines are published monthly for the rockhound trade. Most public libraries in the state have a good selection of these books and magazines.

Museums

Museums are excellent sources for learning more about the earth sciences. Wisconsin has a number of museums with displays that graphically tell the story of the state's rocks and minerals. The largest is the Milwaukee Public Museum, offering sev-

TUMBLING

A barrel-type tumbler

Ingredients being measured for tumbling

Emptying out a load after tumbling

Washing up the stones in the final step

Steps in cutting and faceting a round brilliant stone.

306

eral outstanding exhibits on the earth sciences in Wisconsin. It features one permanent display in which the visitor takes a trip through the full panorama of geologic time from the beginning of the earth to the present. Its dioramas on the state's Prehistoric Indians are without duplication anywhere. In addition, it has an impressive collection of Wisconsin's rocks, minerals and fossils.

Other museums include the museum of the State Historical Society of Wisconsin at Madison; mining museums at Platteville, Mineral Point, and Shullsburg; rock and fossil museums at many of the state's universities and colleges; and museums in many communities displaying some mineral specimens, operated by local historical societies.

The Phetteplace Museum at Wauzeka, in Crawford County, features a collection of sand paintings and beautiful intarsias assembled from mother-of-pearl and gemstones.

Pendarvis, the distinctive Cornish settlement at Mineral Point, is an authentic recreation of an early mining town, dating back to Wisconsin's frontier era when lead mining had its heyday. Nearby at Belmont, the state's first territorial capital has been restored as a state park. Both of these landmarks remind one of the importance of mineral riches during the adolescent period of Wisconsin's history.

State Capitol

Wisconsin's capitol in Madison is a dazzling showcase of stone. Constructed on the outside of white Bethel Vermont granite, it is designed in the style of the Italian Renaissance. Inside, 36 different domestic and foreign marbles in the form of pillars and panels envelop an immense rotunda in a full range of colors from glowing yellow to stately green. Rich blue larvikite (Norwegian moonstone) contrasts with numerous multi-colored stone mosaics.

The state capitol is the fourth highest in the world, topped only by St. Peter's in Rome, St. Paul's in London and the nation's capitol in Washington, D.C. With the rotunda soaring to a lofty 280.9 feet, the state capitol has the nation's only granite dome. Completed in 1917 and maintained since with meticulous care, this architectural colossus is recommended for visiting, if for no reason other than to see the beauty of its stone components.

State Geological And Natural History Survey

Information relating to the earth sciences in Wisconsin is gathered, correlated and disseminated by the Wisconsin Geological and Natural History Survey. Created by the legislature in 1891, the survey is an agency of the state government. Its mission is to study the state's mineral, soil and water resources and to undertake topographic mapping of the state. All these activities are conducted in cooperation with corresponding federal agencies. The results of completed studies are published either by the survey or the federal agencies. Volumes of unpublished information are on file at the survey's office and are available to interested persons. Upon request, lists of publications and indexes

of topographic maps may be obtained free of charge.

The U.S. Geological Survey, an agency of the Department of Interior, maintains an office at Madison and works in close cooperation with the Wisconsin Geological and Natural History Survey. Publications of this federal agency pertaining to Wisconsin geology are available.

A Visit To A Gravel Pit

If you let your imagination go a little foot-loose and fancy-free, a visit to an ordinary gravel pit in Wisconsin can be an exciting experience. Gravel deposits are found in most parts of the state.

A gravel pit and a library have much in common. Each serves as a storehouse for a vast amount of information about the history and structure of the earth.

Since all rocks basically are mineral aggregates, gravel may be described as a mineral potpourri made up of a mixture of loose rock fragments with varying physical properties. The ingredients of gravel come in all sizes. The largest chunks in the unconsolidated mass are called boulders. The medium size pieces measuring from 20 to five inches in diameter are classified as cobbles. The smaller fragments from five to 16/100 inches are referred to as pebbles. And the smallest particles grading down to the size of sand grains are called granules. These rock fragments of different sizes occur in a myriad of shapes. Many are rounded, some are flattened, and a few are angular with sharp edges and corners. The round rocks predominate in most of the state's gravel pits. Their shapes, sometimes pumpkin-like, result from tumbling in stream beds. You'll find them in a full range of sizes including dime-size sling-shot stones, natural bowling balls and huge room-size boulders. The flat rocks are more plen-

A Wisconsin gravel pit is full of pleasant surprises.

308

tiful in some gravel pits than others. Their flattened shapes, sometimes resembling pancakes in the case of sedimentary rocks, were produced most commonly by wave action along the shoreline of some prehistoric lake. You'll find them in many sizes, too, from little skipping stones to foot-wide slabs suitable for patio stones. The angular rocks represent a minority group in most gravel pits. Their sharp-cornered countenances show little grooming by erosive forces and suggest that they were splintered from bedrock in relatively recent geologic time and then moved, perhaps, only a short distance before joining the mineral colony inhabiting a gravel pit.

Gravel is made up of rocks of almost every color of the rainbow — red, yellow, blue and green. Many come in shades of grey, brown and off-white. But seldom do Wisconsin's rocks appear in bright colors. Usually they come in subdued or pastel tones, with a sophistication that befits their very old ages. A friend once spent an afternoon at a gravel pit near Wausau and was impressed with the many colors of the rocks found there. He decided to see how many different colors were present. He picked up small specimens and laid them in a line in order to separate the various colors. Believe it or not, he didn't stop adding stones to the line until the total number exceeded fifty!

You'll always find something of interest among the stones in a gravel pit. Surprises, in the form of some unexpectedly attractive or unusual feature, are the rule rather than the exception.

Some specimens of rock particularly striking in appearance are found in almost every deposit of gravel. Let's take a quick look at a few. Jaspilite is one such rock that seems omnipresent and stands out because of its rich cranberry-red color, usually interspersed with streaks of silver-grey hematite. Similarly, epidote sparkles in bright pistachio green. Multi-colored chert, sporting a prominent glossy polish, flashes in shades of yellow, brown or orange. Ferruginous chert sometimes shines as black as the ace of spades. Pudding stone dazzles the eyes like mod wallpaper, with dark polka dots on a background of light blue-grey. Andesite porphyry stands out in wild geometric designs resulting from the presence of large conspicuous crystals of feldspar. And if you look more closely, you may find small black fern-like inclusions, called dendrites, decorating the faces of some stones.

The next time you visit one of Wisconsin's gravel pits, pick up a handful of pebbles and examine them closely. Try to separate the members of the different families of rocks. Which are sedimentary, igneous or metamorphic? An inexpensive rock and mineral book will help you identify most specimens. Visualize, if you will, the role that each has played in the great geologic events of the past. Remember that each represents a little piece of the state's geologic history. Does this one relate to the ancient mountains, oceans or glaciers? From how far away did it come? Is it a lone wolf in the mineral colony comprising the gravel pit? Or does it have a lot of relatives lying around?

If you should find yourself actually pondering the stories that rocks at a gravel pit have to tell, don't be concerned that your behavior might appear somewhat off-beat because thousands of persons in Wisconsin share this same affliction. Highly contagious and already having reached epidemic proportions, the condition is known as "rock pox" or more formally as "rockhounditis". The infirmity is said to be irreversible . . . once bitten by the bug, always a chronic case! But, fortunately, the treatment is an easy one: Rx — frequent trips to gravel pits and other places where rocks are found. Rocks alone have the therapeutic property required to treat the malady!

The Oldest Known Rocks

When you are in central Wisconsin, stop by and see the state's oldest known rocks.

You'll find them a short distance upstream from where Mill Creek flows into the Wisconsin River, between Wisconsin Rapids and Stevens Point. Their home along the bed of the creek is adorned with a tapestry of white pine, wild ferns, trilliums and paper birch.

These old rocks are outcrops of Precambrian gneiss and schist. Radiometrically dated at an age of 1.94 billion years, they are recognized as the state's oldest known rocks. Although the rocks of the Archean Complex of northern Wisconsin are presumed to be even older, their ages have not yet been confirmed. The origins of the central Wisconsin old-timers are obscure. But, most likely, they came into existence as sediments deposited on the floor of some primeval sea or, less likely, they were spewed from the vent of some ancient volcano.

Deformed by pervasive pressures in the distant past, their gnarled old countenances show the strain of their long period of existence. Once massive slabs of primordial rock, they have wasted away to relatively small blocks, trimmed from time to time to even smaller size by the relentless action of the stream, rain and frost.

They are the wizened survivors of most of the known events in Wisconsin's geologic history.

Wisconsin's oldest known rocks

To understand better the amazing age of these ancient rocks, let's pretend that they received a gift of a single dollar bill for each of their birthdays from the year of their origin to the present. The total amount of the dollar bills would be $1,940,000,000. If all the bills were laid end to end latitudinally where these old rocks crop up, they would encircle the earth more than 14 times!

Epilogue

A Wisconsin geologist recently observed: "To me, at least, knowledge for knowledge's sake in just understanding the geologic history of the earth around us is a worthy contribution. No better documentary can be had than the millions of people who each year flock to our national and state parks to see and learn of the history of the landforms and rocks of which they are made."

In Wisconsin, the opportunity to study the history of the land

310

The state's oldest known rocks in the wintertime.

exists throughout the countryside. The state's richly varied geology is evident almost everywhere.

Whether adding scenic beauty to the changing landscape, serving as commodities to fulfill our material needs or arousing our curiosity through their engaging properties, rocks are an important part of our natural heritage. To know them better is to appreciate more fully the wonderful world of nature in which we live.

Although the resources of the mineral kingdom represent a rich natural inheritance — a legacy of the ancient mountains, oceans and glaciers — seemingly sufficient for our continued use and enjoyment, no longer can we take them for granted. In reality, all are *limited* and *nonrenewable* resources, prone to becoming depleted, in some instances, in a relatively short time, unless properly conserved. In conquering the land, we have become a geologic force in our own right and, more so than any other geologic force, we control the fate of the environment. Whether we admit it or not, we have assumed a stewardship over these things of the natural order. Conserved and treated with due respect, they will provide future generations with much the same utility, beauty and fascination that we find in them. But neglected or unduly exploited, they will become victims of our own thoughtlessness. As with most of the wonderful things of nature, the choice is ours.

Recommended Reading

Brevet's Wisconsin Historical Markers & Sites, N. Jane Hunt, 1974, Brevet Press, Sioux Falls, South Dakota (An illustrated guide covering all of Wisconsin's official historical markers and sites.)

Discovering Wisconsin, Polly Brody, 1973, Wisconsin House, Ltd., Madison, Wisconsin. (An all-inclusive guide to places of interest in Wisconsin.

Ice Age Lost, Gwen Schultz, 1974, Anchor Press/Doubleday, Garden City, New York. (The dramatic story of the Pleistocene Epoch made vibrant and understandable by a talented Wisconsin author.)

The Ice Age, Bjorn Kurten, 1972, C.P. Putnam's Sons, New York, New York (An authoritative presentation, illustrated in color, on the great happenings of the Ice Age.)

The Physical Geography of Wisconsin, Lawrence Martin, 1965, The University of Wisconsin Press, Madison, Wisconsin. (Classic work on the state's physical geography.)

The Wisconsin Story, H. Russell Austin, 1964, The Milwaukee Journal, Milwaukee, Wisconsin. (A comprehensive history, detailing the building of the vanguard state.)

Various publications on Wisconsin's geology published by the Wisconsin Geological and Natural History Survey, Madison, Wisconsin.

Various publications on Wisconsin's fossils and prehistoric inhabitants published by the Milwaukee Public Museum, Milwaukee, Wisconsin.

Wisconsin (States of the Nation Series), August Derleth, 1972, Coward, McCann & Groghegan, Inc., New York, New York. (General historic, economic and geographical information, in narrative style, about 30th state to join the Union).

Wisconsin: A State For All Seasons, Jill Dean et al, 1972, Wisconsin Tales and Trails, Inc., Madison, Wisconsin. (A treasury of photographs and articles on the beauty of Wisconsin through the changing seasons.)

Wisconsin Natural Resources Bulletin, Wisconsin Department of Natural Resources, Madison, Wisconsin. (Bimonthly publication of Wisconsin DNR containing a wide range of articles on the Badger State.)

Wisconsin Trails, Wisconsin Tales and Trails, Inc., Madison, Wisconsin. (A beautifully illustrated magazine, published quarterly, featuring articles of general interest about Wisconsin.)

Wisconsin Week-End, Wisconsin Week-End, Spring Green, Wisconsin. (A concise biweekly publication of things to see and do around the state.)

Acknowledgments

Credit due the following is gratefully acknowledged:

. . . for advice and guidance regarding the text:
- Dr. Carl Dutton, U.S. Geological Survey, Madison
- Dr. Philip Bjork, Department of Geography and Geology, University of Wisconsin-Stevens Point.
- Dr. Lloyd Peterson and Prof. G.C. Kingbeil, Department of Horticulture, University of Wisconsin-Madison

. . . for use of published materials:
- Wisconsin Geological and Natural History Survey
- U.S. Geological Survey
- Geological Society of America
- Minnesota Geological Survey
- Wisconsin Department of Natural Resources
- Michigan Department of Natural Resources
- Wisconsin State Historical Society
- Milwaukee Public Museum

. . . for assistance in publication:
- Blanche Hamilton, Wisconsin Rapids, Wisconsin
- John Rupnow and Tom Jewel, Johnson Hill Press, Fort Atkinson, Wisconsin

. . . for loaning mineral specimens as photographic subjects:
- Members of the Heart of Wisconsin Gem and Mineral Society, Wisconsin Rapids, Wisconsin, and Joe Vieau of Merrillan, Wisconsin.

. . . for first describing some of the landforms:
- *Wisconsin Week-End*

GUIDE BY COUNTIES OF LANDFORMS AND PLACES OF INTEREST

Numerals in boldface indicate an illustration of the subject.

INDEX

Numerals in boldface indicate an illustration of the subject.

314

316

CREDITS FOR ILLUSTRATIONS

About the author...

Byron Crowns, a native Wisconsinite and a graduate of St. Norbert College and the University of Wisconsin-Madison, is a practicing attorney in Wisconsin Rapids, free-lance writer and occasional teacher. For many years, he has written, lectured and taught in the fields of geology and physical geography. Byron and his wife, Gail, are known statewide by rockhounds as two of the proprietors of the House of Suzanne, a popular rockshop in Wisconsin Rapids. Byron is an active member of the Heart of Wisconsin Gem and Mineral Society, which he has served as a director and chairman of its educational committee.

Byron and Gail Crowns

Ralph and Babe Boyer

About the photographer...

Ralph Boyer is a longtime Wisconsin Rapids resident. A graduate of the University of Illinois and retired chemical engineer, Ralph is also a free-lance photographer. He and his wife, Babe, have traveled extensively around North America and especially around Wisconsin on photographing expeditions. Well-known as an articulate rockhound and out-of-door photographer, he has presented numerous programs to audiences throughout the state. He is a past president and director of the Heart of Wisconsin Gem and Mineral Society.

318